The Talking Cure

The Talking Cure

Tam Hoskyns

HAMISH HAMILTON · LONDON

HAMISH HAMILTON LTD

Published by the Penguin Group
Penguin Books Ltd, 27 Wrights Lane, London w8 5tz, England
Penguin Books USA Inc., 375 Hudson Street, New York, New York 10014, USA
Penguin Books Australia Ltd, Ringwood, Victoria, Australia
Penguin Books Canada Ltd, 10 Alcorn Avenue, Toronto, Ontario, Canada m4v 3b2
Penguin Books (N Z) Ltd, 182–190 Wairau Road, Auckland 10, New Zealand

Penguin Books Ltd, Registered Offices: Harmondsworth, Middlesex, England

First published 1997
1 3 5 7 9 10 8 6 4 2
First edition

Typeset in 11½/14pt Monotype Garamond by
Rowland Phototypesetting Ltd, Bury St Edmunds, Suffolk
Printed in Great Britain by Clays Ltd, St Ives plc

A C I P catalogue record for this book is available from the British Library
ISBN 0-241-13711-X

Prologue

It happened when I was sitting in Bill's car. Waiting for him, as usual. He was after a story somewhere in Bloomsbury and we couldn't find a parking space. So I was keeping watch. On a double yellow line.

I had a sixth sense about that journey before we even set off. The kind of sense that I only used to feel with my twin, that something was going to happen and I had to be there. I was meant to see it, I know. I have no doubt about that.

And if I hadn't been looking for it, I dare say I'd have noticed the incident anyway, or at least noticed the eventual body, but I noticed the killer too, because I was very focused on the old boy as he was trying to cross the road.

He looked so broken up. Like a child's discarded toy. He had sacking tied around his feet for shoes, he shivered uncontrollably inside his rough tweed overcoat, his face was hidden under a haystack of matted grey hair and he was filthy. He was waving two white sticks in the air, white for a blind man, so that traffic stopped for him.

He stumbled across the road towards me, brandishing the sticks fantastically, enjoying his meagre power. But then he fell against the bonnet of my car and his face swung round to curse me, or to curse the air, or whoever was there. As he lifted his face towards me, I saw that in fact he was a woman.

The face was extraordinary. Fine-featured. High-cheekboned. Big-eyed. Even in rage and age, filthy as it was, with its milky, opaque eyes, it was quite beautiful.

I was about to get out of my car and guide her on to the pavement, perhaps even slip her some money, when another woman approached her. I couldn't see this other woman's face. She had approached from behind me and she was too close up in my rear-view mirror for me to see much more than her coat. An elegant coat, well-cut. She breezed past my window like a bird, moving swiftly. I had the impression that she was rushing to help the old woman on to the steep kerb, but although she had taken the old woman's arm, and appeared to be engaged in some kind of effort with her (she had her back to me and was masking the old woman almost completely with her coat), it was very soon apparent that she had not helped at all. She had in fact hindered. She had left the old woman to fall to the ground, racing on as fast as she could without breaking into a run.

I got out of the car then, when the smart young woman had disappeared from view, to find the old woman bleeding profusely, her worn tweed coat absorbing the dark liquid like a sponge. She was already dead, her eyes staring their opaque blue at me, her body limp as cloth. No pulse.

I held her in my arms, as I had held my own stillborn boy, ten years previously. Bloody and dead. She must have died from the shock before the knife had even cut through the thick of the tweed.

Now the absurd thing was that because I had touched her, and because I had seen a woman, not a man, do this deed, I had the irrational conviction that I would be accused. So I didn't report it. And since the old lady was already dead, I saw no sensible reason to risk reporting it. Instead, checking myself for any stain of her, I got back in the car, pulled away from the kerb and searched for a meter a few roads down.

I never reported it. This was, perhaps, the most regrettable thing I have ever failed to do, given the events that followed. I didn't even tell Bill. He would have wanted the story too much and I was too afraid. I searched the newspapers frantically for days afterwards, but there was no mention of it. If it hadn't been for my cowardice, she could have been caught then. Before she did any more harm. I could have caught her myself.

But at the time, my cowardice seemed as nothing compared with my perverse delight. There was an unwelcome part of me that found it all quite thrilling.

It wasn't long after this incident, this murder, that Howard telephoned. Only a week or so later. My mind was turning over dust like a detective's mind, wondering why a smart young woman would murder a poor old tramp who looked like a man but was in fact a woman. So when Howard turned up with his face beaten in, he somehow fitted into the same perplexed part of my brain where violence was done. And where the thrill was felt. Even then I knew that the two things were linked. Although I couldn't see how for months afterwards.

I

He was my third client. The first one gave up after four weeks, the second left the country after two. My supervisor said, did I think this was because of the thing I do of not saying what I think?

'Maybe it is,' I said.

'It creates a distance. You must stay close. Try to stay close,' he said.

As a child I used to think that staying close meant being nice. Now I know that it means admitting what you're most afraid to say, and hearing what they're most afraid to say, and staying side by side. Equals. You don't steal their power from them. And you don't give your own power away.

Why did I find this so hard?

My sister was unsurprised to hear of my failures when she dropped by. She was the expert, after all. She even laughed at me.

'Another triumph, eh, Mo?'

'Well . . .' I mumbled.

'What is it with you?' she said. 'You fail at everything.'

'We can't all win,' I said.

'Spoken like a loser if I ever heard one.'

You'd think that if you were doing as well as Kate, you'd be more generous.

'It's a different kind of therapy to yours, Kate. Less directive.'

'How fascinating,' she said, but didn't mean.

'Yes,' I said and meant.

Pause.

'I'll get the hang of it. If anyone else gives me a chance.'

But plainly she didn't think I would.

'Why don't you try Cognitive Behavioural?' she asked.

'Because I've only just started Person-Centred, Kate.'

'Person-Centred is for people-pleasers, Mo! Everyone knows that. Cowards who can't tell the truth. You're so scared of being disliked, aren't you?'

'Well . . .' I mumbled again.

'I wonder if it's really your thing at all,' she said. 'Therapy. Don't you?'

'Do you?'

'Mmm,' she said. 'And I have to tell you, so does Bill.'

In fact Howard called when I had given up hope of working in the field at all.

'I need some help,' he said.

'Who is this?'

It turned out I'd met him somewhere. I didn't remember. He reminded me.

'Oh, Kate's . . .' But I was thinking of Bill. Of what she'd said about him.

He was quiet. I knew that he knew that I still didn't know who he was.

'It was a big party,' I offered, excusing myself.

'You admired my tie, if that helps.'

It did help. He was a striking man, I recalled. Awesome, even. Tall. Dark. Grave. One of Picasso's naked, heavy-limbed women had wrapped herself round his tie, unbelonging as colour to stone. He might have been stone himself:

sculpted, carved, cold, contained so within the outline of himself.

'I remember,' I said. Bill had been away then, too. Bill was always away.

I had talked about my training then, apparently. At Kate's. Or so he said. Which was why he was calling me now. Was I practising yet? Could he make an appointment? Maybe tomorrow?

'Sure.'

Tomorrow was a stormy Monday in October, the London air thick with rain, clouds weighing so heavily up above that daylight had almost turned dark.

I rehearsed my opening lines so that they sounded spontaneous but they didn't, ever, and when I opened the door to him I was dumb.

He seemed no less awesome, more so, if anything, a giant of a man towering above me, his black umbrella killing the remaining light. At last he let it fold down, as though disarming himself, and allowed me to take him in.

His face was a mess. Cut. Swollen. Bruised. I think he attempted a smile but his top lip refused to comply.

'Hello,' he said with forced cheerfulness, eyes avoiding me.

I don't remember what I said, or how he came to be sitting in the room I had prepared for my practice, months previously. I only remember thinking how serious this was, how, despite all the training in the world, I would perhaps always feel inadequate to the task of another person's life in my hands. Kate would laugh at that. But then, we're different.

I remember noticing that he sat with his back to the window, blocking out what little light there was.

*

Bill was away. I didn't know where. I missed him. We lived in a large house then, one that anticipated children who still refused our efforts to conceive them. Occasionally their unborn spirits would enter, softly and strangely padding out the place with their bulk, but only when sleep had persistently eluded me. More often, I could hear nothing but our own echoing lives bouncing back at us like hollow balls from the walls. When alone, I couldn't even hear this. I was frightened there, alone.

I was very nervous that particular day, even before Howard arrived; I know I must have been because I remember I checked my exits, and tested the panic button wired to the burglar alarm. And I think I even prayed. Uncharacteristically. I don't know what I feared, but my tutor's words rang loud in my ears. 'Never see anyone in your private practice alone unless you feel really secure.' She was adamant.

A hot feeling of shame coursed through me. Words like 'impulsive' and 'irresponsible' welcomed me home. I knew that I was taking an almighty risk, that anything could happen, but I also knew that this was my last chance. The big adventure of my dull, barren life. Nothing would stop me.

Funny. My heart is racing even now, as I look back. Standing on the edge of that decision, which had already been made, and yet which had to be made over and over again. Even when it was all over and his great cold back was turned away from me, I had to decide again that I had done the right thing.

Because I knew more certainly than I had ever known anything that as soon as I stepped into the unfamiliar terrain of this particular man, nothing would ever be the same.

Although I had done my training and had read a forestful, as he sat there waiting I could only remember a suggestion to forget the lot. Put theory aside and engage wholly with your client's particular life, I had heard or read or even written somewhere.

'So . . .' I ventured, leaving him to finish off.

Silence.

I felt instantly crowded with fears. I tried to put them aside, to be available to this third client of mine, but they waited for me and called out still.

Breathe, I told myself, and made a mental note to return to therapy myself.

'So . . . what? Mo.'

The way he said my name, thumped it on the end like that, implied a menace somehow, a desire to intimidate me.

Leave it for now, I told myself.

'So! I'm all yours. I'll need to ask you a few rudimentary questions at some stage during our first session but essentially the time is yours. All sixty minutes of it!'

Why so jocular? Relax.

A longer silence this time. He was looking me up and down.

How like a game of chess, I heard myself think. Move by move.

I wondered if he was playing a sort of power-game. But I hardly knew the man. Looking me up and down might have been a mark of respect. I was frightened, that was all, and I was looking for reasons why.

Calm down, Mo, I ordered, but then I caught myself. And don't repress. Admit and put to one side. I am fucking terrified.

'I'm rather wary,' he said, picking a small particle of dust from his knee.

I emitted what I thought was an encouraging grunt to assure him that I'd heard his first tentative disclosure, but it effectively silenced him.

'It's new to me, all this . . .'

I didn't believe him. God knows why. A hunch.

'I'm wary too,' I confessed, keen to draw him out.

He didn't want to be drawn.

'Well, more nervous than wary, but –'

'Oh?' he suddenly asked, looking up quizzically. 'Why are you nervous? Are you nervous of me?'

I shrugged vaguely, very unwilling to say.

He looked back at his knee, as if admiring the weave of his expensive suit, restored to its former glory now without that speck of dust.

'You know, Howard, I really want to ask you what you've done to your face.'

'I thought this was my hour?'

'Sorry?'

'It's my hour, isn't it?'

'Yes.'

'I'll decide what I tell you and when.'

'And I don't think there was anything in what I said that implied a demand to the contrary.'

I wanted to add that short of inflicting grievous bodily harm, it was unlikely that I could exert any control over his disclosures whatsoever, but I checked myself in time.

'You have no right to interrogate me,' he said. 'Do you understand? You're here to serve, not to rule.'

I remember feeling unsurprised at that moment that someone had beaten him up, but I can just about forgive myself now. I knew so little of this whole process then, and even less about Howard North himself. And besides, assumptions are natural enough. The skill is in admitting them.

In the silence which followed, I dared to ask:

'I'm wondering what happened there.'

I was doing everything by the book. Even down to 'I'm wondering'.

'What "happened" there?' he said drily, mocking my tone.

'In that little exchange we just had?' I ploughed on through his ridicule: 'Because, you see, I felt some misunderstanding there. I expressed my desire to ask you a question – some curiosity about the state of your face – a natural concern, I would say –'

'I'm sure you would.'

'But it seems to me that you perceived my concern as – in some way – presumptuous? An imposition?'

I was careful to intone this as a question.

'I perceive most of your psycho-speak as an imposition, Mo.'

'Uh-huh . . .'

Nothing if not direct.

'I don't want to listen to your textbook jargon labouring under the guise of "concern", when it's plain as day you're not really interested in *me*. Do you understand?'

'Uh-huh.'

Only too well. Back came the fear again.

'Don't give me this odious fake-sincerity lark you all do. It disgusts me.'

He paused for my response. I realized that I had only heard his tone of voice, and not the words themselves. Not the meaning. Fear was in my way.

'I'm sorry – could you repeat that, please?'

He narrowed his eyes suspiciously, as if doubting that I could be quite as inattentive as I seemed.

'I'm here to be heard,' he said, more plainly.

'Yes,' I agreed, following that much, at least.

'It would assist me greatly if you paid attention to what I say, therefore.'

'Right.'

'Furthermore, I am here to be heard clearly – that is, either with genuine concern, or with a rational mind, or both.'

'Uh-huh . . .'

'I am not here to be patronized by the kind of half-baked pseudo-integrity that so plagues your profession these days.'

He left a silence, during which he sat so rigidly still that he might have been a model of himself.

'Do you know quite a lot about my profession?' I asked.

'Enough,' he said.

'Why choose a novice like me? Or was it a deliberate choice?'

He chose not to answer me. Which was an answer in itself. Here was a man who made every choice deliberately, who weighed up every tiny speck of dust.

'Do you work in this profession yourself?' was my next question.

It had already left my lips before I remembered that it wasn't my business to interrogate him. That I was there to serve, not to rule.

'If you ask me one more of your idiotically direct questions . . .' he yelled.

'I'm sorry. OK? I'm sorry. No more questions, I swear.'

I suddenly needed Bill. I wanted him home. I wanted my husband home.

Howard released a controlled sigh, drawing my attention back to him.

'I'll do the talking now,' he said. 'First, I have to fill you in. I can't tell you anything about this –' he pointed to his face – 'this ridiculous little uninteresting scratch, until you know all about this –' He thumped his heart with a tight fist, holding the moment theatrically, daring me to speak, which needless to say I did.

'Can I just stop you there?'

He sighed with exasperation.

'What now?'

'I just want to be sure I've understood you so far –' I pleaded, and I launched into my textbook paraphrase, knowing that I tempted his wrath.

'You feel that my concern for you isn't real, that it's not genuine somehow. You object fiercely to my questioning you. You find my behaviour towards you invasive, or imposing, as though everything I say is out of a textbook rather than because I care about you, is that right?'

'"The paraphrase",' he sneered.

'Is it accurate?'

'You tell me,' he challenged.

'I think there's some truth in it, yes, I'm sorry to admit. I don't know you yet, so I'm using what modest skills I have to speed up the process.'

Pause.

'May I go on?'

'You mean there's more?'

'I understand that you want to tell me about your deeper feelings – your heart –' I mirrored his gesture, thumping my own heart with a fist.

He interrupted, his own fist involuntarily back at his chest.

'I want to tell you about me!' It was almost a shout. He stopped still, as if somewhat surprised by himself, then explained more soberly, 'I have to tell you the story so far, the sequence of events, before I can tell you how I scratched my face.'

'OK,' I said inadequately, moved by the sudden passion in him.

He waited a while, clearly expecting some further response

from me, something to kick up against, but I was not forth-coming.

When he was sure, at last, of my more sentient attention, he began.

'There was only me. And her.'

He was studying me already for some trace of emotion, before I knew even who or what he meant.

'My little sister was drowned when she was tiny,' he said, his own emotion absent as air. 'I mean, tiny.'

He held his hands apart to indicate her approximate size. About a foot and a half. Then one hand tilted slightly, as though to cup her head. As though to say what could never be said.

'So very small, she was . . .'

Even my breath seemed indelicate against her tiny frame, but holding it in felt like a kind of drowning too.

He bent his head down to listen to her heart or her breath or both, I didn't know which, I didn't ask, but he smiled unfathomably.

I thought of the old woman and her absent pulse. He looked straight up at me, as if sensing her.

'What?' he demanded, dropping the baby like a ball.

'Nothing.'

'What happened?'

'Nothing.' But he didn't believe me. 'I remembered some-thing. That's all.'

'What?'

'I don't want to talk about it.'

He punished me with a silence, which I broke.

'She really mattered to you, didn't she?' I asked.

He sneered at me contemptuously.

'God almighty,' he said. 'You're the limit.'

'I'm sorry?'

'I don't think this is going to work,' he said wearily.

'Why not?' I asked, the panic rising in my voice.

'I really can't tolerate this pseudo-insightfulness of yours — this pseudo-everything of yours! You're like a walking textbook! Is this what they taught you at school? I thought you admired Neville Hoare?'

'I do! I —'

'Surely not! Would Hoare approve of this? Be yourself, can't you?'

'I wasn't aware that I was being anyone else.'

'There's a great deal you're not aware of, Higgs.'

'Such as?' I demanded hotly.

'Don't you see?' he asked. 'If I'm going to reveal myself, the intimate details of my life, to another person, then it has to be on my terms.'

'But it's on my territory.'

'So?'

'So it would be courteous if you checked your terms with me before we agree to proceed.'

He looked surprised. For a moment, I think, I had his respect.

'Very well. My terms are that you remain silent unless you can be yourself. I don't want a "therapist", I want a human being.'

'And the reality is that you've got a human, being a therapist.'

He looked at me with unutterable contempt then. I had surpassed the credible. He could only close his eyes in response, as if to eliminate me entirely from his world.

'Joke,' I apologized.

He reopened his eyes, somewhat reluctantly, squinting in the suddenness of sun. Then he got to his feet.

'Do you mind if I let down this blind?'

'Go ahead,' I said, flattered to be considered at all.

When he was sitting in the armchair again and I had switched on the desk-lamp so that I could see his face, he said:

'You're an intelligent woman, Mo. That's the part I want.'

Something about the way he said this froze my blood. Or was it the way he looked at me – as though he could see exactly what he wanted from me. Something that I couldn't see.

It was with sudden intimacy that he leaned forward to confide the next:

'I was there when she found her.'

I waited for more but none came.

'Who?' I asked, humanly curious and not denying it.

'I don't know how I was there,' he said, ignoring me. 'That's what perplexes me. If I hadn't done it, why was I there? How did I know where to look?' He paused briefly, scouring his memory. 'Or was I not looking for her at all? Perhaps I was just – there? Was I just – in the area?'

'Which area, Howard? Where?'

He glanced at me irritably, as if to explain himself would be a tiresome inconvenience that I might spare him if I had even a modicum of skill.

'The area of the pond,' he said acerbically.

'Uh-huh . . .'

'The pond where she was drowned.'

'Was drowned or drowned?'

'Eh?'

'She was drowned there or she drowned there? There's a big difference.'

He looked at me as if I'd said something remarkably profound.

'Good God. How extraordinary.'

He seemed suddenly wrapped up, like glass, in impenetrable layers of thought.

'Is it?' I probed.

He looked up at me.

'Is it extraordinary?' I asked.

'I've never seen that before,' he said, looking through me. 'How have I never seen that?'

'What?'

'She never even allowed that possibility. It might have been an accident! Why not? Isn't that an obvious possibility? And yet we never even considered it. Why on earth not?'

He was asking me directly, staring me straight in the face, but somehow looking through me, too, at the tiny drowned child in the pond.

Then he turned away and laughed to himself. A sad, broken laugh.

'She knew it was murder. That's why.' He paused to realize more. 'And how? Because she did it herself. I didn't do it. She did. How could she know, otherwise, if she hadn't done it herself? Or did she watch me do it? Is that how she knew it was me? And if so, if she watched me do it, then she was complicit too; she did it with me, she was guilty too.'

He fell silent, as if into water himself. I broke the surface of it.

'I think I follow,' I said. 'Your little sister was drowned, but you don't know who by. Possibly by you. Or her? Is – "she" – your mother, then, or –'

'Yes, of course,' he said briskly, covering my voice with his own, in case anyone should hear, then whispering, 'My mother. Of course. Yes . . .'

He sank into silence again. I felt like a deep-sea fisherman hauling in the dead weight of a whale. I wanted more, much more, than I had grasped so far.

17

'So . . . your sister was drowned by someone? Your mother or . . . ? Or possibly you? Or . . . ?'

He wasn't helping. He wasn't there. He was where it was happening. Then. Not here or now at all.

'I just don't know,' he said, shaking his head.

I shook mine too, sympathetically.

'The difficulty is that we scarcely spoke of it again. My memories on the subject are so distant. Vague. I was only five, for God's sake. And yet I remember it bound us so tight, so close together, the collusion of it, the confusion of it, the mutual forgiveness, somehow, the mutual uncertainty of it . . . How will I ever know for sure?'

'I don't know,' I said, keen to remind him I was there.

He looked up at me then and seemed startled, caught off-guard, as if suddenly re-entering the three-dimensional world.

'So that's my first memory,' he announced somewhat formally. 'Or non-memory. My first encounter with the Plague. I call it the Plague.'

'The Plague being . . . ?'

'What?' he snapped.

I was very careful to sound like a human being:

'What's the Plague?'

'If you say a word of this to anyone . . .' he warned.

'It's confidential.' I nodded blithely. 'Except –'

'Except no one,' he said.

'Well, I will actually have a supervisor, in fact, who –'

'No one, Mo.'

He was at once intensely present, the black circle around his luminous grey-blue eyes underlining, like ink, his emphatic words.

'No one.'

I had the feeling that he was holding on to me, if not

physically then mentally. I might as well have been dangling from his grasp. I couldn't move. Only when he was satisfied that I had heard his instructions with every single cell of my being did he let me go.

The reminder of the session was a strain, perhaps because he'd said too much too soon for either of us. Certainly I was full up. The only further disclosure he made, that undressing his sister had been a curious pleasure for him, was one too many for me. Murder sufficed for one day.

He seemed concerned to emphasize that there had been no perversion in this curious pleasure of his. No abuse. He had simply been 'interested' because she didn't have what he had 'down there' – just that funny little line, as he used to call it. As a boy he had even looked it up in a library book to put his mind at rest.

'Howard,' I said, 'I'm aware that we're running out of time, so can I just stop you there and tie up a few loose ends before we close, and then next week we'll have more time and we'll be able to –'

'Next week?'

'Yes.'

'Can't I see you tomorrow?'

'Er – well –'

'The day after?'

Pause.

'Can I call you about that?'

Another pause.

'Very well.'

'Which brings me to the practicalities – I'm going to need a contact number from you, for a start.'

He handed me his card.

'Thank you.'

I went through my rehearsed routine – what kind of therapist I was, when I liked to be paid, whether he had any medical history that I ought to know about, etc.

He paid me my modest fee. I showed him to the front door. It was raining again outside, the sky as unpredictable as North himself. He hovered in the doorway, huge again as he fumbled with his umbrella. It flew up like a bird, carrying him out on to the top step.

'Goodbye, Mo.'

2

As soon as Howard had gone I started shaking, almost fever-ishly, as if I'd been infected by him. His word 'plague' came to mind. I knew that the stabbing in Bloomsbury had set my nerves on edge, and would do for some time. And I knew that another client was an important, loaded thing for me, that I had a lot at stake, a lot to prove. Especially to Kate. And Bill. But this? I was a caricature of fear, my bowels lurching into interminable action. Every tiny sound sped the adrenalin through my body like a drug, perversely pleasurable.

That same evening I received three anonymous telephone calls. None of them so much as whispered to me. Or breathed, even. Was this North? Or was it the murderess, intimidating witnesses? Or was it just Bill at last, sorry at last, loving and missing me and trying hard to get through on his useless mobile telephone?

Sadly, although this last would seem the most likely scenario to any outsider, to me it felt the least likely of all. He called less and less often as the years went by. I was not so much a lover as a burden to him now. He would admit that, too. He would admit to his disappointment in me and I would listen almost politely and then I would feel a sharp needling pain as if he had stuck a hat-pin in me, so thin that at first I didn't feel it sink in. Then there'd be a row, of course. And then I'd go back to thinking how much happier he would be with Kate. If Kate wasn't married to Cliff.

At midnight the doorbell rang. I assumed that it was Bill, returning as suddenly as he had left. I only checked my impulse to answer at the last moment, as I stood in the hall.

Why would Bill ring the bell? Hands full? Lost his keys?

The visiting shape was vague through the opaque glass of the door, while I was quite clear in the bright light of the hall. I moved slowly towards the door, half-amused by my antics and half-petrified. I pressed my face against the peep-hole, peering through the tiny convex lens.

Nothing. Pitch blackness. Whoever it was had covered the lens with their hand.

Then the telephone rang. For the fourth time.

My heart beat so loud now it was like a great drum in my ears. I backed away from the door. Slowly. I realized that I hadn't double-locked it, that, unconsciously hoping for Bill's imminent return, I had in fact left it unbolted so that he could get in without waking me up. Perhaps whoever it was had seen me doing this and was in full possession of the fact that only a Yale lock, a fragile, kickable-in Yale lock, stood between me and him.

When I was almost out of view I ran up the stairs, pausing on the landing to listen. I don't know what I expected to hear above the telephone, which continued to ring. I crept into the bedroom, as if my stealth would somehow conceal my obvious whereabouts.

I didn't dare answer the telephone. I could no longer fool myself that the persistent caller was Bill. To answer it now seemed plainly dangerous.

I picked up the receiver and put it down immediately.

Then I called the police. It took an age to get through, and the doorbell rang again. I sat on the bed, trembling with the thrill and the fear of it, waiting to be saved.

A few minutes later I heard the lock turn. Someone had opened the door. I listened above the din of my heart for a clue. Where was he? Standing in the hall? Waiting for my first move? Silence. I held my breath but my heart was unstoppable. *Where was he?*

Then he spoke.

'Are you up?'

It was Bill.

I breathed. Then I went downstairs, smiling mildly, as though everything was all right.

'Hi,' I said easily, kissing his cheek.

'Sorry I'm so late.'

'I wasn't expecting you, early or late. It doesn't make much odds.'

'Right.'

'In fact these days I hardly dare expect you back at all.'

He glared at me, and then passed through into the living-room. I followed.

'Sorry,' I said.

He said, 'Give me a break.'

'You've just had a break,' I said. And then I said, 'I need you, Bill.'

He let out a great big sigh which told me all I needed to know.

'I've got a new client,' I said, changing my tone. 'A very clever man.'

'Oh, yes,' he acknowledged, but he was only half-listening.

'The trouble is, Bill, you say you want love, you want commitment, but when I give it to you, you just throw it back in my face.'

'What are you talking about?'

'I'm talking about you.'

23

He had just stood up to pour himself a drink when the police arrived. I'd forgotten about them. I felt rather ashamed and rather relieved and greeted them cheerfully. They had saved me, after all, from facing up to the truth.

'I'm so sorry, it was my husband – I thought he was an intruder but –'

'Very good, miss. Could we come in for a moment?'

And the two of them eased their way into the hall, eyeing Bill suspiciously.

'What the bloody hell's going on?' said Bill.

'Can we just take a statement from you, sir?' one said, his pen already poised. 'Only we have to take a statement now.' And the other constable took me into the next room.

After our respective tales had been told, they advised caution in opening the door without a door-chain, congratulated me for using the peep-hole, and were gone.

'Using the peep-hole?' asked Bill, pouring himself a Scotch.

'When you rang the bell.'

'I didn't ring the bell.'

I slept atrociously, slapping Bill with fitful arms. I was weighing things up. I had to make a decision the next morning about Howard North. When to see him again. It should have been 'whether' not 'when'.

At six o'clock I slipped out of bed, kissing Bill's face when he least minded it, cushioned on the pillow, asleep. Dead to the world.

I thought of her little body. Floppy, wet and dead.

I sat at my desk with a cup of coffee, black and thick as bitumen, and flicked through the tentative notes I had made.

I'll get better at this, I told myself, as I searched for some clue.

I felt more like a detective than a therapist as I tried to piece together the man's beaten face, his dead sister, his mother, and what it was he wanted from me.

Bill shuffled in at eight o'clock, squinting in the shock of sunlight through the window, his yellow hair everywhere.

'What are you doing?'

'Just working.'

I resented the objection he was about to make.

'At what?'

'Darling, I did actually tell you last night that I have a new client now –'

'Yes, I know. But he's not here, is he? What can you do? It's eight o'clock in the morning.' He was building up to nagging me.

'I can read my notes, I can ... think ... I can try to –'

'He sounds like a sicko, Mo, a bloody psychopath.'

'Just because he might possibly have rung the bell? Is that so sick?'

'You can't "save" him, you know.'

'Who says I'm going to save him?'

'Isn't that what all therapists do ... ?'

'And anyway, who says it was him last night? It could've been anyone.'

'Sure,' he said drily. 'Why pick on the psychopaths?'

I didn't respond.

'I know – why don't you send him to see Kate? Get him live on her TV show. She'll sort him out. She's the expert, isn't she?'

He knew this would hurt.

'Hardly,' I muttered sourly, unable to credit her with any talent at all.

'Or, better still, have him certified.'

I put down my pen, swung round in my chair and glared at him furiously.

'What d'you want?'

'Nothing.'

'Come on. Tell me. What?'

'Forget it. You're in a mood.'

'I'm not in a mood. What do you want?' I insisted, spoiling for a fight.

'Doesn't matter . . .' he muttered wearily, shuffling out again.

'Jesus!' I shouted. But he didn't respond, sensibly enough.

I was livid. I wanted a bloody great row, I realized. I wanted to hear myself justify to Bill all my reasons for a second session with North, against all his best arguments.

I tried to understand why Howard North was so important to me. I couldn't. I didn't have the insight, or the hindsight, then.

THINGS TO DO, I wrote on my A4 pad.

Top of the list went CALL STEPH HARRIGAN.

Do things by the book, I told myself: therapist, supervisor.

Next on the list went CALL SUPERVISOR, and, although I intended to, I knew it would take me a while. I was too excited to risk losing North. And I was also too scared. I'd been warned, threatened even, to speak to nobody.

I stared out at the garden in defeat. The autumn leaves were dripping from the stag's-horn sumach like fresh red blood. A big fat jay was sitting on a branch of it. He seemed almost to be the violator, spilling the blood himself.

Ugly birds, I thought. Lonely scavengers. I was feeling more antipathy towards this bird than I had ever felt towards a bird in my life. It reminded me of someone, I realized. I was in there somewhere, but it wasn't just me. The flash of brilliant cold blue reminded me of North.

What does Kate know about him? I wondered. Maybe I'll ask her.

After breakfast with Bill, who was punishingly uncommunicative behind his newspaper, reading his own article about 'The First Grey Hair' and cursing his copyist, I called Howard North.

'What time?' Bill was intensely irritated.

'Why does it matter what time? I wasn't expecting you back today, anyway.'

'Listen, this is my home and if I –'

'Oh, don't start this again.'

'No, listen –'

'No, I bloody won't.'

I went into the kitchen. He pursued me hotly.

'Don't just walk away!'

It was a small kitchen, but he managed to pace up and down in it.

I said very quietly, so as not to agitate him further, 'There's nothing to worry about.'

He stopped, his eyes searching mine. I looked away, because in truth there was plenty to worry about that he might see.

'I get in at midnight, you're being very weird but you won't tell me why, you've called the police after someone's rung the bell and put their hand over the peep-hole and someone else has phoned up four times without speaking to you, I ask you about this guy Leslie North –'

'Howard.'

'Leslie Howard –'

'Howard Nor –'

'Whatever the fuck he's called!' he bellowed. 'I ask you about him and you won't tell me a single bloody thing!'

'I've told you his name. I shouldn't even have told you his name.'

'You're off with me, you can't sleep, you hit me all night, you tell me you're scared but you won't say why since you saw this guy, or you say you don't know why, and now you invite him back! Without even seeing whoever you need to see or talking to me about it or anything!'

'I can't talk to you about it, can I? It's confidential.'

'Crap.'

'It's not crap. It's part of the job, Bill. A very important part.'

'But I'm not going to tell anyone, am I? Who am I going to tell?'

He almost pleaded with me. I was reminded of playground secrets at school.

I said, 'That's not the point,' because it wasn't.

'Well, I'm sorry, but I think the whole thing stinks.'

He kicked the fridge door.

'Yes, well, you would, wouldn't you? Because you can't stand me being interested in anyone but you, can you? So you can reject me all the time –'

'Bollocks.'

'You're secretly quite glad we can't have children, aren't you, because it means you get all my attention, twenty-four hours a day.'

'Are you serious?'

'But now suddenly that's threatened, isn't it? Because I've got clients now. Thank God it's only clients, not kids, or what would you be like?'

'You should've stuck to architecture, love. You can't do people, can you?'

'Other way round, in fact.'

'You can't do either, in fact.'

3

Bill left me unforgiven in the kitchen, slamming the front door so hard that the whole house shook.

In the afternoon Kate dropped by, minutes before Howard was due. It was the second time that month. She didn't usually drop by. Usually she rang to make an appointment a few weeks in advance. Or, more usually still, I would ring her and she'd try to fit me in. Twice in one month was keen.

'Mo,' she said. I often thought she was saying 'No' when in fact she was saying 'Mo'. An inherent order seemed to lurk somewhere inside her emphasis.

'What a surprise,' I said, not altogether pleased. I leaned forward to kiss her but she pulled away, wincing slightly. It was then that I noticed.

'What have you done to your face?'

'Nothing.'

'It's swollen.'

'No,' she said lightly. 'I've just got make-up on.'

'Why?'

'Why what?'

'Why have you got make-up on?'

'Why shouldn't I?'

'Because you hate it.'

'So?' She stumbled, which was odd for Kate. 'I've come to like it.'

'I see,' I said. 'Very nice.'

'Oh, for goodness' sake, Mo – I haven't come round to discuss the merits of make-up with you!'

No, I thought. You've come round to see Bill.

'What do you want?'

'Look, I'm really sorry to – not to warn you . . . I just wondered if you could do me the most enormous favour.'

'What?'

'It's just – it's half-term and I've got to reshoot an interview and –'

'No,' I said, like she says Mo. I glanced at the carload of children she had sweetly brought round for me, poor barren aunt.

'Well, thanks,' she said bitterly, 'I knew I could count on you.'

'I'm busy,' I said. I was longing to tell her. My trump card. Mr North.

'You seem busy,' she said.

'My new client is due any minute now.' I tossed this lightly at her.

She stared at me in uneasy disbelief. How she betrayed herself.

'Your new client?' she said uncomfortably. 'What new client? You never told me you had a new client, Mo.'

'Why should I?' I asked blithely, reinforced by this tiny success.

'No reason.' She paused. 'Except you're my twin. We didn't used to have secrets, did we?'

'We've always had secrets, Kate.'

'Well, professional secrets, of course. To disclose them would be unethical.'

'Exactly,' I concurred, placing my ethical secrets in the same professional league as her own.

She looked at me with a familiar mixture of hatred and pain.

'I have another client, Kate. Aren't you pleased for me?'

'What's his name?' she asked, unable to be pleased.

'Who says it's a he?'

'Well, is it?'

I longed to resist her, just once.

'Yes, Kate. It's a he.'

At that very moment Howard approached in his car, slowing down as if to park but then suddenly changing his mind and driving on, driving straight past us down the road.

Kate turned to see what I was looking at, her eyes following his car.

'Is that him?'

I didn't answer. Her face was full of unexpected rage.

'*Is that him?*' she bellowed, but then she saw herself in my face, staring back bewildered at her.

'I'd better go,' she said.

And she did, without saying goodbye. Screaming off in her black BMW.

He chose the same seat in front of the window, his face in shadow again, the sun bright in the garden outside.

'Hello, Textbook.' He grinned playfully as I sat down opposite him.

I smiled. How harmless he seemed in the warm afternoon light. Surely he couldn't be last night's terrorist?

'You seem . . . happy? Today?'

'Ha-pp-y!' He said the word as if it was foreign, something new to learn, somewhat puzzling. 'To-day?'

'Mock on,' I invited, good-humouredly. His face clouded over.

'Was that Kate?' he demanded.

'On the doorstep?' I asked. He simply glared at me, waiting for my reply. 'Yes,' I said.

'Does she know I'm seeing you?'

'Of course not.'

'Are you sure?'

'Quite sure.'

'Good.'

He was silent.

'You seem very troubled, Howard, by the thought of Kate.'

But then he seemed instantly untroubled, as if to conceal the very thing I'd observed so plainly in him.

'No!' He smiled broadly. 'Not troubled at all!'

'I'm wondering if perhaps it's a little confusing for you that Kate and I look so much alike?'

'Perhaps.'

'Do you know her particularly well?'

'Is that your business?'

'No. Probably not. Although it concerns me, certainly.'

'She thinks she knows me particularly well,' he said drily.

'Uh-huh.'

'The arrogance of idiots. Always so blind and so sure.'

'Strong words.'

'True words. Can we move on from your twin sister, charming though she is?'

'It's your hour,' I conceded, putting curiosity aside.

We fell into a well of extraordinary silence that seemed to echo back through his life. I sensed an almost inexpressible grief swallow up the room as his eyes searched mine. How could I find words that would adequately answer a sorrow like this?

He breathed in deeply but quietly, releasing the air with even, measured control.

'I feel I understand your silence better than your words,' I confessed.

'What do you understand of my silence?' he challenged defiantly.

'Something of your – sadness?'

'What sadness?'

'I don't know. I only know something of the measure of it.'

'What does it "measure", then?'

'Oh, Howard, I don't know. In silence perhaps I can see you better because you aren't pouncing on every word I say!' I said this without edge, since it was true that his silence had won a small piece of my heart. But I said it with strength, for once unusually fearless of him.

He half-smiled at me.

'Very good,' he said.

'I wish I didn't feel you were marking me out of ten all the time,' I said, more spontaneously still. 'I find it such an obstacle to the progress of our relationship.'

'What progress?'

'Precisely!'

He smiled again.

'You're on form today,' he said, allowing a score of roughly eight, I guessed.

A long silence.

'I was thinking of a woman I loved,' he said, eventually.

I didn't say anything.

'And lost.'

I made the tiniest movement with my head which he might, if he wanted, mistake for a nod. I had finally seen that I must answer his quiet, hidden language with my own if he was to trust me at all.

'She killed herself in the end. This year. Ten years later to the day. She left me everything, for some reason. After all that time apart. I thought she had forgotten me, but amongst those pathetically humble possessions of hers were her diaries. And amongst the detailed documentation of her diaries were her frequent confessions of love. For me. She was full of love for me. Which was how I found out, how the question asked itself all over again.'

I waited.

'I was glad to learn she loved me, after so many years of doubt, but what I wasn't at all glad to learn was . . .'

He looked at me, then closed his eyes, breathed out, shook his head.

'I must be mad,' he said.

'Why?'

Pause.

'Let me start again.'

Pause.

'It's very – it's problematic to communicate one's . . . one's life.'

I waited patiently.

'I might do better to begin at the beginning and work my way through.' He thought about this for a while. 'You see, I have a very particular reason for seeking your help, which unfortunately I can't explain to you without frightening you off. I have to come at it in the right – from the right direction, you see.'

I didn't see, but nor did I say so. The less I said, the more he revealed himself.

'There's a mystery to solve, if you like. That's a good way of putting it. And I need your help in solving it. I can't ever seem to get to the bottom of it. I need an ally, that's what I really need.'

I nodded as indiscernibly as I dared without seeming contrived.

'The most important thing for you to understand is that . . . is . . .' He trailed off, losing his conviction again. 'I've done this so many times.'

'What, exactly?'

'This! All this talking it through! Trying to make sense of it. Trying to believe in this therapy thing. It never bloody works.' He paused, as if thinking better of his petulant defeat. 'But one has to believe in something, I suppose – and God seems very unwilling to make his presence felt in my life.'

I thought I knew why most gods would avoid Howard North. A god is a god, unlikely to kow-tow to exacting mortal terms like his.

'They thought my father killed Cassie, in the end.'

'Cassie?'

'Cassandra. My sister. Because he left the country so soon after the funeral. And never came back. Perhaps my mother put the idea into their heads, as a kind of revenge. Who knows? At first they believed it to be an accident, which for some reason my mother could never allow . . .'

'She never allowed that it might have been an accident.'

It was my first return to textbook technique, but he didn't seem to notice, or if he did, he didn't mind.

'Odd, that, isn't it? One might imagine that a mother's love would persuade her of an accident where there was none, or where there was in fact real malice, but not the other way round. If that makes any sense at all.'

'Uh-huh.'

'In the worst-case scenario, if we postulate that I did in fact kill my little sister, and that my mother did in fact see me do

36

it, how might one expect a mother to behave? Or if she didn't see me do it but assumed that I had done it, how might she then behave? Or if she had done it herself, and I had found her immediately after the deed, how differently might she behave then?'

We both wondered, although he had clearly wondered so often before that he seemed to be hoping more for my insight than for his own.

'The possibilities are endless,' I said.

'But what possibility crossed your mind so clearly just then?' His sharpness tripped me up.

'I was thinking about power,' I admitted.

'Say more.'

'I don't know your mother.'

'But you know your own.'

'Exactly. And every mother is different. We're all unique.'

'Talk about your own mother, then. There may be something in it, something I might see that I . . . do – please . . .'

'Power. That's all. Mothers enjoy power over their children when they lack it significantly elsewhere.'

'Which she did, most certainly.'

'So if she wanted your fear, your submission to her power, whether you did it or not, she'd behave judgementally, she'd make you work for her approval, for her faith in you. You'd want that more than anything else, wouldn't you, as a small boy? Her belief in you, in your basic goodness. Your lovable-ness. You'd need that.'

'Yes,' he said.

'Everyone needs that.'

'Yes,' he said again, in a small, quiet voice.

'You look sad,' I said.

The sadness filled up the room. I felt overwhelmed by it, but he seemed relatively unaware, determinedly unaffected, even oblivious to his own consuming grief.

'Of course it has crossed my mind that my father might have been the guilty one – that my mother and I were picking up the bill, as it were, for my father's crime. But . . .' He trailed off into silence again.

'But?'

'I don't think so. I remember getting a letter from him, knowing where he was in India, looking it up on a map, in my atlas, and wondering if . . . but then . . . then we lost touch. He moved. No one could track him down. And they hunted hard for him, believe me, because he was a suspect by then – a wanted, hunted man. They never found him, though. In the end we assumed he was dead.' A moment's reflection. 'My own private theory was that he'd thrown himself in the sea. He'd lost his daughter, whom he loved more than anyone in the world, and the grief was too much for him.'

Silence. The echoes of my own lost child, bloody, limp and dead as he slipped out of me, came wailing back.

'But now . . .' he said mysteriously, as though secure in some knowledge, some clue that he wouldn't reveal to me, 'I'm sure he didn't do it.'

'You don't think he did?'

'I know he didn't,' he said peremptorily.

'Right,' I replied, brought sharply out of myself by his decisiveness. 'So that's a little part of the mystery solved, then, is it?'

'Not that I was ever really in any doubt. But one's subjective view can be so blinding at times, can't it? Which is why it's so essential to keep talking it through. It was astonishing for me yesterday, for instance, to discover I'd never allowed for the possibility of an accident. Which is a perfect example of blind subjectivity. Or what a Buddhist would call karmic vision . . . narrow. Quite astonishing.'

I wasn't listening.

'Have I lost you?' he asked.

'I was thinking about your mother. You must hate her, don't you?'

I put this too bluntly, but I sensed that he preferred frankness to gentleness. He trusted it more.

'I can't seem to.' He said this as though it were a serious failing, as though it cost him more than he could tolerate. 'I wish I could, somehow. I'd be free of her then.'

4

I envied Kate. Well, there was plenty for anyone to envy about her. She had her own TV show as the country's first live therapist. She had a glorious home in Holland Park, she drove a gleaming new BMW, she was married to a successful and stunningly handsome man and, most enviably of all, perhaps, for me, she had two children, effortlessly born (and conceived). Should one of them not have been mine? At least one?

And yet, ironically, it wasn't any of these things that really hurt me any more. What I envied most about Kate by now was her ruthlesslness. Her ability to get her own way. To pick people up and put them down again without any remorse.

I realized as a child that, with this ability, she would outstrip me always, by a distance that I would never be able to cover as long as I lived. A literal analogy of our distinctly different personalities and the relationship between them was a race that I can remember running as girls – in which we stumbled over a lame dog that I stopped to nurse, while she flew on by like a bird. Winning, of course. She would always win. It wasn't that I couldn't run as fast, but I would always be held up by my heart. Somehow the more compassionate I was, the more heartless she became. And the more heartless she became, the more demonstratively (and remonstratively) compassionate I was.

Sometimes I wonder if there was only so much to go round between the two of us, and it was a question of who grabbed what first. Since she was born first, she grabbed everything she wanted just seconds before me, including her first breath, while I took what was left.

People used to speak highly of my 'kindness', because it served them well, because kindness serves everyone well. Except the kind. What they never saw was that I longed to be free of it. I longed not to care.

'Oh. Hi.'

She was cold.

'Can I come in?'

She walked away from me down the hall, leaving the door open. I was not welcome, but I could come in if I had to come in. Twins can read each other better without words.

'What do you want?'

Her abruptness was nothing new, but it still threw me.

'Er – well, I just wondered . . . I just wanted to ask you if –'

'I mean to drink. What do you want to drink?'

'Oh. Tea. Thanks.'

I paused.

'Why do I always feel that you're punishing me?'

'"Punishing" you!' she sneered. 'Is that a Person-Centred term?'

'You'll find it in any standard dictionary,' I said, trying to give as good as I got. 'If anyone should be punishing, it's me.'

'Why? What have I done?' she asked, laughing coquettishly.

'You tell me,' I said.

'God, you're pathetic, Mo. I'm a thirty-seven-year-old woman. Perhaps you still have time to "punish" people like some five-year-old, but having children of one's own makes that quite impossible.'

'Children and maturity in one,' I mumbled inadequately.

I saw myself in her as she spun round on me.

'What have you come here for?'

But I couldn't say.

'Because I haven't got time to be analysed by a heavy-handed, half-trained therapist just now.'

She poured the water from the kettle into the tea-pot, while I bit my lip.

'You have no idea what kind of therapist I am.'

'But we're about to find out, aren't we?' she said with forced good humour, filling the jug with milk and loading up the tray.

'What does that mean?'

'It means you've got a client who's a psychopath –'

'How do you know what kind of client I've got?' I demanded indignantly, wondering if Bill had already spoken to her, if they'd both been laughing about me.

'Howard North, as he calls himself. A psychopath. Everyone knows that.'

'Who told you I was seeing Howard North?' I watched the confidentiality clause slipping out of my grasp.

'I saw him, idiot. I know his car.'

I chose to deny it, if all she saw was his car.

'I don't know who you're talking about. Who's Howard North?'

'Bill seems to know who I mean.'

I felt the same old pang of jealousy. Had he come here this morning, then, when he'd stormed out of the house? Or was he here now, God forbid, hiding in some cupboard somewhere?

I followed her out of the kitchen and into the conservatory, my eyes looking everywhere for clues.

'Howard North is a very dangerous man,' she said. 'I'm really concerned about you.'

When had Kate ever been concerned about me?

'How well do you know him?'

'Well enough,' she said. 'You met him at my party, didn't you?'

'Lovely tea,' I said, resenting the fact that my new client was somehow hers too, that she could lay claim to him too, as well as everything else.

'He's a killer, Mo.' She was serious.

'What do you mean, he's a killer?' Was she deliberately trying to frighten me? 'What was he doing at your party, Kate, if he's a killer?'

'I didn't know he was a killer then,' she said, draining the blood from her face as if to order. A special effect.

'Who has he killed?' I asked, whitening a little myself.

'He killed his own sister, for one.'

Had he really? How much did she know?

'Tell me you're joking,' I said.

'I wish I was,' she said.

'How come he's a free man?'

'He was only a boy when it happened. And nobody's proved it. Yet.'

'Yet?'

'They're still trying to, especially — since his . . .' She stalled.

'Since his what?'

'Nothing,' she said. She was shaking.

'Are you all right?'

She ignored me.

'And he also drove a lover to suicide. Although I do wonder if it really was suicide . . .'

'How do you know all this?'

'I just do,' she said.

Did she? Or was she weaving a web of intricate lies and half-truths to wrap around me?

43

'Why do you wonder if it was really suicide?'

'I can't tell you,' she said. 'I can't tell you any more.'

I wasn't going to push when she had already said so much.

'Are there any others?' I asked.

'Not yet. As far as I know.'

I shuddered. I didn't entirely believe her, but I shuddered to convince her I did.

'You must feel weird,' I sympathized, feeling pretty weird myself. 'Was he a close friend of yours?'

'Very,' she said. The 'very' gave her away.

'Oh, Kate. How awful.'

'It is rather,' she said.

There was something hidden in the way she said this. I didn't know why, but at that moment I saw his lips meeting hers as if this had actually happened, and as if there was still something 'very' unresolved hidden in her heart. At least if this were true, perhaps it was Howard and not Bill that she loved.

There should have been relief in this, but there wasn't. In some curious way, Howard was becoming almost more important to me than Bill. Was it because he promised me some meagre success? While Bill and I had almost vowed to fail? Or was it just because he liked me? Because he needed me?

'Have you had a scene with him?' I asked her intrusively – but then she was always intrusive in my life, as if it were a right, somehow.

'Mo,' she said, like 'No' again, warning me. 'This tea's foul, isn't it?' she added, changing the subject.

'It's quite strange. What is it?'

'I don't know. Rose Poochong or something. Bloody Cliff. He never stops buying these awful brews. Have you seen the range of coffee beans we've got? It's like a bloody shop.'

She laughed almost hysterically. Really quite out of proportion to the joke, I felt.

'How is he these days?'

'God knows. I practically never see him.'

'Why not?'

'Too busy,' she said curtly, puncturing my curiosity. 'And Bill? How's he?'

'You tell me.'

'How should I know?'

'You see more of him than I do, Kate.'

She dismissed this as 'nonsense', and loaded up the tray.

But it wasn't nonsense. He spent far more time with her than he did with me. Whether they were actually screwing or not wasn't the point any more. The semantics were irrelevant. The point was that Bill and I didn't even feel married any more, we had grown so far apart.

In retrospect I can see that I had finally accepted this. I had stopped fighting for him. In some tacit, effortless way I had managed at last to let go. Which in turn (although he would never admit it) made him frightened to lose me.

'Have we sorted that, then?' she said.

'Have we?' I asked, unsure of what she meant.

'Leave well alone.' She meant Howard North.

She was so crisp and defined, Kate. Her therapy was a million miles from the anti-authoritarian ideals I cherished about my work. She always had to be in control, telling one hopelessly confused individual after another how to change their lives by subscribing to her view. Her will. But, oh, so charming, so charismatic, so clear. She made you believe in order, simplicity, sense. As if she could find a cure for every single problem you ever put to her. All you had to do was obey. If Howard had kissed her, it was his overpowering mother that he'd seen and desired in her.

'I've got to go,' she said.

5

Howard's next visit was a week later. I still hadn't seen Steph, nor anyone else that I could talk to with any candour. I'd left a message for my supervisor, but hadn't seen him either. I assured myself that as long as these two people were lined up for the future, all was well. One hour's supervision to four hours of client contact was the standard requirement for beginners. I was still 'ethical' – just.

His face was almost human again. The swelling in his lip had gone down substantially. The cuts and bruises had healed. I had forgotten quite how striking he was beneath that beaten face. Like carved marble. Eyes a steel-blue sky. Thick black hair painted grey at the sides, rolling back in waves from his broad forehead. A face you couldn't forget. Nor his body, which either stood like a statue, perfectly proportioned and still, or moved with an athlete's ease. There was grace in Howard North. A big man's grace.

I felt rather tatty in my old tweed suit. Not glamorous enough. I wanted to be very glamorous suddenly and to wipe the floor with Kate. I reminded myself that he sought my help because of who I was, because of something he wanted from me in particular, and that my physical image was not of great concern to him. But if Kate had won him, then I had to win him too.

He didn't greet me at all or even smile, but strode in through the front door as if it were his own territory. Purposefully.

'I shan't be coming next week,' he said as he sat down.

'Uh-huh.' I felt the pulse of failure in my blood. 'I'm sorry to hear that.'

His eyes stared intently ahead, straight through me, at some furious image far beyond me that I couldn't see.

'Is there any particular reason why?'

'Why what?' he snapped.

'Why you can't come next week?'

'Is that your business?' he demanded irritably, a palpable coldness in his eyes.

'Not if you don't want it to be.'

We sat in silence a while. A long while.

Eventually I asked, somewhat timidly, 'Are you angry with me?'

He looked at me as though noticing me for the first time.

'I don't particularly care for the female sex, if that's what you mean. And your precise colouring and features are more aggravating to me than any other combination of the two at this exact moment in time.'

He was a different man today. Rageful, tyrannizing, seething through my frailty like a hurricane.

'But don't take it personally,' he said.

'It's hard not to!' I tried to lighten the atmosphere, but the harder I tried the darker it grew.

'Have you ever been persecuted?' he asked.

'Aren't I being persecuted now?'

'Imagine yourself locked up in some metaphorical prison,' he said, ignoring me, 'and then someone turns up who tries to let you out – someone very particular tries to release you . . .'

'Uh-huh.'

'As this person is struggling to undo the lock, you both talk,

48

you laugh and cry together, you get to know each other and even to love each other, profoundly, in this time.'

'Uh-huh.'

'Then just as the lock is freed and you push open the heavy prison door, they thrust you back inside again. They betray you utterly. Everything you've ever told them about yourself in that intimate time when they were trying to release you is used against you now. You have no hope of escape. You are utterly lost. No one believes you. No one will ever try to release you again.'

Silence.

'Think about it,' he said.

I did. It was a torturous picture he'd painted, and it lived on in me.

'I may not be back the week after next, either. I may never be back.'

'I'm sorry. I'd hate not to see you again,' I said.

'Would you?' There was surprise and even tenderness in this first inquiry, but it was soon followed by a great outburst of rage.

To my astonishment, and perhaps to his own, too, he suddenly leapt to his feet and all but upturned my desk, pushing it violently towards me so that everything on it crashed to the floor.

I kicked the panic button with my foot until the alarm was screaming at us. He stopped in his tracks, a statue again.

'What the fuck do you think you're doing?' I said in half a voice as I left the room to switch off and reset the alarm. When I returned I found myself almost laughing I was so nervous.

'Jesus,' I said, shaking my head.

'I'm sorry,' he said.

'What were you doing?'

'Warning you,' he said, intensely.

'By turning my desk upside-down? Is that really necessary?'

He didn't answer.

'It's a very startling and aggressive thing to do, isn't it?'

'It's in proportion to the offence,' he said.

'What offence? I'm not even aware I committed an offence.
What was the warning for?'

He didn't answer.

'Look, Howard, I made it clear to you very early on that I
don't tolerate violence in my practice. Under any circumstances.
I'm afraid I must ask you to leave.'

'That's interesting,' he said.

'I don't know if I'm willing to go on seeing you at all, in
fact.'

'Heavens above! How on earth does anyone tolerate such a
whimsical woman as you! You're married, aren't you?'

I didn't answer.

'You don't have children, do you?'

'Why do you ask?'

'I can't imagine them surviving you, that's why.'

'Please leave now. I won't allow this abuse in my practice.'

'There's that darling word again – impossible to escape it.
Everything's abusive, Mo. You'll be shaking your impotent fists
at the empty universe soon, crying out that death is abusive
too, that social workers should put an end to it.'

'I'm sorry, Howard. If you don't go, I'll call the police.'

He looked genuinely nervous for a moment.

I got to my feet and reopened the door. Nervous or not, he
kept me waiting there a good minute before he stood up. He
was smiling. At the door he stood very close to me so that his
breath caressed my cheek. I kept my eyes on the ground, waiting

for him to pass me but he didn't move. He lifted my chin very gently until our eyes met. Then he smiled again.

'You're out of your depth, aren't you?'

That stayed with me, that sentence, for a number of reasons. First, because it was exactly how I felt. Second, because he seemed empowered by the fact and was evidently glad of it. And third, because little Cassie was out of her depth when she died.

Bill returned – from Kate's, I assumed – shortly after my session with North was through. As far as I could glean from either of them, they were co-writing a complex piece that was to run over several weeks, about paedophilia. It involved a great deal of research, so he spent hours in the library, poring over books from which he would select a short-list for Kate.

His work was creeping surreptitiously into my field and beyond, into the mind-bending world of analysis. Kate's world too, of course.

We were strangers; we avoided each other like reluctant lodgers in their own private worlds. Monosyllabic greetings were the best we could do.

I was in the hall, hovering redundantly, when he came home.

'Hi,' I said.

''llo.'

'Good day?'

'Not bad.'

Pause.

'Good.'

Pause.

'You?'

'OK.'

He made himself a cup of tea, my Bill, my big old tree, while I shut myself in my room.

If this was the end of my contract with North, it felt like the end of my life. Emptier now than it had ever been.

That night we lay still and apart on our backs, studying the crack in the ceiling. It was an ominous crack that we'd filled and refilled through the years, but it was beyond filling now, threatening to bring down the roof itself.

In the morning, with the sun up and glorious on a wealth of golden leaves, Bill still deep in sleep, unconscious as a corpse, I ached with a sudden longing for my childhood home.

I could see my father in my mind's eye, walking down the garden path to fetch the papers and milk. 'Dada!' I heard my early voice cry. Protector from all harm. Loved one. Dada. Man. Don't die. And I could see my mother too, wearing her old straw hat, taking his arm in hers as she breathed in the heavenly day. And I wanted to be there, back there, I wanted them both back, to keep the depth of them for ever in my life. The loss of them was still an unbearable agony.

And now Bill was dead, too. That's how it felt.

'What's the matter?'

He was awake now, squinting in the bright day.

'Nothing,' I said.

'We've got to do something about that crack,' he said.

'I miss Mum and Dad so much.'

He didn't say anything. What could he say? He had listened to my grief for so many years, as a penance almost, for his affair with Kate at that time. What could he say now, with the rift between us so deep and so wide?

'I seem to miss them more, not less, each year.'

'That's probably good, isn't it?' he offered half-heartedly. 'Means that by the time you die you'll probably have forgiven them for every petty harm they did. You might even stop competing with Kate for their love.'

He might have been talking about himself, with his harm done and my competition with Kate for his love.

'If she stops competing with me,' I said competitively. Why should I feel ashamed of minding what they'd done to me?

'I have to go to Wales today,' he said, throwing on a T-shirt through which his morning erection muscled for attention.

I watched him dress. How clumsy and lovable he was in his tousled, half-conscious fumblings. Zips, buttons, hair, even socks, all defying his best efforts to master them. I dozed off again, dreading full consciousness and all the dilemmas it would bring.

'See you, then.' Bill was standing by the bedroom door, looking down at me.

'Mmm?'

'I said see you, then. I'm off.'

'Oh. Right. Bye.'

But he stayed there.

'Bill? Are you OK?'

'This guy North,' he said, 'he's not your lover, is he?'

I almost laughed.

'Is he?' he demanded.

Good God. Was he jealous? After all these years of quiet indifference to me, was he finally jealous again? Jealous like he used to be, wildly, furiously? Or was he just curious to know?

And when I still didn't answer, he added that, frankly, he had understood it to be what Kate called 'unethical' to see a client without a supervisor, or a therapist.

'Without a The Rapist' he said, as if this joke hadn't been cracked with all the same cynicism before.

'Fuck Kate,' I said. 'Why can't you be as cynical about her?'

'Grow up, Mo.'

'And anyway,' I said, 'I'm seeing Steph today.'

'Well, good, I'm glad,' he said, but he was furious. 'Maybe she can persuade you that North is a psychopath. Nobody else seems to be able to.'

'Do you want me back after all?' I said.

'What?'

'As soon as somebody else might want me more?'

'I just don't want you hurt.'

'That's news,' was all I could manage as he walked out, the words seeming to echo in the hollow of the hall.

6

'What I'm picking up is that you're . . . deeply involved with him in some way – intrigued by him? Drawn? That you can't – that you don't want to let go of him? But there's also something else . . . there's a real fear of him – or of holding on to him? Of keeping him in your life?'

Steph always 'picked up' the truth, and never more incisively than she did then. I loved the way she felt around for the words, for the sense of what you were telling her, always questioning, never assuming a thing. Except that I did notice more of a statement than a question in 'there's a real fear . . .'

Originally I had found Steph's method of working almost ridiculous. She verged on the mystical, as though convening with another world. A spiritual world? Perhaps she would claim that she was. Personally I'm fairly cynical about all that. Perhaps if I'd had a little more faith in something spiritual I might not have suffered such intense and ongoing fear, nor invited what I did. But we are who we are.

She was waiting for my response like an alert field-mouse, her beady eyes smiling at me patiently.

'Yes. That's it. That's exactly how I feel. Compulsively fascinated, as if I have to get to the bottom of it.'

'It?' she asked, but as if she was sharing the feeling somehow.

'I don't know what "it" is at all. It's like a sixth sense, as if there's some mystery, some secret I've got to get my hands on. It's like a challenge . . .'

'And what I immediately think of, when you say a challenge, is Kate . . .'

'Kate?'

'We talked last time you came about her success, how it challenges you?'

I didn't want to talk about Kate.

'And I also think, when you speak of a sixth sense, of your husband . . .'

My husband. How strange the word seemed.

'Uh-huh.'

'You described – with some envy? – his instinct for a good story, his sixth sense?'

'Yes, I did, you're absolutely right.'

'Perhaps it was a projection of your own? Or –'

'Well, I – sorry – or?'

'Or is there a parallel here? Between Bill's investigative journalism and this curiosity you have about Mr North? As if – and this might be way off-beam – as if you're competing with Bill somehow, but you're in a different profession?'

'But, Steph, you have to admit there are many similarities.'

'Between the professions? Are there?'

I felt slightly ashamed then, as if my motives for choosing the profession I had were in some way unclean.

'And are those similarities what attracted you to this profession in the first place?'

'I feel as if I've done something wrong.'

'At this moment?'

'Mmm.'

'OK. Can you say more about that?'

She really did stay with me all the way. I thought of what I'd learnt in college, and of how ineffectually I put it into practice when I compared myself to Steph.

She was waiting again.

'As if you're shocked by my curiosity,' I said.

'OK. D'you want to know my real response?'

'Mmm.'

Not really, I thought.

'I'm not at all shocked. I was aware when I said "curiosity" that I was using my word. Your word was "fascination". And I was using my word because that's often what I feel in this job. Really curious!'

She laughed easily, quite at peace with this part of herself. I thought how interesting it was that with certain parts of ourselves we are perfectly at ease. We'd had a good look at them, they wielded no power, they were under our control. But there were other parts of ourselves which erupted from within like wild animals: uninvited, unwelcome, unknown. We became different people then. Awkward, shifty, ashamed. Frightened of ourselves.

'Are we travelling together still?' She beamed warmly at me.

'Yes.' I smiled.

'Where did you go?'

'I was just thinking about repression.'

'And I was thinking how repressed this area is for you – isn't it?'

'Which area?' I asked defensively. I'd forgotten how uncomfortable it could be on this side of the therapeutic exchange.

'This healthy curiosity you have, you seem quite – ashamed – of it?'

'Yes, I suppose I am.'

'Can you say more?'

'Like what?'

'In what way you're ashamed, or why, or . . . ?'

I was really uncomfortable then. I think I even blushed. I didn't want to say more.

'You seem very embarrassed, Mo.'

'Mmm . . .'

'Do you want to say what that's about?'

I let out a heavy sigh, which she mirrored.

'This whole area is still so . . .'

'So?'

She was unremitting in her efforts.

'So uncomfortable.'

'I can feel that,' she said, and she started wriggling around slightly in her skin. 'Feels tight in here, constraining . . .'

'Mmm . . .' I acknowledged the accuracy of her physical insight rather begrudgingly.

'Are you cross with me?' she asked pleasantly.

'Yes.'

'Thought so!' She smiled.

'I don't want to break new ground and I can feel you pushing me to.'

'OK. Let's leave be.'

She fell silent, which was very clever of her. She just left me with the door half-open on a whole powerhouse of feelings which might really help me. They might throw some light on North, or ease the tension with Bill, or possibly both. Unexplored, they promised miracles.

'D'you know, I think it's to do with sex?'

'Yep. That's what I think, too.'

How dare she, I thought. How dare she be so at ease with this dark secret in me?

'This man – Howard . . .' I began.

'He sounds like an attractive man . . .'

'Does he?' I pounced, greedily.

'Does that make it OK?'

'Make what OK?'

'That he sounds attractive to me. Does that make it OK for you to be attracted to him?'

I hadn't even admitted to myself the attraction I felt for North. Why should I admit it to her?

'Maybe,' was all I said.

She fell silent again, smiling kindly, encouragingly, determined not to push. I had the sense that she could see something I couldn't see, something I was blind to that everyone could see except me, a most intimate part of myself that I didn't even know was exposed.

'I'm supposed to be the good girl. Maybe that's it,' I said.

'Say more, if you can?'

'Kate's bad, I'm good. I'm not allowed to be bad.'

'So where does the badness go?'

'Lock and key, Steph! Repressed! Group 104 security!' I was trying to laugh at myself. I knew I could say more to Steph than to anyone else in my life about who I really was, but could I tell her what I hadn't even told myself?

'And the badness – what is it exactly?'

I could feel my heart sink through the earth, burying its secrets in the dark, enclosing soil.

'I don't know,' I said. Nor did I want to.

'Not just sex?'

'God, no.' I laughed. 'If only it was just sex!'

'If only it was just sex,' she repeated, so that I could hear the words, hear the admission I had made to something far more troubling.

'Can we talk about something else?' I said, uncomfortably.

'It's your hour, Mo.'

How I imitate her, I thought.

'I need to talk about Bill. Me and Bill. We're just so – I don't know . . . We're so estranged.'

'OK.'

'It's not OK,' I said, exasperated by her glib, easygoing response. 'It's terrible, and it's my life. It's the whole of my once-happy life turned upside-down!'

'Your once-happy life?'

I felt that she wasn't with me any more, that she was outside me, looking in.

'Don't just sit there like the big I AM, Steph, as if you know what's best for me. You don't. You haven't got a clue.'

She smiled and nodded and tried to stay on my side. She was struggling.

'What are you trying not to say?' I asked. 'You might as well tell me.'

'What I'm thinking is, I don't have a memory of this happy life with Bill. I don't recall hearing about that.' She was puzzled, furrowing her brow.

Silence. Like the truth. Like a boulder in the middle of the room.

'Before we were married it was good.' But was even that true?

'Uh-huh. And when was that? Ten years ago?'

'I haven't forgiven him. That's what the real problem is. Ten years, and I still haven't let it go. It's my fault, Steph. And now I'm taking revenge.'

'Revenge?' She was surprised. 'Doesn't sound like revenge to me.'

'Doesn't it?'

'Sounds to me like you're getting some attention for once.' She watched me take this in. 'He respects you, Mr North, doesn't he? He values you.'

'But what do I do about it?' I pleaded, my panic audible.

'What do you want to do? Depends how attracted you are,' she said calmly.

'Or how frightened I am.'

'Or are you just frightened of yourself?'

I didn't think I was. I was genuinely frightened of something I could sense in him, but I didn't say so. Nor did I tell her anything that he'd told me about himself. I didn't want her to spot a danger so great that she would intervene in some way, abort my adventure before it had even begun.

'Perhaps that's all it is.' I nodded. 'I'm frightened of the feelings . . .'

'And they're just feelings,' she said.

7

For days afterwards I awoke each morning with a heady feeling of anticipation. Of what, I really didn't know. It was mixed in with a deep feeling of remorse, and neither feeling won the day. I felt pulled equally between the two. Perhaps I was anticipating midnight callers again. If I was, none came. The remorse was undeniably for Bill, but North was in there, too. I didn't hear from either of them and I didn't contact them. I didn't contact anyone. Every night I retired to bed restless, disappointed, and alone.

Then one day I woke up late, too late for either feeling to get the better of me, and hurried to be on with the day. I switched off the alarm, grabbed the post, and made myself a cup of coffee. I sank on to the sofa we had taken for ever to choose and missed Bill. His familiar ordinariness.

I flicked through the pile of letters and put the brown envelopes aside for later. A postcard from Bill's mother, as usual addressed only to him, from Malaga. She had bought a timeshare there and was always inviting him out to cover an ever-unfolding story about some expatriate. This card was no different. 'A big wet kiss from your loving Mum. XXX.' Mothers and their sons. An invitation from two close friends to their wedding anniversary, which somehow emphasized our own current separateness. And finally a letter written in handwriting both distinct and unfamiliar, an elegant swift run of black ink on a cheap white envelope. A London postmark.

Mo.

I was sorry to have frightened you. Truly. I seem to have been blessed with an alarming ability to terrify. Especially women. I had rather hoped you might be the exception. I do honour your decision not to see me again, but I wonder if you might agree just to meet me for a drink somewhere? Do telephone.

North.

The letter was so uncharacteristically polite. I thought of how effectively he had frightened me, and of how harmless he now seemed, if only because of this admission of his. His 'ability to terrify'. I even felt sorry for him. Perhaps this was his intention. If it was, it worked.

How could I trust my fear, my instinct for danger, when I had only recently witnessed a brutal murder in what had seemed to me to be harmless circumstances? In my efforts to identify reality I still doubted what reality was.

I telephoned. There was hardly time for it to ring before he answered.

'Yes?'

'Howard?'

'Speaking.'

'Mo.'

'Mo.'

And then a pause.

'Er – I got your letter . . .'

'Good.'

'Would you – well – where would you like to meet?'

He gave me elaborate directions for a place by the river overlooking Tower Bridge and then asked:

'Shall I pick you up?'

'Thanks. I'll make my own way there.'

Just in case, I thought.

We arranged to meet at six. At five, I soaked myself in a long, hot, scented bath. Exotic smells. There was the undeniable feeling of anticipation back again, bounding about inside me like an excitable dog. Thoughts of Bill came knocking at my heart but I locked the door on them.

I chose my clothes carefully. I thought they exhibited an easy naturalness, a wearing of the world like a loose garment round my limbs. But when I looked at myself in the mirror before I left, I saw restraint. A wildness hemmed in.

I found the place early and sat a while in my car. Tower Bridge glowed in the winter evening sun like a fairy-tale castle, a magical palace that didn't really exist, or that had shot up through the water like King Arthur's sword. Excalibur.

Howard was also early, I noticed. He stood with his back to me, gazing out at the same magnificent sight. Did it thrill him as it thrilled me?

I got out of the car at six o'clock and he turned instinctively towards me. He looked different, although the same elegance lent itself to his form. His whole presence seemed gentler, less forbidding.

'Hello,' was all I could manage. I felt shy of him now, in this different context.

He didn't reply but smiled, ushering me into the bar. He made his way determinedly to a table by the window and pulled out a chair for me.

'What will you have?'

'Apple juice? Anything soft.'

I watched him struggle with his impatience as he waited at the bar. When at last he returned I was so absorbed by the river-life, the boats, the nostalgia that these evoked in me, I didn't notice him.

'Mo.'

He was already sitting down opposite me.

'Oh. Thanks.' I gulped down the cold juice.

'Do you like boats?'

'They remind me of my father,' I said, and then wished I hadn't.

'Is he a sailor, then?'

'No. He just loved boats. He wanted to live on one.'

'Now that I can understand.'

I didn't want him to understand. I didn't want him to know anything about me. I wanted to go on being a mystery. Our previous relationship had allowed me that. Now, even with this small revelation, I felt the power run out of me like blood from my veins.

'I'm afraid this meeting really disqualifies our counsellor—client relationship,' I announced somewhat formally, retrieving a little control.

'Why?'

'It would be unethical to continue.'

'According to whom?'

He had a conceited smile on his face that implied a superior knowledge, but also a gentle teasing of my pomposity.

'Generally it's considered quite inappropriate,' I said.

I feared another outburst of his rage as I crossed him once more, but he remained calm and amiable, still half-laughing at me.

'What was your training? I've forgotten.'

I didn't believe he had forgotten. I remembered at Kate's party his enthusiasm for the man whose ideas I most admired, his delight at my admiration for their unconventionality, his constantly bringing the conversation back to my training and beliefs.

'Neville Hoare,' I reminded him.

'Of course. The man himself.'

Surely he was laughing at me?

'I'm surprised you've heard of him.'

'Why?'

'Few people have. Even fewer like him.'

'Is that so?' he said thoughtfully. He went quiet for a while. 'I don't know much about him. I've heard Kate mention him once or twice. He sounds quite unusual. Not your run-of-the-mill soul-saver, is he?'

But I didn't want to talk about a complex man like Hoare with someone who hardly knew his work. And anyway I was thinking of Kate, of her bruised, swollen, made-up, covered-up cheek.

'How do you know Kate?'

'Kate?'

'Have I asked the wrong question, Howard?'

'Can a question be wrong?' he asked rhetorically.

'A question can be compromising, can't it? Let's not play with words.'

He looked at me in silence for what seemed like an eternity. An untroubled grey-blue gaze. Or was he looking at Kate? A smile carved its way into his lips.

'You're extraordinarily beautiful,' he said.

My heart sank. This was a moment I had longed for and dreaded, both. In equal measure. It wasn't the flattery, but the intention behind it that so thrilled and daunted me. I looked away, out of the window at the boats. Dada and his boats. This infant in me, seeing so subjectively still what I might take from the world. Me, me, me. Nurture my baby soul. Mama, Dada, both. Love me all. Love no one but me all. Do not have eyes but for me. Bill. My Bill. Be man. Be Dada for me, father me so, and I will mother my son. Give me back my childhood better than it was and I will mother you.

'Have I said the wrong thing, Mo?'

I looked back at him. This stranger. This danger to me.

'Possibly.'

He took my hand and turned it over in his, toying with it like a cat with its prey.

'How tiny it is. Like a child's.'

I snatched my hand away and stood up, betraying my confusion and fear.

'I think I'd better go.'

'Very well.'

He kept his eyes trained on me, bewildered now, reluctant to lose me.

'You needn't fear me,' he said.

'Oh, really? You needn't be so frightening,' was my quick retort.

Pause.

'I expect that's true,' he conceded.

'It's difficult without rules to follow, isn't it?' I said, a little more kindly.

'Doesn't your guru disapprove of rules?'

'If you must know, he's not my guru. And, yes, in many ways that's quite true.'

He smiled.

'What's so funny?'

'Nothing. I'm interested. Go on.'

I didn't believe he was interested at all. I believed he wanted to watch me hold forth ridiculously so that he could patronize me.

'Basically, Hoare posits that rules are fundamental to identity, but only if some of them are broken. By choosing which rules to break, individuals define themselves. If the rules are good and true, they won't need to break them. It's only the repressive social rules he likes to see broken.'

'And our rules? Which are they?'

'Well – they're the ethical rules by which one abides as a counsellor.'

'One?'

'I. By which I abide.'

'Are they dictates, or are they rules you choose for yourself?'

'Both.'

'And ours?'

'Ours?'

Somehow 'ours' seemed excessively intimate.

'Yours and mine?'

'We've broken our rules already, Howard. You broke my rule by upturning my desk. I've broken another of my rules by meeting you socially. But one rule I won't break is to see you as a client again, having met you like this. It would be unethical.'

'Is that what Mr Hoare would say?'

'It's what I say. Neville Hoare isn't some god to be obeyed.'

'Is he still alive, this man?'

'I assume so. He still writes the occasional book.'

'You've not met him, I take it?'

'He's totally elusive. I don't know anyone who's met him. Makes you wonder, doesn't it? It could be a monster we're all studying.'

Howard smiled again.

'Sit down,' he said. 'Please? Just for a while.'

He took my hand and drew me back to my seat.

'I seem to keep upsetting you. I don't mean to, Mo. There's no one I'd rather please.'

I avoided his eyes, staring hard at my beer-mat. I kept

thinking of Bill, of our courtship, of how thrilling it had been.

What am I doing here?

I fitted the round base of my glass centrally on to the beer-mat. We do these things when there is nothing else we can do.

'I've had a difficult – unexpressed – life,' he said. 'I wanted to tell you. Tell you about it. The whole story.'

When I got home the lights were on and Bill's car was parked outside. I felt the keen edge of fresh deceit cutting into our lives. My deceit now, not his. His was something we already knew about, a part of the marriage that we had somehow contained. Or had we? Had we ever?

It was easier to be the victim, I realized, than to inflict the wound.

Our mutual deceit had now become a lethal blade, severing all communication between us, all heart-to-heart transfusion of the truth.

'Bill?'

The television was on. *Newsnight* was reporting crime statistics for the 1990s. There had been a decrease in burglaries but an increase in violent crime. As if we hadn't noticed the latter. Bill was asleep, his face squashed up against a cushion like a child's. He was always asleep, it seemed. Either away or asleep. For once, I felt relieved, and turned to go, anxious to deceive him further by changing out of my silk dress into something more demure. But he stirred and opened his eyes.

'Hi,' I said, braving his cold eyes. 'How was Wales?'

'Fine.'

He looked away, watching the television studiously. News was, after all, his subject, and had often been a useful focus when awkward emotions emerged. I watched it, too, perching on the end of the sofa.

'How can they say it's gone down?'

'What?'

'Burglary,' I explained, aware that he wasn't actually listening to the programme at all. 'I thought it was so popular now they were teaching it in schools.'

'They're manipulating the figures, that's all. What they don't say is that most of the crime is burglary-related. They just call it "violent crime" instead of "burglary" so it looks like they've got a result – in one department at least.'

'Oh, the deceits of this world . . .' I mused idiotically, asking for trouble.

'Tell me about them,' he said.

He said it like a world-weary journeyman whose last flicker of faith in human integrity has finally been blown out. Was it my flame? Or his?

I felt that my own deceit was rank, that he could smell it on me. Was I even deceiving myself? I had agreed to meet North 'as a friend' the following day. To hear this whole story of his. Whose 'friend' was I?

Bill switched off the sound with the remote control and looked at me. Finally.

'Where have you been?'

'Out.'

'Where?'

'To a pub.'

'Who with?'

'A friend.'

'Who?'

'No one you know.'

'Male or female?'

'Does it matter to you?'

'Male or female?'

'Male.'

'Who?'

'A friend, Bill. Just a friend.'

'Who? Friends have names, don't they?'

'I'm not going to have this conversation now.'

I got up to leave the room but he grabbed my arm and pulled me back down on to the sofa. He stood up and paced about in front of me, glaring at me wildly. I hated this side of him. Perhaps I should have been pleased that he cared, but it was too late for that. I didn't want him to care.

'You look very smart. For a pub. Best silk dress.'

'So?'

'Sure it wasn't dinner?'

'Yes, Bill, I'm sure it wasn't dinner.'

'First time I've known you to dress up for the pub.'

'There's a first time for everything, I guess.' Did he hear the irony?

'Howard, was it?'

'Who?'

'How is the dear psychopath?'

It was then that I noticed Howard's letter lying open on the table. I had left it there, of course, without the faintest notion that Bill would be back that night. He snatched it up and waved it under my nose.

'Heroic Howard North who rings your bell in the middle of the night. Literally, I mean. Only you can tell us if he rings it metaphorically, too.'

'Don't be ridiculous.'

'Oh? Is that ridiculous? Kate says –'

'Kate! Have you been talking to Kate about this?'

'Something wrong with that?'

I felt instinctively that there was something very wrong with that, something far beyond their treachery, which I couldn't put my finger on. But I did my best to conceal this from Bill, making light of what I could.

'Not at all, Bill. Why should there be anything wrong with talking to Kate so intimately about me?'

'That was ten fucking years ago!'

Was jealousy all we had left to share? A petty possessiveness?

'I loved you, Bill,' I said.

'Kate says he's a very attractive man.'

'Kate married Cliff. If that's her idea of attractive, she's welcome to it.'

'Oh, come on, Mo. Everyone knows that Cliff is an incredibly good-looking man. He's practically famous for it!'

In fact this was true. But Cliff was Kate's, and anything of Kate's was becoming less and less attractive to me.

'I'm talking about personality, Bill, not face or physique.'

The argument was facile but inevitable. We would shortly have to discuss the merits or otherwise of Howard's physical attributes, both of us knowing full well that sexual charisma lay like a buried treasure, far beneath the surface level of skin.

'He's got personality, too, I hear,' Bill said.

'Well, honey, just for the record, he made such an impression on me the first time I met him, I couldn't remember what the fuck he looked like when he called.'

He laughed at this, at what he thought was yet another lie. In fact it was almost the first truth I had told.

'She says he's the archetypal hero of every woman's dreams. Would you agree with that? Just out of interest?'

What was she doing, feeding Bill's frightened imagination with images like these? Did she want to drive him frantically back to me? And if so, why?

'I've no idea,' I said.

His distress, such an unusual feeling for him to experience in relation to me, was fast turning into rage.

'Surely you would. You'd agree with Kate. You are twins, after all.'

'So?'

'Presumably you fancy the same men.'

'Why should we? We're not the same people, Bill. You should know that.'

'But the same men fancy both of you.'

Back came the cruelty. He could hurt me in spite of everything, and he revelled in it. I came up for air.

'I don't want to know, Bill.'

'But it's not news, is it? You've always known I fancy Kate. And that she fancies me. We were lovers, for God's sake!'

'Jesus, Bill . . .'

Did he mean me to feel that old panic again? The panic of losing him. The rush of jealousy, the urge to possess what I didn't even want any more. I had spent our entire married life trying to hold on to his love, when he had thrown it away at the very start.

'I must say, I don't blame you. We haven't made love in so many years, you must be crying out for it.'

'What about you? Aren't you, if I must be?' My voice was trembling.

'*What were you doing with him?*'

It was a sudden cry of pain, as if he could sense something far worse than ever I had forecast.

We stared at each other. It was one of those moments when you choose a direction that changes the whole of your life. Full of renewed feeling, full of compassion again, do you love and forgive, or do you draw the line? Do you volunteer for more pain, or do you say never again?

73

I chose to draw the line. But I kissed him full on the mouth, as if this could somehow wipe out the truth of what I had done.

He devoured my mouth as if it were food, a food he hadn't tasted in years. His hands groped at my breasts as if kneading dough, before clawing at the stockings beneath my dress, wrenching at them greedily so that they burnt my thighs, his fingers digging into me. He tore the offending dress from me so that it ripped at the seams. Then he threw me on the floor and penetrated me in almost every way that he could, before collapsing in a half-satisfied, half-tortured wail of relief.

He had raped me, effectively, since I'd had no will for it, since he had used such force. But I had surrendered, so . . . In a court of law they would say that I hadn't struggled enough. I could have hit him or screamed, but I feared more force still. And somewhere at the back of my mind I thought I deserved it. I even wanted the finality of it.

In the early hours of the morning I woke sweating feverishly, plagued by a recurring nightmare.

Ironically, although I was suffocating with heat, I had been dreaming of a terrible coldness, of living on a strange planet colder than any coldness I had known. Was it Europa, Jupiter's fourth moon? Frozen over like a cracked white eggshell, bleeding blue water from its wounds? Wherever it was, I couldn't ever grasp its laws. It seemed much like earth, in that it was peopled by the same human race, but every human instinct I possessed was alien to them and punishable by law. In vain I endeavoured to grasp the logic by which they lived so that I might belong to their world. I longed for their immunity to the cold.

It was killing me. Killing the warm heart of me.

I woke startled and ached with the loss of Bill. For ever a loss now.

When eventually he and I had climbed into bed, he had offered me his back, and I had offered him mine. And there would be no turning back.

8

I didn't sleep for the remainder of that night but lay staring at the crack in the ceiling until birdsong and first light. They brought rain. As I slipped quietly from our bed I felt the sharp edge of cold air. It was shocking to me, a hard, shuddering cold. November now. Winter was waiting for me, summer finally done.

I wandered downstairs at a distance from myself – a distance of both the head and the heart, as though watching myself on a screen, an unscrupulous anti-heroine for whom I felt only contempt. Perhaps if I had exercised some of the empathy then that Neville Hoare's teachings had always urged me to, things would have been different. Even before trying to forgive or understand Bill, I might have sat down with myself, reached out a hand, tried to understand where I'd strayed. But my empathy was all used up on North. I hadn't learnt to apply the same generosity to myself.

After a fresh coffee and two Cox's apples I stole back into the bedroom for clothes, any clothes, I no longer cared which. Bill stirred in his sleep as I opened the wardrobe door, and the sound stopped me short, as a healthy conscience might, but, once sure of his continued sleep, I crept away to dress. I wanted to be out of the house before he stirred again. It was still relatively early, only seven o'clock – my rendezvous with North was at nine – but I chose to leave then rather than risk a further confrontation with Bill. Sure that the sound of my car would rouse him, I pulled away fast enough to qualify for the Grand Prix. I dreaded the sight of his face at the window, his tousled crop of fair hair above his smooth skin creased by the restless sheets, his lips mouthing questions at me. I didn't look up.

I had two hours to kill. Or an hour and a half. The drive from Shepherd's Bush to the Isabella Plantation in Richmond Park would take half an hour at most on a Saturday morning.

I knew that Howard lived in Chiswick — he had given me his card at our first session — and I felt an overwhelming curiosity to see the house itself.

My heart was pounding in my chest as I turned down the road itself — a road full of fine Georgian houses, ablaze with burning-red Virginia creeper. A distinguished, wealthy air pervaded the comfortable half-asleep street. Each house was fronted by wrought-iron railings or high walls and gates, generous porches, handsome front doors in rich hues of green, blue, crimson and black, their brass accessories gleaming in the rain. And yet they conveyed somehow a contrived, sober modesty which served only to adorn their splendour further, like a thin veil over a face. Beauty is always best hidden. Flaunted, it courts enemies.

I thought of our plain old Shepherd's Bush house, dull and big as an over-large frock. How envious I felt of these elegant homes. How ashamed, too; how inadequate I felt that Howard had even seen our place. Had he anticipated something like Kate's place, at the very least?

I drove slowly down the road, searching for his house, his number, his home. It was easily the finest of them all. Exquisite as his tailored clothes. An immaculate old Mercedes lazed in the drive, a demure gun-metal grey.

I pressed down on the accelerator, terrified of being seen. I looked a mess. What could I offer him now, disempowered as I was? No magical skills to promise him, no therapist's role to play. Nakedly myself.

At the end of the road I discovered the river gliding easily by. I envied its complacence. In fact I envied everything then. I watched myself with loathing, wanting all that wasn't me. I stepped out of my car, unsteady on my feet, into the pouring rain, and took a deep breath. It was the cleanest London air I had breathed since a walk on Hampstead Heath in the spring, but a damp, cold air now, sweet-smelling as the sea. I longed for the sea, for the countryside by the sea to swaddle me in swathes of peaceful green.

I was drenched by the time I roused from my half-conscious reverie. It was already 8.30 when I heard a door slam shut. I saw Howard's Mercedes pull out of his drive and glide towards me, glide like the river, glide like the sky, a gliding gunmetal grey . . .

Then Howard's figure was towering over me, lifting me up from the pavement, carrying me to his car, sitting me on the front seat, my soaking body marking the leather upholstery. I had collapsed. I was shivering uncontrollably with the cold, or the fever, or the Plague. We rolled back into his drive, the Mercedes grumbling about its cargo, I felt sure. I could almost hear its low, refined drawl reprimanding North for his choice: of all the women you could have, this drowned rat of a thing . . . But as soon as the engine's quiet hum was switched off, the lazy beast was silent again. Hugo, I christened it privately. Over-privileged, over-indulged, under-extended. Indolent.

I was almost hallucinating, I realized.

'Can you walk?' asked Howard, opening my door.

'Of course I can walk,' I said, but I fell out of the car on to his gravel drive and had to suffer the indignity of being carried in.

*

78

When I returned to full consciousness I was sitting beside a roaring fire, wrapped in a green silk dressing-gown. Swathed in peaceful green. I had nothing on underneath. Howard was sitting opposite me, frowning slightly, staring hard at the fire. I half-expected a woman's presence to waft into the room, but none came.

'Feeling better?' he asked, without looking at me.

'Yes. Much. Thank you.' I paused. 'I mean – I wasn't aware of feeling worse, in fact. Although obviously I must've done.'

'You collapsed.'

'Yes.'

I paused again, trying to read the expression on his face.

'You were very cold.'

'Was I?'

I wondered just how cold. Surely he hadn't undressed me himself?

'How cold was I?' I ventured cautiously.

He smiled, plainly aware of my discomfort but offering no reassurance.

'Very cold indeed.'

I blushed, feeling suddenly very hot.

'Did you . . . ?'

I looked down at the silk dressing-gown tied neatly around my waist, the too-big swathe of green. He knew exactly what I was wondering, and seemed to enjoy my uncertainty.

'It was somewhat necessary,' he finally confessed, 'under the circumstances.'

An involuntary smile danced over his lips. He looked down at the thick Persian rug, but I could see him quite clearly struggling to wipe it from his face. When eventually he looked up again, a stony seriousness had taken its place.

'I do apologize.'

'Where are my clothes?' I demanded indignantly.

To my astonishment he had the audacity to smile yet again.

'I'm so sorry. You have every right to be angry –'

'I certainly do.'

'But you must understand that – in spite of my best intentions – it afforded me the greatest pleasure to . . .' His sentence trailed off, but his eyes stayed focused on me, speaking volumes of their own. 'I must say, you do have quite the most beautiful . . . the most beautiful . . .'

He was frowning again, just slightly, as though discussing a work of art, not quite sure whether it really was so fine after all, and if it was, then what exactly it was that made it so exceptional.

'How dare you?' was all I could say.

He looked away at the fire, his glowing face suddenly sad, as though some thought or memory had swept him away from me. A great distance stretched between us.

'Your clothes are in the laundry-room,' he said dismissively, his voice suddenly cold – hostile, indifferent.

I think I was expected to leave then, quietly and graciously, like some meek, obedient slave, understanding, as no one else could, her master's troubled temperament. I stayed.

He continued to ignore me, surrendering wholly to his thoughts, which excluded me utterly.

It was this habit of withdrawing from me, I later realized, that made me determined to draw him out. His sudden stubborn silences created an urgent longing in me to hear this story of his, this whole account of his life.

'Howard?'

He seemed startled by the sound of my voice and, looking up, was plainly amazed to find me still there.

'What are you thinking about?'

He didn't answer, but looked away again at the fire. I thought back to our first session together, to his sister's 'funny little line' and his own 'curiosity'. I was wondering uncomfortably what pleasure my unconscious naked body had in fact afforded him when suddenly he got up from his throne of a chair and left the room.

I looked around me for some clue to the mystery he was. The room was heavy with atmosphere, panelled from floor to ceiling in wood. There were large, incongruously modern paintings on the walls. The thick lined curtains of eggshell blue exuded a musty-sweet smell. I studied the books on the shelves behind me, many of them classics, bound in old red or green leather. One shelf alone – the lowest – was confined to modern writing, paperbacks and hardbacks alike. It was crammed with books, in fact, as though struggling to contend with the weight of history above. To my astonishment, many of these books were modern psychology books. But more astonishing still, since he had denied even a nodding acquaintance with the man's work, he had every book of Neville Hoare's. Admittedly their spines looked untroubled by exercise.

Maybe he's only recently bought them all, I speculated.

I was about to pick one from the shelf and look at it when I felt the soft impact of flying clothes at my back. I turned round to see Howard, who had presumably thrown them at me.

'They're more or less dry,' he said.

'Thank you,' was my more or less dry reply.

'I must ask you to leave now,' he said.

'Sure.' I picked up my clothes. 'Tell me. Why the sudden change of mood?'

'Please get dressed. This is too familiar,' he said.

'I didn't ask you to take off my clothes,' I retorted.

'I don't mean familiar in that sense of the word.'

He turned his back to me sharply, looking out of the window at his gleaming car. I climbed discreetly into my underwear and then into my overwear until I was fully dressed.

'Shall I see myself out?'

He turned round suddenly, surprise and confusion blatant on his face.

'Don't go yet,' he said. It was an order, not a request.

'I find I'm happier with consistency, Howard – you know? I like a person to say something and stick with it – at least for a minute or two.'

'Sit down,' he said, plainly unamused.

Although the masochist in me enjoyed his domination, the freedom-fighter did not. Went to war, in fact.

'I'm so sorry, I didn't quite hear what you said.'

'I said, sit down.'

He hadn't sensed the edge in my voice. I persevered.

'Yes, I thought you said "sit down". My ears attempted to transmit the words to my brain, but there was something in your tone which my brain didn't recognize – hold on – I'm getting the message through now . . . it's just processing . . .' I paused dramatically, as if listening to my brain, and then said, *sotto voce*: 'Ah. I see. That's why . . .' before readdressing him. 'Apparently the tone you used was quite archaic – no longer in common usage – something to do with male domination? Tyrannical bullying? Make any sense?'

'Very good,' he said drily. 'You've come a long way.'

Absurdly, I was flattered. But I found the statement disarmingly patronizing too.

'Not literally, of course – you haven't actually covered any distance. You're merely treading water. But that's better than nothing, isn't it? When you're out of your depth.'

I thought of her again. Tiny dead weight in his hands. Or hers.

'What makes you think I'm out of my depth?'

'Aren't you?'

'What depths are they, Howard? If you could give me some indication of how deep I'm in, I might be able to say.'

He studied my face, examining its dimensions thoroughly, cocking his head to one side to get a fresh perspective on it.

'The likeness is remarkable,' he said.

I always hated these comparisons, common as they were.

'Can you imagine being a twin, Howard? How frustrating it is?'

He put his head straight again guiltily.

'Not easily,' he confessed.

'Imagine if people were always making assumptions about you because of how you looked, because of what they knew about your twin, because they'd screwed her or –?'

'I wouldn't like it at all.'

I felt that he was trying to cut me off somehow, to stop me explaining further, but I wanted to drive the point home. I wanted to see what he would betray of his intimacy with Kate.

'People I've never even met – men particularly – behave as if they have an intimate knowledge of me, simply because they've slept with Kate. Men I wouldn't even look at, let alone sleep with.'

He was silent. Intensely so.

'And since she sleeps with a different man almost every week, it makes life rather difficult for me.'

Pause.

'Does she?'

'Does she what?' I asked.

'Sleep with a – so many men?'

'Well, she's never been one to tire of it, put it that way. She enjoys her power too much. Even in her work. I expect she'd call it all work, mind you. Research or experimentation or something. She is a sex therapist, after all. Amongst other things.'

I said all this in a very matter-of-fact way, which indeed it was, but he looked decidedly uncomfortable.

'I've often wondered what would happen if her power failed her . . .'

'Her sexual power, you mean?' he asked, too urgently.

'She assumes she can conquer everyone who comes to see her – she would say "cure", but generally she cures by conquering, it's the conquest that motivates her –'

'How do you know what motivates her?' he demanded furiously.

'Because she's explained it to me,' I said. 'Am I upsetting you?'

'Not at all,' came the swift, suddenly calm reply. 'I can't abide assumptions, that's all. You seemed to be guilty of the very thing you were criticizing in others – namely that because you're twins, you must be alike.'

'We couldn't be more different,' I said, in my defence.

He fell silent.

I wondered whether I should leave, whether I had far outstayed my welcome there, but he scarcely seemed aware of me, so deep in thought was he. Then having said nothing for at least ten minutes, he offered me a coffee.

'Thank you.'

When he was out of the room I looked at his books again. He even had *Beyond the Law* – Hoare's most recent work. I still hadn't finished it myself. I flicked through its pages, hoping it would fall open at a passage that would change my life, that would reveal the world to me as I longed for it to be. Uncannily, it fell open on a chapter about sex. 'In this particular domain,' it read, 'the law-makers are the law-breaker's victims, since only they know what price they have had to pay.' I didn't get any further before he returned with a tray.

'Any you don't recognize?' he asked.

'Of . . . ? Oh – you mean the books?'

'I do indeed mean the books.' He poured the coffee.

'I certainly know all of Hoare's work,' I said, and couldn't resist adding, 'I thought you didn't know much about him?'

'I don't,' he said soberly. 'Honestly. If only I did.'

'But you've got everything he's ever written!'

'Do you know much about him from what he's written, Kate?'

'Mo.'

'I do apologize,' he said, immediately contrite. 'Mo.'

'Yes, I feel I do know something of him from his work.'

'What do you think you know?' He passed me a cup.

'I know he's an honest thinker,' I said devoutly. 'Thorough. He shines a light in the darkest corners of the soul.'

'Goodness.'

'He goes where no one has dared.'

'Brave, then?' he mocked. 'Honest and brave!'

'Very brave,' I answered gravely, resisting his ridicule. 'But I imagine he must be very lonely, too.'

'Why lonely?' He seemed suddenly disconcerted by this.

'Because he makes people so uncomfortable.'

'Ah. Indeed.'

'People like to be told life is simple and everyone is good.'

'Do they, Mo?'

'Whereas he tells them they're not good. Quite categorically. He tells them life is complex. Not simple at all.'

'Which, undeniably, it is. Complex, I mean.'

'But you'd be surprised how many people would rather think they were stupid or confused than admit that life is complex and difficult.'

We sipped our coffee thoughtfully.

'Do you really think that's true?' he finally asked.

'Yes.'

'Does Kate deny complexity, too?'

'Possibly,' I said, wondering why we were back with Kate. 'She's very single-minded. She doesn't like paradox, or complexity. You can see that in her TV shows. She believes in straightforward answers. Solutions. God help her if she ever meets with the truth!'

'Don't you believe in solutions?'

'Yes, of course. But it's always better to face unpalatable truths than deny them, isn't it?'

'Is it?'

'What's that line of Hoare's? "If you deny it, you are immobilized, if you admit it, you are resourced."'

'What a trite little saying!' He cringed.

'I don't think it's trite.'

'Of course it's trite. Anyone can write that crap.' He spat the words contemptuously.

'I think it's very profound.'

'Unadulterated faeces, Mo.'

His sudden mood swing left me bewildered. He was like two people, one cultured and civilized, the other thriving on anarchy.

I dug in my heels, determined not to lose myself.

'I don't agree. I think Hoare is immensely courageous. Wise and –'

'How can that kind of simplistic rationalizing be "wise"?' He

86

cut me off abruptly, almost shouting at me. 'For all his tribute to complexity, how does a comment like that take into account all, or any, of the complexities we struggle with every day?'

'His writings are as capable as anyone else's of addressing life's complex entirety.' I was fierce in my defence of this great man, this hero of mine. 'He addresses life's whole better than anyone I know.'

'Life's hole?' echoed Howard, making a circle of his forefinger and thumb.

I moved towards the door, but he grabbed me.

'Don't be such a ridiculous, sentimental cow.'

He was holding me by the shoulders, his face furious and betrayed in mine.

'Use your fucking brain,' he said desperately. 'I need your intelligence, Mo, not your sentimental fairy-tales.'

'How is what I've said sentimental? I don't see it.'

'You're obviously in love with this bloody Neville Hoare. That's sentimental, isn't it? He can do no wrong in your eyes.'

'I'm sure he can do wrong.'

'Think for yourself, Mo. Don't think through books you've read by anonymous guru-men. I need you to think for yourself.'

Hugo the Mercedes grumbled slightly with old age as the accelerator was pressed down.

In Richmond Park we left him lined up with his inferiors, before setting off for the Plantation in wellington boots and coats. I was wearing an old oilskin which Howard had found buried in his cloakroom under countless jackets. It reminded me of a coat that Kate used to wear, the glossy black against her dyed yellow hair.

'Whose was this?' I asked, fingering the worn creases in the arms.

'No idea.'

He stood still for a moment, breathing in the damp, leafy air as if it were the scent of God. In that instant he seemed to transcend himself. And when he exhaled, a heaviness seemed to expel itself from his limbs.

'Ah.'

I fell in love with him then. I believe there is always a precise moment in love when we suddenly recognize the other person's soul, like an old photograph we know profoundly well, that for some reason we've kept and at last understand why.

He beamed with pleasure.

'Isn't it lovely?'

I nodded, hopelessly tongue-tied.

'I'm glad you're here,' he said easily, as if it cost him nothing.

'I am too,' I said clumsily, because it cost me everything I had.

We walked on in silence. I felt as though we were new lovers, too full up for words, bursting with the sweetness of life.

But, in concluding some long process of thought, he suddenly said:

'Women are the lovers, aren't they?'

And at once I felt found out, left out, guiltily alone with this new passion burning in my heart.

'What about men?'

'Women are the choosers. They hold everything together or rip it asunder with love. Love they choose to give or withhold. Women have the ultimate power.'

I was baffled by this out-of-the-blue generalization, which swept aside my whole experience.

'Are men only women's victims, then? Can they do no wrong themselves?'

'It's not a question of right or wrong,' he said impatiently.

'It's a question of the truth. It's beyond morality, thank God.'

The irony of this juxtaposition of concepts made me laugh.

'What's so funny?'

'Nothing,' I said, contrite. 'So whose fault is what, then? Or do you blame women for the lot?'

'You're looking for good and bad, Mo. The old morality. It's nobody's fault. There's no one to punish. It just is. The truth.'

We walked on in silence again. What experience had forced this conclusion on him, I wondered. Or was he right? Was it really as simple as that?

'Tell me about yourself,' I said.

The invitation was perhaps too general. He remained silent and thoughtful, as though waiting for the next, more particular question.

'Tell me about your mother, then,' I said.

'What about her?'

'Her story. Before – before the . . .' I couldn't say the words. The dead little face, eyes open, was staring up at me from my own arms, the luminous blue eyes like the tramp's eyes in Bloomsbury, the same beautiful face, only fresh and round and young.

'Before the drowning,' he said.

'Yes. Before the . . .'

He waited to see if I could say it now, but I still couldn't.

'My mother, then,' he began, pausing to collect his thoughts. 'She was born in India to a tea-planter and his wife. Darjeeling tea, it was. She was . . . heavenly. Is the word. I've seen photographs. A most beautiful child . . .'

He digressed dreamily into his own memories.

'But she was mostly ignored,' he resumed. ' "Starved of attention" would be an accurate description. Her father was drunk all the time, or out chasing other women, while her mother was forever resting. Resting! I love the lies they told! Presumably she was in fact trying to cope emotionally with her husband's infidelities, and his drunkenness.'

We passed through the big iron gates of the Isabella Plantation. I had only visited it in the late spring, for the cool pinks, crimsons and whites of the camellias and the rhododendrons, but now the trees had their own glory, a dying chaos of oranges, yellows and reds.

'Needless to say,' he continued keenly, 'she grew up to be a beautiful woman. An exquisite beauty. She dazzled Calcutta. All those hungry British men, dreaming of a white woman's breasts and . . . "Stiff upper lips, stiffer lower dicks" . . .'

He laughed at his own little joke.

'Ever heard that one before?'

'No,' I said, embarrassed by his sudden crudeness.

I kept my own thoughts to myself. They were unclear, anyway. Mothers, breasts, mother's milk, sex, and finally Howard's dick. I should have been a Freudian . . .

'My mother was allowed to be desired, you see. She was white. The British could openly worship her. It must have been tough for the whores, who were used to being preferred by the British. The Indians themselves treated their whores with utter contempt, since an Indian whore was living evidence of their own inferiority, but the British romanticized those whores.'

'Poor whores,' I said, 'passed to and fro . . .'

'Indeed,' he said. 'But imagine the desire my mother kindled then – in the Indians and the British alike – rich and beautiful as she was. A perfect woman, even amongst her own kind. I can't think of a woman who could equal her . . .'

High praise indeed. Too high. There was something odd

about it. I thought of his earlier admiration of my own modest beauty — of my face, on the first occasion, and of some other region that he had come upon that morning, on the second.

'She soon learnt to steal the attention of every man from every other woman in the room. That was her career, if you like. Securing the devotion of men. She was very good at it. She acquired a lifelong taste for it. If she didn't have a man's total devotion, she'd go to any lengths to secure it.'

He paused. His voice was less excited now, sober and dull.

'When she married my father, however, it was his devotion alone that she sought. Primarily because it was unattainable. Unfortunately for her, and for him — for all of us, in fact — she could never secure even a fraction of his devotion. He simply loved someone else. But because she was Indian, he couldn't marry her. That was the social unacceptability of the day.'

'How sad,' I said.

'So my mother married him instead. Of all the men to choose! She chose a man as unavailable to her as her father had always been.'

I thought of my own father, endlessly absent from my life. Was Bill his substitute, always away working somewhere?

'I could go back through each generation and show you how the patterns repeat themselves tirelessly. Even down to me. "Consciousness cracks the Code," as Neville Hoare would say. But I haven't noticed it.'

He was quiet now, falling into the inexpressible grief that swallowed up the air.

'I feel for you,' I said.

It was the wrong thing to say. He stared at me blankly, stranger that I was, an intruder suddenly in his private, painful world, where the past and the present – and doubtless the future, too – were woven like a net around him.

'Don't pity me,' he spat contemptuously. 'Just let me tell my story. From start to finish. I don't need your bits and pieces thrown in. Everything has a beginning and end, an action and reaction, a cause and effect. You have to see the whole.'

'It's OK. I'm listening,' I said. 'I'm trying to see the whole.'

'Use your head, Mo, not your heart.'

'My heart rules my head,' I said. 'I'm not here because you're an intellectual challenge to me, Howard. I feel for you.'

He looked truly horrified by this, almost disgusted. Everything about him hardened. I could feel the chill paralyse me. I wanted to say that I was confused by him, that I hated his abrupt changes of mood, that he was frightening me again, but I couldn't persuade my brain to move my lips. It knew better than I did that Howard North was two different men. One I now loved, the other I feared.

He walked on again slowly, safe in the knowledge that he could tyrannize me into submission whenever he wanted to. Or so it seemed to me.

I wondered how Bill was. My once-beloved Bill, now a cold stranger to me. He seemed so far away. On another planet, almost. In spite of myself, I missed him. However hollow our marriage had been, I missed the known quantity it was. The familiarity. But I relished the new, too. It seems that the mind craves change as the belly craves food, or it will atrophy. And if it cannot discipline itself to value as new what is old and familiar and worn, then it will seek novelty. Shots of adrenalin. Like a drug. Ultimately violent.

'I need you, Mo.'

It seemed to come from nowhere, unless a statue has needs. But he had moved up close behind me and I could feel his breath on my neck. I turned, and was met by his smile, the lips soft and open now, inviting me in.

The rain was pouring over us like honey, heavy and sweet.

'I want you,' I said.

'Now, Mo –' but I stopped his mouth, and his lips covered me.

Now, yes, I will have you. Take you. Admit you. Find, if you will, the deep entrance in. Under the evergreen glossy-leaved camellia tree. Penetrate me.

But that wasn't what he meant. He meant, 'Now, Mo, I will tease your desire.'

He brushed my cheek with the back of his hand, stroking it softly up and down, up and down like love. I longed for that hand to be seized by the same rapacious hunger I felt for him, but it teased on, while my senses frenzied themselves. Did I dare to make the first tentative move? To reach out, touch him, stir his desire? Find out what spoke to him there?

'Are you happy?' he asked.

'I love the rain,' I said.

'We're fairly drenched, aren't we?' He smiled. 'Let's go back.'

And back was what he meant. All the way back through his life. He took my hand and led me away. Led me astray. I let him. I had surrendered by then. He could lead me anywhere. Wet as a drowned babe.

9

I suppose, in effect, that he kidnapped me. It didn't feel like it at the time, but he never asked if he could drive me to the West Country. Not that I minded or had anywhere else to go.

'I was adopted, you know. I'm not my mother's natural child,' he announced, somewhere near Salisbury cathedral with its head in the clouds. 'No blood between us.'

I assumed he was denying the murderous blood, not any blood spilt.

'Where are we going, Howard?'

'Home.'

'Whose home?'

'Did you hear what I said?'

'You're adopted, yes.' But I hadn't really taken it in. 'Are you?'

'Cassie wasn't. But I was, for some reason.'

'But you were older than her –'

'That's right,' he said, in the same clipped tone he used to close most sentences he didn't want opened again. As one closes the lock on a full suitcase. Click.

'So she suddenly became fertile, your mother, or . . . ?'

He didn't reply.

'Howard?'

'I've no idea. It's anyone's guess. Perhaps they didn't have a – didn't enjoy a full . . . It's possible that they didn't – or couldn't – consummate the marriage until much later, is what I'm trying to say.'

Why does it cost you so much?

'That would be unusual,' I said. 'I mean – it's an odd way round, isn't it? Usually it's the other –'

'Yes.' He cut me off. 'As I say, I don't know.'

I wasn't going to leave it there, even if he was.

'Maybe with his Indian lover still haunting him, he couldn't – you know – sort of keep it – up. With your mother. So to speak.'

I was suddenly blushing absurdly, infected by his own dis-ease.

'As I said, anyone's guess.' He had the same click in his voice.

'Did he resent her terribly?' I asked.

'How on earth should I know? He left when I was five.'

'Didn't you ever see him again?'

He was silent, not to be drawn.

We pulled up, soon after, beside a large old family house with its own long drive. Georgian, again. Graceful, simple, clear. The sort of house that can look you straight in the eye with no secrets to hide. But, oh, how misleading those first impressions can be.

'So this is home? Your country seat, or . . . ?'

'This is where I grew up,' he said.

I took a deep breath.

'Right.'

'And where my sister was drowned.'

An ominous feeling crept over me. The excavation into his past had only just begun, I could feel that now. I sensed that he was pacing himself, like a runner, for the long distance ahead, while I was merely limbering up for a jog.

'Funny old place,' he said.

'Beautiful, isn't it?'

He was thoughtful. 'I haven't spent any time here, really, over the last two years. I came down to find my mother, that was all. About six months ago.'

'To find her?'

'Well, to look for her. I needed to talk something through.'

'Does she still live here, then?'

'My mother?' he asked, amazed. 'My mother's dead.'

Good God, I thought. Why is that such a shock?

'I'm so sorry,' I said. 'I didn't realize.' Pause. 'She must've died very recently?'

'Very recently.'

'For some reason I thought she was . . . still alive.'

'No. As it turns out. She's not.'

There was a perplexing fury in his voice, as if the audacity of her death had enraged him. Or something about it had. Something that was far beyond grief had deeply troubled him.

'I'm sorry,' I said again, feeling that it was somehow my fault.

He got out of the car and stood looking at the house for some time. I felt that if I got out of the car too, we would be there for days, weeks, possibly, so I stayed where I was until he opened the door for me and took my hand. We stood looking at the house together, my hand wrapped up in his like a lucky charm.

'I can't tell you how sick it makes me feel.'

'Sick?' I had been admiring the graciousness of the place. 'Why does it make you feel sick?'

'Can't you sense it? An overwhelming toxicity? Like chemical warfare. Gas.'

'A kind of malevolence?'

'Exactly.'

I could sense something, in fact, but I wasn't sure if it was coming from the place or from Howard. What I sensed precisely was not malevolence but despair.

'How long did you live here?'

'For as long as I can remember.'

'When did you leave?'

'I didn't.'

Could he mean that?

'I don't understand . . .' I said. 'You never left home?'

'No. Why? I lived here for . . . let me think . . . forty-six years? Yes, that's right. I'm forty-eight now.'

'Gosh,' I said, for want of a better word to express the astonishment I felt.

'Two years ago, I bought the house in Chiswick, so, if you like, I left two years ago, but . . .' he trailed off.

'But . . . ?'

'It wasn't a formal thing, ever. I just – didn't come back.'

He spoke of the situation as though it was relatively normal. A little unhealthy, perhaps, to an outsider, but nothing at all serious. If anything was serious, it was the fact that he 'just – didn't come back'. That was the thing that had been wrong. Leaving Mother had been wrong.

'So you left without telling her?'

'And without telling myself, more to the point. I just walked out. I packed a suitcase and walked. It was a late summer afternoon – Kittie was asleep on the sofa –'

'Kittie?'

'Katherine. My mother. Kathy, Kittie, Kate . . .'

'Kate?' I repeated, uncomfortably reminded of his intimacy with my twin.

97

'Occasionally, yes. Kate.'

'A strange coincidence?'

But he wouldn't be drawn.

'When did you first meet her?'

'Who?'

'My sister. Kate.'

'Mo. Behave yourself.' He smiled, pinching my cheek affectionately. 'It's not your business to interrogate me.'

'It's not your business to pinch my cheek,' I said.

For a moment he seemed delighted with me, smiling at me just long enough for me to feel quite shy.

'How beautiful you are,' he said.

I looked away. The Wiltshire landscape with its generous rolling hills lay like an indolent cat, hiding its feline teeth and claws in soft lolling lines. I felt his hand on the nape of my neck, caressing me gently, sending a fierce charge through the whole of me.

'Please, Howard –'

But he stopped my mouth with a kiss like no kiss I'd ever known. Perhaps because it was so unexpected? Exotic as an unfamiliar fruit. Soft. Moist. Extraordinarily sweet. Then he fixed his eyes on me again, as though sharpening the focus of a lens, before pulling away.

We stood in silence; the current between us seemed so strong to me now that it was almost tangible. I felt the dull ache of longing in my limbs, like pain. But he seemed immune to it. He was looking at the house again, as if the house itself had stirred the desire in him, as if I just happened to be there. There, but dispensable.

'Do you want to come in?'

'Sure.'

He took my hand once more and led me to the peeling black

front door. I presumed that he would unlock the door himself, but instead he rang the bell.

'Who lives here now?'

'I'm – renting it out,' he said, unconvincingly. 'This old boy – he was homeless and . . . He's nutty as a fruitcake. You'll see.'

We waited an age for the old boy to answer the door. His white head of hair appeared first, as though charging at us. In fact he was charging after a cat that had just leapt out of his arms and was running through my legs. He straightened up, defeated by the chase.

'Kitty!' he shouted, presumably after the cat, although this wasn't entirely clear, since he was staring straight at Howard.

'Kittie?' Howard looked horrified.

'Hello, there, Mr North. I told her you'd be back. Kitty!'

'Told who?'

'Kitty!' he shouted for the third time.

'I think he means the cat,' I whispered as quietly as I could.

The old man bent down to retrieve the marmalade cat that had been the cause of so much confusion already.

'I do indeed mean the cat,' he said, straightening again and smiling politely – but icily – at me. 'How are you, madam?'

'Mo,' I corrected him. 'I'm fine, thank you. How are you?'

Confused, he smiled and nodded vigorously and said, 'Yes yes!' but wouldn't shake the hand I extended to him. Nor did he suggest a name for himself.

'Whose cat is it?' asked Howard, irritably.

'Whose are you?' was the old boy's reply.

'I'm sorry?'

'Who do you belong to, Mr North?'

'It's a heavenly beast,' I interrupted amiably, stroking its purring back.

'Do they have beasts in heaven?' he inquired.

I was getting the impression, pretty fast, that the old boy didn't like me very much, and that he liked Howard even less.

'Look, can we come in, just quickly? I don't want to invade your privacy or anything but . . .'

The old boy waited for Howard to hang his sentence clumsily in the air, unfinished, like half a car off a cliff. He left him suspended there for some time before rescuing him.

'My house is your house,' he said finally, which was obviously more of a fact than a hospitable gesture. 'Come and go as you please.'

Howard was climbing the stairs when the old boy grabbed my arm and whispered, terrified, in my ear:

'I can't find it anywhere. I swear.'

What on earth was he talking about?

Howard glanced back at us, frowning slightly.

'Is he bothering you?'

'Not at all,' I answered pleasantly, keen to investigate at my own leisure.

'Are you suggesting that I am harassing her?' asked the old boy indignantly, winking conspiratorially at me.

'Do come on up, Mo. I want to show you around.'

'Is she *another* woman, then? I understood you were married, Mr North?'

Howard didn't answer this rather intriguing question, but instead said:

'Please don't feel obliged to follow us about, sir. We shan't be long.'

The old boy stared up at him reproachfully from the bottom of the stairs like a banished child.

'Very well, very well . . .' he mumbled, withdrawing obediently.

Howard walked me straight into his mother's bedroom. He was clearly profoundly disturbed by the place.

'Nice view,' I said.

The view looked out over the garden at the back, a hopelessly overgrown tangle of climbing roses and broken pergolas, but the sweep of the hills behind was stunning.

'It's beautiful,' I said.

'Yes,' he muttered, his troubled gaze finding its way to the window. 'Yes, it certainly used to be. Katherine had a real feel for the garden. The colours – well you can hardly see them now – they were still flowering a couple of months ago, but – well, they complement each other so well.'

I was looking for water. Even a small boggy puddle would have sufficed to convince me that this had been the place. But I couldn't see it anywhere.

'It was filled in after the – after Cassie's death. It's overgrown now.'

'The pond, you mean?'

'Isn't that what you're looking for?'

'Yes.' I felt guilty, caught out. 'Where exactly was it?'

'Over there.' He pointed to the far left-hand corner of the garden. 'It used to catch the light from this room so vividly, gleaming like a silver coin. It was as if Cass was trying to haunt us. So Kittie filled it in.'

There was a long pause, which I left because I didn't know quite how to ask my next question, and which he left because he was haunted still.

'What actually – happened to her – I mean to her body? Once she was dead?'

He looked so frightened.

'I don't know.'

'I mean, was it reported, or was she buried, or – what?'

'I really don't know. My father dealt with it.'

'Of course, your father was still around. I forgot.' I thought about him. 'Do you think he knew?'

'That Cass was murdered? I've always assumed so, yes.'

'And do you think he knew who it was? Who did it?'

'Again, I've assumed so. I've always assumed he thought it was me. Mother would've told him it was me, I'm sure.' He thought about it, at once less sure. 'I suppose it's possible he didn't know. She might have lied to him to protect me, or . . .'

'Or to protect herself? She might have told him it was an accident?'

'It's possible, I suppose.'

'Although he might not have believed her, of course. He might have been convinced it was she who'd killed his little girl. It would be as good a reason as any to leave your wife, wouldn't it? And he did leave her, didn't he? Pretty soon afterwards.'

'Two weeks later, yes.'

He fell silent. Thoughtful.

'Did you never see him again at all?'

'No, not until . . .'

He didn't finish the sentence. In fact he plainly regretted having started it. He had let something slip unintentionally. He coloured a little.

'Until when, Howard?'

'Until never. I never saw him again. At all.'

He smiled nervously. He could see that I didn't believe him.

'But I did hear from him. That was all I meant. He wrote when Katherine died. To say how sorry he was. It was rather a surprise, since I'd more or less given him up for dead.'

'Perhaps you should correspond with him. See what he can remember. He might finally be able to put your mind at rest.'

'Wouldn't that be a glorious thing?' he said, like a hunted man for whom the word 'rest' implies an impossible, longed-for dream.

'He might know something really crucial,' I said.

'Yes. I haven't had time, unfortunately, since Katherine died, to ask him anything . . .'

We stood staring out of the window like two goldfish, side by side. His proximity thrilled me unfailingly from that day henceforward. That falling-in-love day. I thought about the probable quantities of women in his life. I tried to imagine one or two. Why did he never mention them?

'That woman you loved,' I ventured bravely, out of the blue, 'who was she?'

'Which woman?'

'The one you lost.'

'I've lost many women, Mo.'

Was I merely one in an endless line, I wondered.

'The one you spoke about before, with the diaries – the one who killed herself.'

'Oh. Lizzie. Yes. Lizzie,' he said reflectively.

'Lizzie?'

'Yes, she was the first.'

'The first – woman? Or the first one to kill herself?'

'The first one to run!' He was making light of it, but it didn't seem especially light.

'You said that reading her diaries brought something up for you, some question came up . . .'

'Did I?'

His eyes were like the lens of a microscope now, focusing on the centre of my soul. He seemed to be assessing whether I was worthy of a further confidence.

'Lizzie and I were – engaged. My first true love.'

'How old were you?'

'Thirty-eight . . .'

Thirty-eight seemed too old for a man's first love, but I said nothing.

'The question that came up in Lizzie's diary – well, it's the same question. It's the question I have about Cass –'

'Murder?'

'Attempted, in this instance. But murder, yes.'

Don't panic, I told myself. Hear him out.

'According to her diaries,' he continued, 'and I had no knowledge of this until I read them – but apparently, the very night after we'd announced our engagement, while she was staying in one of the guest bedrooms here, someone tried to suffocate her.'

'Jesus. Who?'

'In the middle of the night. Pitch dark. She had no idea who it was. She couldn't see anything. She even lost consciousness. Presumably whoever it was thought they'd killed her. The following morning she left, unsurprisingly. She never came back.'

'God,' was all I dared say, in case he was about to confess.

'There were only two people in the house. My mother and myself.' He paused, letting the silence speak for itself. 'It's the same problem, isn't it? It has to have been one of us.'

'Was it?'

'Lizzie assumed it was me. My mother had already frightened her enough with tales of Cassandra's murder. Why wouldn't she suspect me?' He looked at me as if hoping for a reason why not, but sadly none suggested itself. 'She killed herself all these years later because she "finally couldn't face the evil in the world". And who can blame her?'

The old fear crept back. However much I wanted to trust him, I couldn't. I couldn't believe in his innocence until he believed in it himself. How can you trust someone who tells you they can't trust themselves? All you can do is offer your company.

I searched his face.

'You think it was me, too,' he said.

'I don't know, Howard. I don't know what to think.'

'I need proof. That's what I need.'

'How are you getting along?' came a piping, cheerful voice behind us. The old boy was beaming from ear to ear. How much had he heard, standing in the doorway unobserved?

'I do hope I didn't frighten you,' he said.

'Not at all,' said Howard, disguising his agitation poorly.

'Only I wondered if you'd care for some tea?'

'Thank you. Why not?'

'I shall be in the kitchen, then,' he said, and he left us to follow him.

We stood in silence for a while, smiling at each other like old friends with old jokes to share. But the seriousness soon returned.

'I only read Lizzie's diaries after my mother's death,' Howard explained, 'a month ago,' as if the timing was an important factor to grasp.

'How come?'

'Well, I had very little interest in her by the time she died. Ten years is a long time. And I'd cut her out entirely from my thoughts when she left. I was very hurt . . .' Pause. 'Kittie was a great comfort to me, though, during that time. I was soon back to normal.' Whatever 'normal' was, I thought.

The kitchen was damp and grubby, its paint an ageing custard yellow. An old Aga of the same colour had been chipped and dented over the years, but spread a general warmth throughout the room. I wondered if it was the same kitchen Howard had known as a child. He looked about him with a certain nostalgia. And a certain hostility, too.

The old boy seemed to be studying us out of the corner of his eye. Some hidden agenda that I couldn't begin to guess at was absorbing him.

'Lovely cup of tea,' I said.

'Indian,' he replied. 'Always the best.'

Howard looked up at him abruptly.

'Indian tea!' said the old boy again, playfully shouting at him.

'What about it?' asked Howard coldly, but no explanation was offered.

'I went to India once,' I said. 'I loved it. I remember my journey up to Darjeeling most particularly, on a tiny two-carriager – '

'Isn't that a terrific little trip?' said the old boy enthusiastically.

Howard looked up from his tea again in disbelief.

'Have you been to India?' he asked.

'No, no, not at all,' said the old boy adamantly, 'I've only read about it.'

'Then you should be careful, sir. You make yourself sound like a man of the world!'

He was half joking and half putting the old boy down. I didn't like it.

I looked out of the window at the garden. It looked sinister in the half-light of the dusk, an inextricable knot of roses and thorns. The evening was coming in fast. It was still raining hard, the sky dark and gloomy and promising more of the same.

'I ought to get back to London soon,' I said.

'And so you shall, so you shall . . .'

I had expressed my wish to Howard but the old man had answered me. Howard was deep in thought.

I wondered what I was doing in this remote place with these two strange men. I could feel the malevolent atmosphere contaminate me like a disease. Like a plague? Contracted through thin air?

'Howard? Shouldn't we be getting back?'

'Back?'

'To London.'

'If you like.'

He didn't seem keen.

'If you want to stay, I can easily get a train. Just drop me at the station. Salisbury's not far, is it?'

'No, we'll go.'

Pause.

'You could always stay over. Rough night for a drive,' suggested the old boy.

Howard looked at me for some hint of willingness. I felt none. In fact I positively dreaded the thought of a whole night there.

'That's very kind, but I have a husband to get back to. He must be wondering where I am.'

This felt like a lie, so remote were Bill and I from each other now. But as an excuse to escape the toxicity, it served me well.

'A husband! Well, well!' he exclaimed. 'The other one has a husband, too, as I remember it! So many husbands and wives.'

'Can we wash up for you before we go?' Howard cut in.

'What other one?' I asked.

Howard began to stack up the plates and cups.

'The other woman,' said the old boy.

'Who?' I was asking Howard now.

'I don't know what he's talking about.'

'What other woman?' I asked the old man.

Just as he was about to answer me, Howard dropped the

pile of crockery on the cold stone floor. When the noise of it stopped echoing in my ears, I looked at Howard's trembling face.

'I'm so sorry,' he said, seeming as baffled as I was by his action. He knelt down to retrieve the scattered pieces of china. 'I'm terribly sorry, sir. I shall replace these, of course.'

Had it been deliberate, then?

I was burning with curiosity about this other woman, but with great self-restraint I let things be.

'D'you want a hand?' I offered.

'It's quite all right, thank you. The least I can do is clear it up myself.'

After a short silence, I found myself spilling over with laughter – the kind of laughter I used to restrain as a schoolgirl, nervous and totally inappropriate, making it doubly compelling. The old man also began to laugh, for reasons of his own, emitting such wild, shrill noises that even Howard was amused. By the end of the evening we were all laughing uncontrollably. But at quite different things, I felt sure.

10

I woke early. It was still so dark that I could barely see where I was. What little I could disntinguish was only vaguely familiar to me. How had I got here? Had I been drugged? Reviewing the previous day's excursions, I surmised that it had to be one of two places: Chiswick or Wiltshire. With North.

Neither possibility seemed wholesome at that early hour. I wondered why. I had always found the first hour of the day to be the most illuminating, the time at which I could hear most clearly the good sense of my unconscious mind. The common sense, deep in all of us. Like a conscience, or a god. That morning the sense was especially distinct. I had taken a wrong turning. I had lost my way.

The filled-in pond like a home-made grave haunted me. I dreaded the morning light, dreaded finding myself in Katherine's room, seeing the room again, the pond again, the tangled garden below. But although I missed my regular days, safe as a timetable, I felt no immediate urge to return to them. How could I forgo this adventure in my life for mere safety's sake? I was enthralled. I can think of no better word. Afraid, but enthralled.

This intelligence Howard wanted from me, this head, not heart, of me: why was it so crucial to him? Or did he really mean detachment? Objectivity? He certainly wasn't encouraging any emotion in me. Not willingly, at least. My feelings were troublesome enough as it was. He was asking for analysis, almost. But then, why come to me? I believed in empathy, above all. Objective thought was for people who could no longer see the wood for the trees. Couldn't Howard? Was that it? Was he too much in the thick of this to find his own way through? How dense a wood was it, then?

I imagined a mass of enmeshed branches strangling each other, strangling anything in their midst, suffocating all life. I thought again of the garden, the wild roses and thorns, menacing as snakes in the half-light. I could see Howard in there, gasping for breath. The image was surely a warning of sorts.

Would I have to join him there?

I had the sense of being asked to visit hell itself, with no guarantee that I would ever return.

I did go back to sleep. The sedative of sleep. I dreamt of the cold again and woke to find myself naked beneath a single sheet in a room now light enough for me to recognize. Katherine's room. Panic set in. I had lain awake, I recalled, for much of the night, anticipating suffocation at the very least. Now I half-expected to find Katherine standing over me with a knife, grinning like a fiend, a fearful menace in her eyes. I breathed deep and long, until the rhythm calmed me. What was I so afraid of in her? What dread beast threatened my life? Certainly she was the particular form that my terror took, but did something far worse lie beneath the mere symbol of her?

Before I had climbed out of bed, let alone considered the full implications of this question, there was a gentle knock on the door.

'Who is it?'

'Mo?'

Howard's voice, like a timid boy's.

'I'm not up yet.'

'Can I come in?'

'Hold on, I'll just . . .' I reached for my T-shirt in amongst my discarded clothes and slipped it over my head. 'OK, come in,' I said.

He opened and closed the door without a sound, seeming to breathe more easily as soon as this was done.

'What's the matter?'

'Nothing. Are you all right?'

'Why? Shouldn't I be?'

'Did you sleep even half-decently?'

'Not bad,' I said, lying. 'You?'

'I found it quite impossible to – er – to sleep, myself.'

He was propping his exhausted body up against the door like a stringless manikin.

'It must be hard for you, coming here.'

He was staring at me very intently, not really listening to me. He was deeply preoccupied.

'What is it?' I asked, uncomfortably. 'Why are you staring at me like that?'

'I was just . . .' But he changed the subject abruptly. 'Look, do you want to go back up to London today or can you spend a little more time with me?'

'Howard, I'm a married woman. I have a life of my own.'

I was using Bill like a shield.

'I know that,' he said irritably.

'How do I explain this excursion to my husband?' As if he would care . . .

'He doesn't own you.'

'Neither do you.'

But his face said, yes I do – I own the very heart of you.

'I want to be back by this evening,' I said, matter-of-factly. 'OK?'

He nodded and smiled like a child.

'I want to dig up the pond,' he said, equally matter-of-fact. I shuddered at the thought.

'Why?'

'To see if there are any clues. I want proof,' he said. 'I must find proof.' He paused. 'Help me. You must help me, Mo.'

It was an order, really, lightly disguised as a plea. I flattered myself that I had some choice in the matter, but if I'd chosen to walk away then, I would have found out the truth.

11

The wind was biting cold, eating into my flesh like a parasite. We were crouching over the once-upon-a-time pond, six foot across, and digging away at the compacted soil with hopelessly heavy old spades.

It's going to be a visit to hell and back just digging this bloody thing, I muttered to myself.

'Eh?'

Howard had his back to me, digging the end that faced south. My direction was north, so that when the sun occasionally burst through I could enjoy the warmth of it on my back. One of few comforts that day. Facing north also meant that I could study the back of the house and observe how frequently the little old man's white head of hair appeared at one window or another. By midday I had counted eighteen occasions, and I must have missed a few.

After approximately four hours of unrewarding, unremitting work, I hit gold. The spadeful of dark wet earth glinted at me like a lighthouse at night. My impulse was to tell Howard immediately, before I had even seen what it was, but a deeper, more suspicious impulse suggested that I keep it to myself, just for the time being. The impulse of fear. I fingered the sodden soil like a detective, cautious and respectful of perhaps the only clue – vital evidence that could clear or condemn a soul. It offered up a small gold locket, about the size of a coin. Exquisitely engraved.

I stopped breathing. I was a thief now, hot and furtive, fearful of being caught. I stuffed the treasure into my pocket, committing myself to a more thorough examination at some later, lonelier hour.

'Irksome task, this . . .' Howard shouted across to me in the wind.

He seemed to be enjoying the simple physical objective of the day, a robust and invigorating contrast to his more cerebral preoccupations, whatever those were.

'Telling me!' I called back jovially.

The paradox of our high spirits in the face of this morbid mission did not escape me. Perhaps it was a natural reaction in the face of such a grim pursuit, but I still felt ashamed. And this shame extended to my guilty secret now, burning in my pocket like a hot coal. Howard's insistence upon truth as the ultimate morality had me sinning already. Betraying him.

Hours later the old man brought up a thermos flask of weak Darjeeling tea and inedible sandwiches, and admitted to the name of Rolf. Howard raised an eyebrow in disbelief and smiled discreetly at me.

'What's that short for, then . . . Roland the Wolf?' And he barked at the old man like a dog. 'Rolf! Rolf!'

'Rolf' seemed to find this enormously funny.

'Oh, I see! Yes, indeed! Very witty indeed!' He could hardly breathe for chuckling. 'Rolf! Rolf! Rolf! Rolf!' He barked somewhat ferociously at both of us before adding very flatly: 'It's not short for anything at all, in fact.'

There was something incongruent about him. Something hidden. For a start, I felt quite sure that his real name was not Rolf. Then there was his moodiness which, unlike Howard's, seemed implausibly controllable. It was not as if there was a dark unsettled area of his soul that suddenly pushed through into the light, but a cool, considered change of direction, seemingly designed to put one off the scent. A versatile chameleon disguised as an eccentric old man. Then there was the fact that he was there at all. What would an old man want with a remote country house that size?

'Is this your part of the world, Rolf?' I asked.

'I've lived here long enough!' he said cheerfully, his humour masking his unwillingness to say more.

'How long is long enough?' I persevered, equally cheerfully.

'I've quite lost count of the years, my dear.' He finished the sentence as if with a full stop. In fact he was just about to launch into a new chapter heading when I asked:

'Many years, then?'

'Many years. Off and on.' Another full stop.

'Off and on' intrigued me. Somehow I couldn't imagine this man to be 'off and on' about anything. Was I making assumptions again? I sensed that he was a man who could not tell lies easily and who therefore had to be rather vague about the truths he wished to conceal. After all, the lie of his own name had escaped neither Howard nor myself. It was blatant. I thought I could probably draw the truth out of him with a little time and my characteristic stubbornness, but I was optimistic, as it turned out.

'It's getting dark already,' said Howard, looking up at the heavy sky accusingly. 'God, I hate this wretched time of year.'

'Shall we call it a day?' I suggested, easy either way, but aware of the long motorway journey ahead.

He ran his eyes over me as if they were his hands, caressing my cold limbs. I could feel myself light up like a dry bonfire, suddenly ablaze.

'You want to get back, don't you?' he asked.

I want to lie beside you on white sand . . .

'I really should,' I said.

'Want to, or should?'

'Both. Does it matter? The outcome is the same.'

Howard clearly didn't suspect the old man as I did. He talked in front of 'Rolf' as if he were senile or deaf or both.

'It matters to me.'

'Well . . .' I said blandly, not wanting to be drawn. I looked down at the dry pond, away from him.

I heard him sigh. A sad sigh. I didn't dare look up until I had seen his feet tread a fair distance to the house.

I cannot be all things to all men, I told myself. The fever will pass.

'She loved him, that woman.'

The old man was standing very close to me, his voice steady and sane as it had not yet been.

'Who?'

He didn't answer.

'His mother, you mean?'

'Well, I wouldn't know about that . . .'

'Wouldn't you?' I asked.

He smiled mildly.

'Who then?' I demanded. The other woman, of course, I answered myself. 'Who was she, this other woman?'

'Ah, I could describe her face to you, but her name . . . I never remember names.'

'Not even your own, huh?'

He gave me a long, honest stare. It said: Be very careful. The ground upon which you stand is dangerous. I tell you for your own good.

'I wouldn't like to be in her shoes now,' was what he actually voiced.

'Why not?'

But he looked away towards the house, as if to be sure that Howard was nowhere nearby.

'She was just like you,' he said. 'Only . . . a sure woman. Sure of herself.'

'How much like me?'

'She said she had a twin,' he replied simply. Confirmation of my worst fears.

'Why are you telling me this?'

'For your own good.'

He shuffled away then, leaving me on the uncertain ground of the buried pond.

Kate? What was her game?

I followed him inside, the soft darkness of dusk eerie as the previous evening, uncertain shadows dancing before me. I longed for some concrete truth, some absolute in all this possibility. Glimpses of certainty evaporated like mist in the half-light of impending night.

The same cold, fluorescent tube welcomed me in the kitchen. The old man was stirring some odious concoction from a tin in a heavy saucepan over the Aga.

'Is that your tea?'

'It's Kitty's tea.'

'Glad to hear it. Where's Howard?'

'Upstairs?'

I took off the wellington boots that we'd brought down from Chiswick after the walk in Richmond Park, and made my way upstairs in the almost-dark.

'Howard?'

I knocked on several doors before finding his.

'Hello?' came his disembodied voice.

'Can I come in?'

He didn't answer.

I found him lying on his bed staring blankly up at the ceiling.

'Sorry to intrude.'

'What is it?'

'I was just wondering when you were thinking of heading off.'

'Heading off what?'

'I mean, heading for London. Going.'

He exhaled again, the same sad sigh.

'Whenever you like.'

'There's no need to make me feel so bad, is there?'

'Oh, for heaven's sake!' he exclaimed wearily. 'Here we go again . . .'

'Sorry?'

'Good. Bad. Right. Wrong. Black. White. What's the matter with you? Can't you see how intolerably grey everything is?'

'No, I can't,' I said firmly.

'No, you can't, can you? I almost envy you your simple view of things.'

'There's no need to pass a value judgement on my view of things.'

'I expect you think you're closer to God, don't you, with all that simplicity?'

'No.'

'Of course you do. Just the way you say "no" like that, so smug and sure of yourself.'

Sure of yourself. The words rang in my ears.

I didn't know what was happening. From those caressing eyes to this inability even to look at me. Had he witnessed my exchange with the old man? Was I no longer to be trusted?

I remembered the locket in my pocket and felt for it anxiously. Still there. I was not to be trusted, no.

'I think I'll just call a cab, Howard. Make my own way back.'

I closed the door behind me. He didn't look at me once.

The cab took two hours to arrive. I used the time fruitfully, prowling through the house more stealthily than either Kitty the cat or Kittie the ghost, unnoticed by anyone.

The most surprising and perplexing of my discoveries was the abundant evidence of the latter's presence. Her belongings were everywhere. It seemed as if no one had collected them after her death, as if the place waited for her as it always had done in brief absences. Her name was in every book, her initials on everything from napkin rings to cutlery to hairbrushes, her dried flowers spilt out of old albums, what I assumed were her clothes still hung in the wardrobes, and a virtual tower of mail awaited her on the hall table.

Nothing had been touched. A thick coating of dust covered the furniture, disrupted only by an occasional item of Rolf's, strewn about the place — a book or a pipe or an out-of-date newspaper. In the main the possessions were hers, as was the house. Her return seemed imminent. It waited for her animation like a stage-set ready for a play. Suspended in time, impervious to death, this house expected her.

I would find out. I would find out everything.

Despite my investigative boldness in the house, I did not dare to draw from my pocket the buried treasure I had found. I longed to open it up, for I was sure there was some vital clue inside, but I would do so only behind a locked door in my own home.

Howard did not reappear from his room, and I chose not to bid him goodbye, but I saw the curtain twitch as I climbed into the back seat of the taxi.

12

When I got home Bill was in the living-room listening to Wagner and reading psychology books. I tiptoed upstairs unnoticed and locked myself in the bathroom. I was nervous of what I might find in the locket. I dreaded most some evidence of the dead child herself. Some lock of hair, or a fingernail.

Why a fingernail? The thought was morbid and very unlikely but almost paralysed my willingness to look inside.

I turned on the hot tap and held the treasured clue beneath its flow, careful not to let any water leak into the locket itself. Once free of the mud, I could see that the chain had been broken, as if ripped or pulled from the owner's neck. It was a longish chain, without doubt an adult's. No small drowned child had once worn a chain this long. The locket must have belonged to Katherine, and been wrenched from her in a struggle by the pond. With her husband? Or with Howard? Or with little Cassie herself? This was evidence of sorts, wasn't it?

My own fingernails were short and struggled in vain to release the catch. Frustration eclipsed any hesitation I had felt. My impatience mounted into an intense battle with this small delicate thing. I applied a nail file, tweezers, nail scissors and finally a razor-blade without success. I found myself about to stamp on it like a petulant child. Intelligence, Mo, I told myself. Head, not heart . . .

I studied the locket right up close. It was as tight as a fresh mussel, stubborn, unyielding, like a safe casement hiding its secret from me. Then suddenly, without any interference from me, it sprang open and her face was staring at mine, a mirror of mine, her eyes as large and seeing as the sun.

My heart hit at my ribs like a frantic animal trapped in a sudden cage. She seemed in the room with me for that instant. It shocked me as an accident would, leaving me dazed and confused, surprised by my continuing breath. The effect was so overwhelming, it was as if I had met a ghost, as if I had been visited by another's will, a presence, a force of some kind.

I sat on the side of the bath, breathing deeply. It was a while before I dared to look at the locket again. When I did, I noticed a second photograph, on the other side. A young man, whose face was strangely familiar, although I couldn't think when or where I had seen it. A face from a Russian play or film, like Chekhov's face. There was the same sadness about his eyes that moved me. They seemed almost to be pleading with me. I didn't feel any visitation when I looked at him, but when I shifted my focus back to Katherine's photograph, I felt her there again, less suddenly and more certainly.

She was undeniably beautiful. Her fine, delicate features framed her exquisite eyes like precious metal around two radiant jewels.

How could any man withstand her? Even her own son must have been in love with her. And how could any woman be both as beautiful as she was and good? Decent? Honourable? Who wouldn't use such a gift as that for their own ends, even unconsciously? Could she know any other way?

I tried to temper my innate hostility, my envy of her, with some feeling of sisterhood, some generosity. It was a struggle. Envy came easily to me after so many years of Kate. I could always see qualities in other people that I failed to see in myself, and somehow it would always seem as though they had got my share.

I saw that in the photograph Katherine was actually wearing the locket, and had one hand stretched out towards it as if superstitiously checking its presence. I could see a frail vulnerability in that hand. She was, of course, gazing intently not at me but at this young man, who must have been her husband. I thought of what Howard had told me about their relationship, and I felt a deep empathy at last. A deep knowledge of her.

This feeling calmed me. I felt able to put the locket away, as though I had heard what she had come to say. I thought it was safest in my own jewellery box for the time being.

I went downstairs to greet Bill but he was fast asleep, snoring lightly. I sat down beside him, needing the warmth of him, the old familiar smell of his life. I felt like a thief again, stealing parts of him without his consent. I drowsed in the rhythm of his breath until I was also asleep.

The curtains had been left open and the early morning sun poured through them in a flood of gold. Particular words ran through my semi-consciousness like the headings of important paragraphs. Home. Warmth. Love. Marriage. Family. Bill. And finally Husband, tagged on the end.

We seemed so close again, lying against each other in the sun. Marriage should be for ever this. Soft bliss. The ordinary warmth of old intimacy, won with the effortful years. But we had lost it for ever in a careless day or two.

As soon as consciousness invaded us, however, the air turned cold. Bill pulled away from me and sat up suddenly, cricking his neck and back. He had an alarming ability to realign his spine without a chiropractor so that it cracked and crunched murderously, threatening to do irrevocable harm.

'Is it all right?'

'Yup,' came the monosyllabic reply.

We were silent, our bodies awkwardly close, with an emotional distance of miles. A vast acreage.

'How's your piece coming along?' I asked, politely, almost, as if of a stranger.

'OK.'

I reckoned that two syllables were better than one and that three might be on their way. I glanced over the titles spread across the floor.

'Heavy reading, by the looks of it.'

'Yup.'

I was wrong about the syllables.

We both stared out at the garden, frozen in the clean, clear sun.

'Is it interesting? Paedophilia?'

'Very.'

'Disturbing, I guess, researching it?'

He nodded.

'I think it's much more common than people realize,' he said.

A whole sentence encouraged me further.

'The actual practice of it, you mean, or just the desire?'

'Both.' He climbed over me and stood up. 'Want some tea?'

'Please.'

Please don't turn away, old friend. Allow me my adventure. Please?

He went next door. I glanced again at his books on deviant sexual behaviour. Why was he allowed to delve deep beneath the safe surface of things if I wasn't? Why condemn my small curiosity?

123

I thumbed through one of these books, intrigued despite myself. *Young Sexuality*, it was called. There were other, less appealing titles that I chose to ignore.

Bill returned with two large mugs of tea and a packet of biscuits.

'I didn't get to Sainsbury's, I'm afraid.'

He struggled with the impenetrably tight plastic wrapping. I gulped the hot strong tea. I held the book oafishly in one hand, like an unwelcome visitor in my own sweet home, wanting to reach into our lost marriage for a handful of ease.

He finally freed the biscuits and offered me one.

'Thanks.'

We ate them quietly, glancing at each other and glancing away.

A silence full of unsaid things.

'Have you been with . . . ?' he asked tentatively.

'Yes, I have,' I said plainly. Cleanly. Unsuggestively.

He picked up a book. One might call this a displacement activity, but it seemed well-placed to me. It seemed like sorrow.

'People always talk about children as if they're a different breed, like dogs or something,' he said irrelevantly. He was waving the book about as if referring to it, but he was distracting me with it, in fact, while his eyes searched me for tell-tale signs of betrayal.

'A different breed?' I said, letting him search, letting things be what they were.

'As if they only become human when their sexuality begins . . .'

'But it begins at birth.'

'Exactly!' he said. 'But everyone pretends it begins at puberty. Why? It obviously doesn't, does it? Doctors-and-nurses starts at about age three.'

He fell silent again, looking at me as if I was someone he didn't know very well.

'I don't think that's true, actually,' I said. 'Paedophiles often make out that the kids lead them on, don't they? As if they're very sexual.'

'That's what I'm saying, Mo. They act surprised that the kids lead them on. Why? Kids are openly sexual little beings. They want to explore sex. Why expect them to be paragons of virtue, innocent of sexual desire? That's when the harm is done.'

'Maybe,' I said.

'The harm is done when adults pretend their kids aren't sexual. They seduce them in all sorts of subtle ways, and then when the kids reach puberty and they can perform sexually, the shit hits the fan.'

I wondered why this was all so important to him.

'It's a difficult line,' I said.

'What is?'

'Sex and kids.'

'Is it?' he said, as if it shouldn't be a difficult line.

'I can sort of understand how it happens, can't you?'

'Can you?'

He was shocked, as if my empathy meant that I condoned it in some way, or even that I was capable of such abuse myself.

'I can see how the line gets crossed, how it becomes hazy, ill-defined. A lonely adult, with the undivided attention of an adoring child of the opposite sex who wants to touch and be touched. I can sort of understand. I mean I find it very hard to understand how an adult can do actual sex with a kid. But subtle seduction, or "molestation", as I suppose it would be called, I can see how that happens.'

He looked disgusted by me.

'Thank God we lost our child in that case.'

I felt as if I'd been knifed.

'I'm not saying I would have molested him, Bill! I'm saying I'm conscious of that capacity in human beings under certain circumstances.'

'And you a therapist! A The Rapist.'

'God, you're so repressed!'

We were heading for another full-blown, hurtful, spiteful row.

'I'm so repressed, am I? So repressed I believe in saving our marriage, is that what you mean? Whereas all your fucking stupid therapy has taught you is how to screw more than one man and still sleep peacefully at night! After everything you've said to me. After everything you've accused me of, you rip our marriage to bits!'

He was shouting now. I was probably shouting myself.

'What fucking marriage? Since when were you trying to save our marriage, Bill? Because I didn't notice. And I don't want it saved any more.'

'Fine.' He took this in. 'Thanks for telling me.'

'There's nothing left to save.'

'I disagree. But you're obviously so obsessed with Howard Nor –'

'How come it's all right for you to go off for days on end, week in, week out, but it's not all right for me? It's not OK for me to want to work –'

'I go away to research a subject. A subject, Mo. You're interested in one person who wants to fuck you stupid. OK. Fair enough.'

'I'm not just interested in him, although I'll admit he's a lot more interesting than anything else that's happened in the last ten years –'

'Are you in love with him?'

'What I'm interested in,' I said, unwilling to answer that, 'is the whole family, the whole set-up, the "story", as you would say. I'm after the story.'

'I'll tell you a story, honey. Just ask, you know? It's my department, stories . . .'

'Why is it your bloody department?'

'Shall I tell you one now?'

'Bill, I'm trying to explain things to you – are you listening or not?'

'Come to think of it, you probably know it already.'

'Know what?' I shouted impatiently.

'It was probably the first thing he confessed to you.'

'Confessed to me?'

The word sent a shudder through me.

'In your intimate little sessions together.'

'Confessed?' I asked again, my voice deserting me, leaving only a whisper. Bill had that smug look of triumph on his face, familiar in cruel children.

'What, Bill?' And, when he didn't answer, 'What's he done?'

'Or maybe you're that fucking nuts that you can hear a confession like that and not turn him in. No, worse than that, set him on a pedestal, set him apart, the Man Who Dared . . .'

I glared at him in horror, knowing that he could mean only one thing. The thing I dreaded the most. He could only mean murder. Little Cassie's drowned body was Howard's doing after all. Bill had somehow found out, with his journalistic prowess, what I was still only guessing at.

'How do you know?'

'How do I know what?'

'Come on, Bill. Don't play games. How do you know?'

'No, wait. What do you know, Mo?'

He wanted the words, the actual words, spoken in my voice.

'I know about a murder. OK?'

'You *know*? You do know?'

'Well . . .'

'He actually told you?'

I was being tricked into breaking any confidentiality that remained between Howard and myself.

'I can't say any more.'

'We're talking about murder, Mo.'

'It's unethical.'

'Murder? You're telling me!'

'I mean I can't break confidentiality.'

'How convenient.'

After a short, shared silence, he added:

'I understand from Kate that confidentiality breaks down when a client is a danger either to himself or to anyone else.'

'So it was Kate who told you, was it?'

'Never reveal your sources. Rule Number One.'

'Not even when they're a danger to themselves or anyone else?'

He didn't answer me.

'Pretty tight with Kate these days, aren't you?'

He didn't answer. He simply stared at me, a look of tired frustration on his face. Then he said in a flat, honest voice:

'There's such a stupid, blind arrogance about you these days, Mo.'

The words hurt, if only because he didn't intend them to. He was just stating a fact. He added:

'You think you're invincible. You think bad things won't ever happen to you. But you're wrong. Be told, Mo. You're wrong.'

'He was only a boy,' I said, as if this was an acceptable excuse. 'He lacked awareness.'

'What are you talking about?'

I was trying to make Howard's crime bearable to myself. Forgivable, even.

'He was only a little boy.'

'He's a fully grown man, Mo!'

'Now he is, obviously. When he did it, I mean.'

'He "did it" about a month ago!'

'What!'

My blood ran cold. We were suddenly talking about something quite different, about which I knew nothing and for which I was not prepared.

'What are you talking about now?'

'Darling, don't you know?'

'What?'

'He was a chief suspect. Or still is. He had no alibi. But because there weren't any witnesses, and there wasn't enough circumstantial evidence, they couldn't detain him. But they still suspect him.'

'Of what?'

'His mother's murder. Howard North's mother was murdered about a month ago. Surely you've just said you know that, Mo?'

'No. I didn't know that.'

'But you've just said he confessed.'

'No, I didn't. I was talking about something else.'

'You mean he killed someone else?'

'No, I don't mean that. Stop confusing me.'

'If you're protecting him, Mo . . .'

'*I'm not protecting him!*' I suddenly bellowed, stunning us both into silence. 'His little sister was drowned when he was a boy. He's haunted by it. Nobody really knows how it happened.'

'I'll hazard a guess!' He was almost laughing, as though the obviousness was too pronounced for any but the most obtuse to miss. 'It's that murder which is weighing so heavily against him now. He's just been released for the second time. Second arrest. Still no evidence. Just questioning.'

I could feel the tears, hot and uncontrollable, coursing down my cheeks. His voice was kind at once, but no comfort to me. Too late now.

'Come on, baby, sit down. It's all right, sit down.'

He steered me back to the sofa and sat me down, cradling me like a baby in his arms, while I wept.

'He didn't do it,' I said.

'It's all right . . . sshhh . . .'

'I'll prove he didn't.'

'That's right . . .' he hummed, humouring me.

'Poor Howard.'

'All right baby . . .' he stroked my hair. 'All right now.'

'I'm fine,' I said.

'Do you want something to eat?'

'Not really.'

'I could go to Sainsbury's – get something nice?'

'Could do.'

He thought I was almost his, almost back again in one piece.

When he was gone I sobbed. My private grief, the grief I couldn't show Bill, betrayed the depth of my involvement with North. It was the same uncontrollable grief that hit me when my parents died. I was up to my neck. Treading water. Feeling only his tides, his particular ebbs and flows.

Bill came back with lobster, cheeses, rye bread and Chardonnay. We ate with the silver cutlery and lit a candle which danced in the morning sun. He said that we should talk of the murders again, the seriousness of them, but that today should be a day of peace.

We would have made tender love in our big bed, if there had been a marriage left to save. But there wasn't. We both knew that.

13

I was sick for days after that meal, or possibly weeks. I blamed the sickness on the lobster, but it was more likely the Plague. In truth, my stomach was such a knot of fear that it would have heaved at anything. I felt as if my body was protesting, as if it was rejecting what I clung to in my mind, or heart, or soul – whichever domain it was that Howard now dominated. I couldn't bear to let him go.

The thought that Howard had murdered his own mother was too repulsive to allow. I would not allow it. I denied it with all my power. And yet curiously, when I almost allowed it, the murder of Cassie seemed as nothing by comparison. This disturbed me, this relativism of violent crime, as though once a line was irreversibly crossed, other lines could be sketched in along the way to comfort the conscience: harms not yet done. So if he had killed his sister, well, at least he hadn't killed his mother. Yet.

I slept fitfully during my illness. At moments of relative calm I would suddenly be seized by a horror so deep that death seemed the only likely relief. I would wonder at such times how anyone who had survived a war could ever find life bearable again. Let alone meaningful. Then I would sleep a little. The drug of unconsciousness. These short bursts of rest would lull me into a false sense of security from which I would wake with a sudden sense of peace. I would feel the shape of hope again.

But then I would start thinking. Howard's words, 'right' and 'wrong' and 'truth', would float through my mind, and I would argue things out in my head. Was he trying to justify a multitude of terrible, hidden crimes with this new morality of his? Was I so lost in the complexities and contradictions of his baffling brain that I couldn't trust my common sense any more? Was I hiding from the dark truth?

If he has committed either murder, I told myself, he has crossed that line. And if he's crossed that line . . . then what? I'll find out the truth. If he is a murderer, I'll turn him in.

I presented myself to myself as something of a saviour, a truth-seeker, on the surface of things. I had a cause, and it gave me a reason to march out of my empty life once more. I had to prove his innocence. I had to keep the truth sweet.

When I recovered physically, I was in a state of such mental delusion that I couldn't even see the danger I was in. I felt that I was – and indeed I could appear to be – as lucid as light itself. But real light illuminates real things, and I had lost my sense of reality by then.

While Bill was struggling to meet his deadline for whichever Saturday national newspaper it was, I packed a few necessities into a small suitcase and left.

He didn't hear the door shut, the car start. He was listening to an interview he had taped, with the volume turned up very loud to hear the voice above the background noise. It was a woman's voice, explaining why she had kept her son in her own bed at night until he was almost grown up.

I stood a short while in the hall, listening.

Her husband had died, she said, when her son was four. They both cried so loud in their separate beds, it seemed a crime not to comfort each other by cuddling up together instead of sleeping apart. And then they just sort of got into the habit of it.

I was tempted to stay long enough to hear what became of them, especially the pubescent son, but my prurient interest shamed me.

I drove past Howard's house in search of some evidence that he had returned from the West Country. He had. The Mercedes was lolling in the drive.

I pulled up by the kerb and crunched a path through the gravel to the front door, where I knocked on the big brass door-knocker. No one answered. I waited for some minutes because I thought I saw a shape or a shadow move across the window of the front room, but if I did, whoever it was didn't want to know me.

Was it Howard?

I felt that I had failed him in some way. Could he sense that I had broken his confidences and even hidden vital clues from him, and that now I suspected him myself? Could he see me for the traitor I was? I felt sure that he could. I sensed that he could see me now, see through me, waiting on his doorstep like a dog. He could see my deceit, my suspicion, my treachery, clear as daylight, and he was shutting me out of his life.

This thought sharpened my determination to force my way back in. I had to prove myself, my worthiness, my trustworthiness to him.

I waited in my car, flicking through a book of Neville Hoare's about personal responsibility. Just to pass the time. It didn't tell me anything I didn't already know.

My car was parked on the same side of the road as Howard's house, hidden from view by the wall that adjoined the gates to his drive. He would have to walk or drive out in front of my windscreen if he was there at all. I would see anyone who came or went from the house.

I was a truth-seeker, I flattered myself, with right on my side. A private investigator, there to see justice done. I enjoyed the self-importance of this fantasy. It glorified my ordinary, unfulfilled ineffectiveness.

I read the end of the book, looking for conclusions, hoping for some affirmation of my actions as valid and worthy. I found instead an essay on vanity. Hoare called it the major motivating force behind most 'good deeds'. I felt irritated and depressed by a world-view that would once have seemed to me honest and sane.

I put the book back in my suitcase and stared out at the road ahead. I must have sat there for at least an hour before anything happened. And then Kate swept past the front of my car and she was out of sight, speeding away in her BMW.

14

On the motorway I tried to remember everything Howard had ever said to me, but nothing formed even half a sentence. My head was a cacophony of words and voices, none of which made any sense.

The road was wet and the rain still heavy. My wiper blade needed changing months ago, in the rain-free summer months, and I regretted my negligence now. Seeing ahead became an art. By leaning forward over the steering wheel, I could extend my focus beyond the drops of water to the road in front of me. But if I sat back, I could see nothing beyond the blur of greasy water thickening on the windscreen. It was an uncomfortable drive, therefore, with my neck cricked back like a cyclist's, but I would get there in the end.

At one moment I thought I saw Howard's Mercedes swim up behind me, but without a wiper on the back window of my car it was hard to be sure. I was driving a Mini, a car so low on the ground that I could rarely see more than a fraction of any car behind. If it was indeed North, he seemed to lurk behind in my blind spot like a spy.

How like him, I thought.

Why did I think it was like him? What evidence did I have, beyond his enigmatic silences? Then suddenly I remembered the doorbell, the evening after our first session together. The shape of him through the glass was indistinct, and I had been unable to see anything through the peep-hole because he had covered it over, but it must have been Howard. I had been so sure it was him. He had hidden from me then, too.

The memory of my fear was like the secondary tremor of an earthquake.

So I was right to feel frightened after all, I told myself. My instincts had been right. And if they were right – since there's no hard evidence to trust, just suppose my instincts are evidence enough – then Howard is following me now.

My heart lurched. I glanced in my rear-view mirror. Wasn't that his car? My imminent death at his hands seemed to loom up from the tarmac in different guises. A crushed car or a strangled throat, a swollen river corpse, a suffocated weight, a hanging manikin.

I drove off the motorway at the next junction and circled the roundabout twice. His car, if indeed it had been his, didn't follow me. As I returned to the motorway on the slip road I scanned the passing traffic for some view of him, but saw nothing remotely resembling his car. I doubted my instinct now as surely as I had fleetingly trusted it.

I came off the motorway for the second time at Salisbury. Once parked, close to the cathedral, I studied the map. I didn't know how I would find the place. I had no house name, number or road, nor even a village to guide me. I had a vague notion of its whereabouts, but the web of minor roads which threaded their way through that area was so dense that I could only despair. Or hope for incredible luck.

By the time I arrived, the day was almost dark. A cold light shone out from the kitchen window, so uninviting that I dreaded my task. What value was any further investigation now, frightened and lonely as I was? Wouldn't I just distort anything I learnt? I wanted to turn my car around and head straight back for London.

I waited a while, reassuring myself. I could see the old man hovering over the Aga, doubtless preparing some concoction for his cat. I thought I could smell it from the road. Would I give him a terrible fright, turning up like this out of the blue? Or would he be half-expecting me?

I got out of the car, into what was now only a slight drizzle. The air smelt so good. I remembered Howard's 'Ah' as he had breathed in the fresh air of Richmond Park. How I had loved him then. How safe I had felt with him at that moment of recognition.

This recollection soothed my agitation somewhat. I stretched my aching, car-compressed limbs into their original shape, my neck making something of the same noise as Bill's.

I walked up to the front door as confidently as I could, to deceive only myself that all was well.

I rang the bell and waited. I remembered from our previous visit that the old man was slow in answering the door. I walked around the front of the house to the kitchen window to see if he was aware of a visitor, but plainly he hadn't heard the bell. He was oblivious, pottering to and from the Aga with a smile. Perhaps he had a radio on, or perhaps he was just rather deaf.

Either way, I decided to leave him to his cat food a while and take a walk. I was enjoying the country air and wanted to snatch all I could before dark. At least I had found the place. I could relax a little now, after so much insanity.

I looked around me at the West Country hills, and a deep feeling of sadness overcame me. I was thinking of Howard, of his growing up in that particular landscape with that particular view. I ached for him, in spite of myself. He awoke in me a feeling that had lain asleep all my life: a feeling of significance.

And in that moment, just as I am told it will at my death,

my life seemed to play before me like a movie that starts so well and features such stars and yet goes nowhere at all. Were we all in this pointless journey together, or was it my unique destiny to fail? To merely exist amidst a series of unconnected events? To have no purpose, to affect no outcomes, to simply pass through life like an idle passenger? I would do something worthwhile, I told myself, and I felt better then, with this secret promise nestling inside me like hope.

Standing on the doorstep for the second time that evening, waiting for the old man to answer the bell, I fancied that I saw a shadow flit past the side of the house. Was it a shadow? Some movement, anyway, although it was so dark now that I might have imagined it. The old fear returned as suddenly as it had left. The thud of my thumping heart was beginning to wear me out. I felt like someone forced, after an all-too-brief reprieve, to ride the same roller-coaster again.

'Come on . . .' I urged under my breath, pressing the bell long and hard.

But still the old man didn't appear.

When I dared to look again at the side of the house, there was nothing to see. I supposed that a cat or bird or any wild thing might cast a moving shadow there. And if not, why, then I had seen nothing, it was fancy, no more. Night-time and fear will always combine to deceive the eye, to play havoc with good sense.

One more long ring on the bell and a couple of knocks on the door with my knuckles, and at last I heard the unmistakable sound of bolts being pulled back.

With the door-chain firmly in place, the old man asked, 'Who is it?' through a chink of light.

'It's me. Mo. Remember? I came to visit – a couple of weeks

ago.' No response at all. 'With Howard North? Don't you remember? Just a fortnight ago.'

I hoped for some recognition, some form of welcome. But when his face did finally peer out from the light, he seemed hostile and afraid.

'What are you doing here?' he barked, the astonishment bright in his eyes.

'Can I come in, please?' I whispered somewhat urgently.

He glanced down the drive, seeming as nervous as I was, as though expecting to see something very particular.

'What's the matter?' I asked.

'Come on in, then. Quick.'

He opened the door wide so that I could pass him, then closed it fast and firmly behind me. This done, he sighed with slight relief.

'What on earth is going on?'

'I might ask you the same question, my dear. What in heaven's name induced you to return, when my instructions were perfectly plain?'

'Your instructions?'

'*Stay away!*' he suddenly shouted, as though I were approaching a bomb about to explode.

We stood in silence for a minute or two, both of us baffled by his outburst. And then he seemed to be listening, above his own pulsing fear, for some evidence of the danger that he had implied.

I had the sense that we were somehow infecting each other with a mild hysteria that could soon get out of hand. I wanted to laugh. We were behaving absurdly for two rational grown-ups.

He eyed me warily.

'Something amusing you?'

'I'm sorry. I don't mean to laugh,' I apologized. 'I'm just — nervous, that's all.'

As he calmed down slightly, I sensed the same seriousness in him that had emerged towards the end of my last visit.

'I should think you are nervous,' he nodded gravely. 'Very nervous indeed.'

There was something immensely sobering about the way he said this. The steady sanity in his voice suggested a superior knowledge, as well as a greater wisdom by far, than I would ever possess.

I was about to ask him what exactly he meant, but he put a forefinger to his lips and with his other hand beckoned me to follow him. At the door of the living-room he made me pause, while he went inside and drew the curtains. Then he invited me to sit down beside the fire.

'You're wet,' he said. 'Come. Dry yourself. Nice and warm.'

He shut the door behind me.

Silence.

I expected him to say something, to offer some explanation, but he just leant deliberately against the door, lost in his own thoughts, as if I wasn't there. I felt impatient, but I restrained myself and tried to relax instead. Just as I was beginning to feel quite hypnotized by the flames, he suddenly asked me a most unlikely question.

'What have you done with Kittie's locket?'

'Kittie's what?' I pretended bewilderment.

'You know perfectly well what. I'd like it back, please.'

'Back? I don't know what you mean.'

'I'm warning you.'

'What are you warning me of?'

A feeling of panic seized me. Who was this man?

'Have you ever known murder, my dear?'

So here was the true psychopath, I heard myself think.

'I asked you a question. Please answer me.'

His question brought to mind the old tramp in Bloomsbury, struggling across the road, waving her white stick at my car. The moment at which the knife must have gone in became vivid now, as if I had actually seen it. A vicious effort of strength against the struggling life of her limbs. Surely Howard could not have done the same to his own mother? Surely no one could? Her sudden collapse jolted me back to the present. The terrifying immediacy of death.

'Yes, I believe I have. Known murder.'

His eyebrows betrayed his surprise.

'Nasty business, isn't it?'

'Are you threatening me?'

He laughed at this. I felt increasingly angered by his changeability, which I perceived as calculated to deflect and control everything I said.

'I might be, mightn't I?' he said. 'And then again, I might not.'

I decided to meet his tyranny with a tyranny of my own.

'When I came down here with Howard, you spoke to me as if you knew me.'

'Did I?'

'You whispered to me behind his back. You seemed very scared. You told me that you couldn't find something. What was it that you couldn't find?'

'I don't know what you're talking about,' he said coldly.

'Yes, you do. Don't lie.' I paused. 'That other woman. The one who was so sure of herself. The one like me. I suddenly thought I knew who she was.'

His face seemed to freeze, in absolute terror.

'Have I said something wrong?'

He was looking beyond me now, at the curtains behind.

He mouthed his next words at me without any voice at all, but accompanied them with gestures: *Don't* (one hand making a dismissive gesture away from him) *say* (the same hand opening from a fist at his mouth) *any more* (both hands making a scissors cut across each other).

I realized that someone was listening to our conversation, though who or why I knew not, that they could not see us, and that plainly it was they who were the danger, not he.

I nodded to reassure him that I understood. My lips were sealed, I indicated, drawing an imaginary zip across my mouth.

Despite the evident danger we were in, I felt relieved that I was no longer alone.

'Are you feeling warmer, now?' he asked kindly.

'Much warmer, thank you.' I found some significance in his choice of words, as if 'warm' was to reassure me of a kindness and integrity that he couldn't otherwise show.

'Good.'

'I love real fires,' I said lightly. 'At home we only have one of those fake coal-effect fires because you can't burn real coal or wood in town.'

'Real fires are nice, aren't they?' he agreed, drawing the conversation to a close.

In the ensuing silence I wondered where the listener was. Had I, as I had suspected, seen a human shadow after all? What was that strong draught I could feel? Was one window slightly ajar? And why had I been made to wait at the door while Rolf closed the living-room curtains? There must be someone outside. Someone who had threatened this frail old man – with murder, perhaps? Someone who knew about the locket and wanted it back at all costs.

Had the old man actually seen me find and steal the locket,

and then rather stupidly let slip what he had seen? And if so, to whom?

My obvious suspect was Howard. It was so obvious, in fact, that I tried to think of other possibilities, despite my fear. Howard was too big for us.

I tried to guess which window was ajar, having decided that the outside was the most obvious place to hide. But the heavy velvet curtains, which the years had faded from a rich gold to a mouldy yellow, gave nothing away.

'Shall you be staying the night, my dear?' the old man abruptly inquired.

I tried to read some instruction from his expression but found nothing. I shrugged but he continued to look straight at me, stony-faced.

It occurred to me that the listener could now, unaccountably, see us both quite clearly. Or could they only see Rolf? None of the curtains in my eye-line had moved. I spun around on the sofa to look at the curtains behind me. I saw a last settling ripple as one fell back into place. I thought I also saw a glimpse of blonde hair, but that was too unlikely. What would Kate be doing out there?

The old man raised a disapproving eyebrow and shook his head. But he said:

'I can't think what you hope to see behind you, dear girl. This isn't a pantomime.'

'Sorry. I felt a draught.'

He nodded and smiled, but then his face froze again.

'I'm afraid you probably did. These windows haven't had any attention for years. They're practically falling apart.'

We sat in silence for a while. I was trying to think what to do. If only the listener *was* Kate, I would have no hesitation in simply opening the curtains and asking her what the hell she was playing at. But of course it wasn't Kate. Kate was in London, and Kate was a lot of things, but she wasn't quite mad yet. Even jet-black hair would probably appear blond with the warm living-room light falling on it through the yellow curtains. I must assume the worst. I must assume that Howard is out there now, dangerous and murderous, and after the locket I had found.

So if I left for London now, how safe was the old man? Did his well-being depend upon my being present or absent? How could I find out?

'Perhaps, since you weren't expecting me, I ought to leave you in peace.'

'As you wish.'

He seemed slightly dismayed.

'Unless . . . I wouldn't want to inconvenience you . . .'

'You wouldn't. Not at all.'

'In that case, if I could stay just for tonight . . . I've packed a few things in the car . . .'

'Do you need them urgently?'

I sensed from his question that retrieving them at this stage would not be advisable, although I was anxious to secure the locket. If it was such a vital clue, I wanted it on my person, for safe-keeping.

'No – I don't really,' I said. 'I can leave my teeth for one night!'

He smiled.

'If I were you, I'd just settle right where you are – it's the warmest room in the house. Doze off by the fire.'

I suddenly had this terrible fear that he might be setting me up. He might be about to leave me alone in the room, with the murderous Howard outside the open window, just waiting for a moment alone with me.

'I'm feeling quite paranoid,' I said, hoping that he could reassure me somehow.

'Paranoid?'

'I don't know anything about you. For all I know, you might be a murderer.'

I felt that I could say this quite legitimately, without endangering either of us, since we had already spoken of murder fairly openly.

He laughed.

'I'm serious. You were certainly trying to frighten me earlier.'

'And so I was, my dear. You needed frightening. Young women are ill-advised to turn up at remote country houses where lone men reside, at any time of day, let alone at night-fall.'

There was no comfort to be gleaned from these words, utterable by anyone anywhere, although not in quite the same formal English he chose.

I wished I believed in angels. I would have summoned one then. I wished I had secret access to Bill, that I could somehow bring him careering down the motorway with policemen on motor bikes, in cars, in helicopters overhead. Like the husband he never was.

'I shall probably kip down here myself if you don't mind, my dear. I don't tend to venture beyond that door much after nine o'clock.'

'By all means,' I said warmly, sighing with relief. 'What's happened to Kitty.'

'She's outside killing things. At this time of night. If she's lucky.'

This sentence wasn't the most conducive to sleep, but he offered nothing further, and was soon snoring loudly in the chair opposite me. He dribbled slightly over the pink blanket that virtually strangled him, its colour more appropriate to a baby of six months than to a tired old man.

I turned out the remaining light and watched the embers glow. When they finally extinguished themselves, I closed my eyes and replayed the evening's events again in my mind's eye.

I didn't sleep at all. At about midnight I heard a car start and saw its headlights peep through the curtains. I leapt up to have a look, fearful that it was my own car being driven away, but I could see very little in the dark. All I could see was that it was not my car. My bright yellow Mini was plainly visible. It sat, like an ally keeping watch, where I had parked it earlier, whereas this car was so dark in colour that it almost seemed not to exist between its head and rear-lights. As it drove past the window I could see only that it was a long car, not a hatchback, and not an estate. A Mercedes would fit the description well.

15

I woke to the sound of birds, the light of the morning sun and a cup of Darjeeling, although which stirred me first I couldn't say. I suspect it was only when the old man had drawn back the curtains and placed the porcelain cup by my side that I was aware of either sun or birds.

The sunlight was a welcome and soothing surprise after so much rain. I almost felt happy. But even the most wretched, dull day would have sufficed to shift my fear.

'Thank you,' I said warmly.

I looked up to smile at the kind old man but, to my horror, discovered that Howard North was towering over me.

My breath left me.

'What are you doing here?'

'I might ask the same of you.'

'I drove down last night.'

'So I understand,' he said sharply, but then, changeable as ever, added gently, 'Whatever were you thinking of? Driving down here on your own?'

'I don't know,' I said, confused by his sudden concern. I rummaged through my sleepy mind for some half-decent excuse.

His eyes searched my face for something. A clue? A betrayal? Or was it the same something he was always wanting from me? An emotional void? If so, it was the last thing I felt capable of giving him then. My feelings were like bubbling nectar waiting to be drunk.

'I just — I just wanted a break.'

'Home-life rather a strain, is it?' he replied curtly, sharp again, as if dismayed by the struggle he had seen in my face.

'It's been easier,' I admitted.

'I can't say I'm surprised.'

'No, I'm sure you can't. It's exactly what you planned, isn't it?' I snapped.

He didn't show any alarm at my irritability. Perhaps he was satisfied that my anger was sufficient proof of my honesty.

'You followed me, didn't you? I thought it was you,' I said.

'Why on earth would I want to follow you?'

'You tell me.' But he didn't. 'What are you doing here if you didn't follow me?'

'I do own this house, Mo. I have every right to be here.'

'Do you?'

'Of course I do. "Only son and heir", that sort of thing.'

'You didn't kill her for this house, did you?'

It was out before I had even thought about it, let alone intended it. A look of such intense fury overcast his face that I feared for my life. But it passed in a split second, like a bird flying high in front of the sun. He then became very calm and clear and, more like a police officer than a criminal, he began to fire questions at me. They came so fast I thought I might confess to a murder myself.

'Who have you been talking to?'

'My husband.'

'And who has he been talking to?'

'Kate, I suspect.'

He clenched his jaw with icy control.

'And what has he learnt from Kate?'

If I tell him, what will he do, I wondered.

'I asked you a question, Higgs.'

'Apparently you murdered your mother.' It sounded so absurd that I thought he might laugh. 'You were the chief suspect, at any rate.'

He stared at me.

'I see,' he said, and paused. 'And you believed him? Of course.'

'No, I didn't. Not necessarily.'

'Didn't you?'

His face was suddenly open, like a grateful child's when someone at last takes his side against authority.

'I found the thought intolerable. But if it's the truth, then I hope you'll . . . own up to it. What else can you do?'

He sank down on the sofa beside me suddenly, his face buried in his hands.

'I was coming to this, Mo . . .' He was frowning, his hands combing through his hair. 'I wanted to tell you the whole story, that's why when you kept asking me during that first session what had I done to my face – remember that?'

'Yes.'

'And I said, let me tell you in my own time, in my own way, from start to finish. Do you remember that?'

'Yes, I do.'

'You see, I was coming to this.'

He stared ahead in perplexity, whatever plans he had nurtured now thwarted.

'I couldn't just start with a murder and expect to be understood, could I?'

'I don't know,' I said, flatly.

'You wouldn't have believed me, for a start.'

'I might have done.'

'The risk was too great,' he said adamantly.

There was a long pause.

'At least you feel remorse,' I offered, to comfort myself more than him.

'What for? What are you saying? I thought you understood?'

Understood what? Murder? I wanted to shout, but checked myself in time.

Every sudden change of his mood seemed to threaten my life.

'I didn't do it, Mo.'

'You didn't do what?'

'I didn't –' he stopped abruptly, glaring at me like a man betrayed. 'Dear God, must I spell it out? Even to you?'

'Yes, I'm afraid you must,' I said.

'I did not kill my mother, Mo. What possible motive could I have? I loved her! I don't want this monstrous house. It's a bloody albatross. I'm stinking rich as it is. What do I want another bloody house for? I was keeping her, for God's sake!'

'What do you mean, you were keeping her? You hadn't seen her for two years.'

'I was sending her cheques. So she could pay bills. She was utterly dependent on me. I'd kept her in money for years.'

'Perhaps you didn't want to keep her any more,' I suggested impetuously.

'Well, I wasn't, by the end. She wouldn't be kept.'

'Why not?'

'She'd all but disappeared. I couldn't get the cheques to her. No one knew where she was. She wasn't cashing them.'

'So where was she?'

He stood up and walked over to the window. Four birds

suddenly arrived from nowhere and danced in front of it, in an unlikely, uniform line.

'They say that when somebody dies, birds often do this – dance and sing like this – as if the spirit were revisiting.'

When he turned back towards me his face showed such grief that I hated myself for ever doubting him.

'I'm sorry,' I said.

'Yes,' he replied, looking through me.

'I didn't mean to be cruel.'

He smiled, a mild, benign smile of resignation, as if I had been his last hope and I had run out on him.

I felt I could have laid down my life for him then.

'How can I help you, Howard? What can I do?'

He looked surprised.

'Nothing. You're very kind. Nothing. You've done enough. You've tried.'

'I haven't done anything. I've let you down, that's all.'

'Nonsense. You've done your very best. I know you have.'

'How can I help you? Tell me!'

He paused, studying my face, as if ascertaining the appropriateness of what was to come.

'If you really – really want to help –' He paused in shyness, his face colouring slightly. 'You see, you mustn't fall in love with me, Mo.'

Of all things. That.

'Why not?' I could feel my cheeks burning.

'If you do, you can't help at all. You mustn't love me.'

He looked out of the window again, as if to avoid my gaze.

'The trouble is, the real difficulty is, that I could fall in love with you. Which would make it doubly hard for you. Because in my heart I would very much want you to love me, too, that's the difficulty. Because I'd end up trying to make you love me in spite of myself, in all sorts of unhelpful ways which I can't seem to control. I think perhaps I'm already guilty of this. But you mustn't love me, you see. However much I want you to. You absolutely must not.'

Even the back of his neck seemed to be blushing as he looked out over the fields.

How could I ever not love him?

We remained silent until I dared to ask:

'What if I already do?'

He turned from the window and gazed at me with such longing that I thought we were both lost.

'Do you?' he asked.

I looked away, unable to withstand his eyes.

'I hope not, for both our sakes.'

He came back to the sofa and sat down beside me, taking my hand in his with all the tenderness of love.

'You see, you must use your head, Mo. Examine the facts. I'll tell you everything I know, if you'll promise to seek the truth. Seek it out, like water. Look for the truth. Not for my answering love. Just for the truth.'

He spoke with all the urgency of a man sentenced to death. The sentence was emotional, I realized, not literal, although he may have felt so lonely by then that suicide presented an alternative hell.

I was reminded, by the content of his words, of Neville Hoare's writings. A passage about courage which I remembered well echoed him word for word, almost. The essential point had been that any search for the truth, be it spiritual or physical, needed courage above all, the courage to face every possibility.

'I'll try,' I said. 'I really will try.'

'Thank you,' he said.

I sipped my tea, which was unbearably sweet.

'Any good?' he asked anxiously.

'A little sweet. But very warming. Thanks.'

'The old boy made it. Wasn't sure if he'd added sugar or not. He seems to add sugar to absolutely everything.'

'What's that burning smell?' I asked, suddenly aware of it.

'Toast, I think. He's been cursing the toaster all morning.'

He hovered over me a while longer before deciding against further conversation.

'Charcoal and marmalade suit you for breakfast, then?' he said, grinning as he left the room.

A short while later the old man came in, balancing a tired brass tray which he rested on my knees. Howard stood behind him, smiling to himself.

'Toast and marmalade, my dear!'

'Thank you. How delicious.'

'A little burnt, I'm afraid. Blasted toaster – got no automatic pop-up, has it? Flipping useless thing,' he muttered at Howard.

'Charcoal's good for you,' I offered.

'I hope it isn't quite charcoal, my dear,' he said politely but very firmly.

Howard pulled a conspiratorial face at me.

'Oh, no. I didn't mean – I meant just the edges being a little – well – burnt. Not really charcoal as such.'

Silence.

'More tea?' he asked, finally.

'I'd love some without – without so much sugar, if you're – making some.'

'Very well.'

He pushed past Howard like a piqued old woman whose whole sense of herself lay in the reception of her breakfasts.

'Oh dear . . .'

'My fault, I think,' said Howard.

There was an awkwardness between us as soon as we were left alone. The shared intimacies hovered around us like the visiting birds, unforgettable. And the way through this dense silence seemed suddenly impenetrable, like picking a path through the tangled roses outside.

Howard took the initiative.

'When all this is over, perhaps we'll be able to . . .' but he trailed off into silence.

'Able to what?'

'Perhaps we'll be able to love each other a little, I was going to say.'

The words ran over me like caressing fingers, their tips finding every secret, sensitive place.

'But I was forgetting your husband,' he said.

16

Howard spent most of the day digging the pond. It had only been a small pond, but it took some digging. He attacked the earth with ferocity, his newly purchased spade gouging out great lumps of soil like a greedy spoon at a thick chocolate cake. There was little I could really do to help with my heavy spade, but what I could do I did.

The knowledge of the locket, tucked away in my suitcase, was beginning to trouble me. I was determined to give Howard this reward for his efforts, this precious clue, but I was reluctant to admit to its theft. I preferred to return it to the mud of the pond, where it could be miraculously happened upon all over again. And yet the double dishonesty of this after his demand for the truth was more troubling still. Why had I held on to it in the first place? He would be as offended by my secretive suspicion of him as he would by my dishonesty. What could I do? I had gleaned all I could from the locket; there was nothing to gain from holding on to it. Perhaps I could simply tell him the truth, and risk a moment's wrath. He'd hardly kill me.

'I'm just going to take a break, Howard.'

'Right.'

'Anything you want?'

'Nope.'

He was barely conscious of me, such were the demands of his mission.

During the morning he had watched my every move – in

anticipation of what, I did not know. He wouldn't even let me retrieve my suitcase from the car, insisting that I looked fine as I was and that my teeth would survive one day's negligence. Was this the beginning of my gradual demise? From one day's negligence into a thousand of self-abandonment? I had borrowed his mother's hairbrush, feeling it was not altogether right to do so, and otherwise I obeyed him. Something was almost broken in me, surrendering. By the afternoon, Howard seemed confident of his control of me. He relaxed his vigilance. I was able to go to the loo without his finding some spurious reason for accompanying me. I therefore assumed that it might be safe to collect the locket at last.

I was also very keen to catch the old man on his own. I wanted to ask him a few important questions before the locket left my safe-keeping. Not least, what on earth had happened the previous evening that had so tyrannized him. Although it was true that my fear of Howard had diminished substantially, I was still profoundly uncertain of him. My fear had shifted. I was no longer personally afraid of him, since he seemed to pose no immediate threat to me, but there was undeniably a darkness lurking within him that might threaten somebody. He himself had made it my business, my duty, even, to find out the truth.

The old man gave a terrified start when I came upon him in the kitchen. He was all nerves still, I realized. His apparent calm at breakfast had misled me into believing that Howard was not a man he feared. I had assumed that all was well again, that whatever had been amiss the day before was amiss no longer. Now I realized that I was wrong.

'What's the matter?'

'Tea, my dear?' he asked, in flat denial of my question and his fear.

'Tell me.'

He eyed me warily, as though expecting some impending violence.

'Nothing to tell.'

He looked away from me, out through the window at the drive.

'You can trust me, you know,' I said gently.

'Nonsense.'

I found his reply baffling.

'Why so sure?'

'Howard thinks he can trust you –'

'Does he?' I was flattered, in spite of myself.

'Not for me to put him right, but I know he can't.'

'I'm sorry?'

'I saw you.'

'Saw me? Saw me what?'

'Where is it?'

He meant the locket, of course. What did he know? I had been so confident of his pliability, and yet he continued resolutely to defy me. I had slipped back into stereotyping, which classified this old man as 'docile', or senile or fragile, or anything ending in '-ile'. In fact he was more alert and shrewd than any of us. He would never be any man's fool again, as perhaps he had been once or twice in his life. He was living on his wits as though he had only just come to them.

I was aware for the first time that he might be a part of this plot, or intrigue, that he might have some stake in it.

'I'll give you some advice –'

'You've given me enough.'

'Give me the locket. Get in your car. Go home. Leave us alone.'

'Who's "us"?'

'You have no idea of the danger you're in.'

'If you'd only be specific about it instead of threatening me, I might have some idea, mightn't I? Who knows, I might even do as you suggest.'

He seemed to be thinking about how much to tell me. He was narrowing his eyes as an artist sizes up a model before painting her. But I felt that he couldn't actually see me; he lacked the necessary insight to grasp my soul. Whereas Howard already had it in the palm of his hand.

'Who are you, Rolf?'

'I'm nobody's fool, my dear, I can assure you of that.'

'I didn't think you were.'

'Least of all yours.'

'I'm flattered,' I said drily.

'Don't be,' he said. '"Flattered vanity/Leads to insanity."'

'That's nice. I like that,' I said, aware that these two short lines headed the first chapter of Neville Hoare's book, which was sitting in the suitcase in my car. Had he broken into my car, rifled through the suitcase, perhaps even found the locket, and was he now telling me so?

'Does it matter where the locket is?'

'A great deal.'

'Why?'

'Do you have it on your person now? Give it to me. Please. Now.'

'You must tell me what's going on,' I said firmly, using a certain authority that I reserved for occasions like this. It often got me what I wanted when all else had failed.

'I can't,' he said, responding in kind. 'Not possible.'

Authority was not going to work with the old patriarch that he was gradually revealing himself to be.

'Why not?' I asked. 'What harm can it do?'

'A great deal of harm.'

'Listen, Rolf. I don't want to cause you any harm. But I can sense that something is seriously wrong. I want to help.'

He seemed so profoundly wary of me that no reassurance, however sincere, was likely to satisfy him.

'I know your kind,' he said cynically, testing my goodwill with this inference.

'My kind?' I asked, testily.

'Your cunning, feline kind – stealing people's secrets from them.'

'I thought you liked cats?' I said flippantly, ashamed of the truth of what he said. The thieving truth.

'I do.' He paused and smiled suddenly, changing direction with characteristic dexterity, like something feline himself. 'Too much for my own good.' And he winked improbably.

The sexual implication of this wink was too awkward to contemplate. And yet he might once have won me for a day. How hard it must be to relinquish one's sexual power to old age, after years of mastery, like a useless tool. He might even have won my heart twenty years ago, attractive and astute as he was, rather like Howard, but he would have broken it, too, I felt sure. I thought of Howard's mother and her broken heart. And then something suddenly dawned on me. I looked at the old man again, studying him closely as he waited for me to say something, and I realized who he was. It was the eyes that gave him away. The sadness around his eyes. Just like the photograph.

I chose to keep the realization to myself, for the time being at least. The more he thought I knew, the less he was likely to reveal.

'What are you afraid I might do,' I asked, 'if you tell me?'

'Who knows? People can do terrible things, can't they?'

He looked strangely haunted suddenly, as if by some memory, like a man traumatized by the horrors of war, who suddenly remembers some gruesome torture inflicted upon him.

'What terrible things are you thinking of?' I asked.

He didn't answer me.

'Were you ever married, Rolf?' I inquired, out of the blue.

'What sort of question is that?'

He was indignant. I felt duly ashamed of my bluntness.

'I don't know,' I mumbled. 'I just –'

'What has it to do with you whether I was married or not?'

'I'm sorry. I didn't mean to pry.'

There I was again, I thought, asking too many questions too soon. In fact I realized that I didn't want to know too much about Rolf, even if he was the man I thought he was. I wanted only the information relevant to the case. It was Howard's story I wanted.

What a task it seems to be to find out the truth, I conceded wearily. Are we all so secretive, or is there something truly hideous buried here somewhere?

'I have to ask you something less personal, then,' I said determinedly.

'How refreshing,' came his dry reply.

'That woman you mentioned –'

He seemed to bristle immediately.

'The one who looked so like me?'

'Yes, I know who you mean,' he replied curtly.

'Did she do something – anything – terrible?'

He looked at me uncertainly, wavering on the precipice of the truth.

'I would have to tell you everything, right from the start. It wouldn't make any sense, otherwise.'

No short cuts, in other words. Like father, like son.

Suddenly Howard was standing in the doorway, still and silent in his soft woollen socks, unannounced by either step or breath. How long had he been there?

'Is she harassing you?' he asked, trying to sound unconcerned.

'You shouldn't creep up on people like that,' said Rolf.

'Just wondering where my assistant digger had gone . . .'

'Any joy yet?' I asked, trying to appear guiltless of any intrigue with the old man.

'Only in seeing you,' he said, with unlikely ease. He must have heard Rolf's ungainly attempt at flirtation and was mocking him.

'Tshh . . .' hissed the old man fiercely.

'Take it on the chin, Rolf,' Howard teased. 'Some of us can still get away with it.'

'Just!'

'And some of us just can't!'

The banter was light, but barbed with sharp, possibly lethal thorns.

'What are you hoping to find out there anyway?' asked the older man irritably. 'You're wasting your time.'

'What the bloody hell do you think I'm hoping to find? Evidence, of course. One tiny clue that proves I didn't . . .'

He shut up as suddenly as he had burst forth, his brow furrowed like one of the ploughed fields outside.

'Proves you didn't what, Howard?' I asked.

'You know what, Mo. Didn't kill her. Proves I didn't kill her,' he said.

'Does she know?' Rolf barked, looking at Howard like an astonished deer.

'Do I know what?'

The old boy looked at me as though I were a tiresome child, always in the way. Then he looked back at the other adult in the room.

'Howard? She doesn't know, does she?' he asked again.

'She knows something,' he said.

'How much do you know?' the old man demanded of me, his face close to mine.

'How much don't I know?' I asked Howard. 'Because I get the feeling that you're hiding a lot from me still. I get the feeling you're deceiving me.'

'What have you been talking about?' Howard asked the old boy irritably.

'I haven't said anything, I swear,' he answered.

Rolf seemed momentarily frightened of North. It was as though he didn't know quite who to be frightened of, but he knew that someone was very much to be feared. Howard, or Kate, or even me. Or was there someone else involved in this whole intrigue?

'I suddenly had the sense that you two were related,' I said provocatively, making the most of their joint anxiety.

They looked at each other for a fraction of a second that left me in no doubt.

'Yes, I've had that sense sometimes, too,' Howard deflected ingenuously. It was neither a truth nor a lie.

'You should check out your family trees,' I suggested.

'Yes . . . perhaps we should . . .' He contrived to be preoccupied, lost in his thoughts again.

'You said "evidence",' I continued, unwilling to let him withdraw. 'As Rolf said, what exactly are we looking for out there?'

'You must have a better idea than anyone,' Rolf accused me pointedly.

'I'm not looking for a body,' said Howard, thankfully ignoring Rolf's indiscretion, 'if that's what you mean.'

'Why not?' I asked. 'The body could be there, couldn't it?'

'How does she know about the body?' Rolf shrieked in dismay.

Howard ignored him. 'It isn't in there, Mo. It was made to look like an accident. She was given a proper burial. Her grave is up at the village church.'

'How do you know?'

'Because –' Howard glanced at the old man – 'because – I remember.'

'But you didn't remember before, did you?' I asked.

'What is this? Some kind of interrogation?'

'You didn't, did you?'

'No, I didn't.' He paused and sighed. 'I didn't know then. I have subsequently done my research. Now I do know. They would have been idiots to bury the body themselves. Can't you see that? Far too obvious.'

'So how did you find out they'd buried her at the church?' I asked.

Another furtive glance at the old man.

'I walked up there and had a look.'

'So there's a gravestone with her name on it, is there?'

'Not her actual name, no.'

'What, then?'

'For God's sake, Mo! I thought you trusted me?'

'Why should a few questions imply that I don't? I'm trying to find out the truth. Trust would, I feel, obstruct that objective process, don't you think?'

He smiled for a moment, almost pleased with me.

'Very well.'

Again he looked at the old man, shrugging slightly.

'Are you two in cahoots?' I asked, feeling slightly paranoid.

'Kahutz?' asked Rolf. 'Where's that?'

We all managed a laugh of sorts, mine rather more constrained than theirs.

'No, we're not. Not in any conspiratorial sense,' said Howard. He took a deep breath. 'God, it's so impossible, this. If we'd only stuck to our bloody therapy sessions, Mo, we'd have covered this ground weeks ago. The trouble is that more keeps happening before I've even told you the essential story itself.'

'Well, perhaps it's time to tell me the essential story.'

'Yes, it is. Of course it is. Only things are getting somewhat urgent.' He furrowed his brow again. 'I'm under quite a serious threat, that's the trouble. And so is – so is . . .'

'Rolf?' He didn't even nod. 'From whom?'

'Too many questions, Mo. Too many questions. Remember your training. Trust your client's process, eh?'

'But you're not my client, Howard.'

'No, I'm not, that's true, I'm not. But I still – I feel rather as though I am, still.'

'Then let's have a session, shall we? Tell me the story. You're expecting an awful lot of me if you think I'll just come along for the ride.'

'Of course.'

He fell silent, his head bowed.

'What's the problem?'

'The almighty risk is the problem, Mo.'

17

He took the risk, or at least a part of it. A part of the whole. It seemed a substantial enough part at the time.

He chose the village church as his venue, driving me there in his grumbling car. 'Not her again,' it seemed to be muttering.

The church stood at the top of the hill, attacked by fierce winds. Like its teachings, it turned the other cheek.

'I'm really biting my tongue, Howard – it's frantic with questions.'

'One thing at a time,' he replied firmly.

The Mercedes mowed over the mud and grass of winter.

He pulled up the hand-brake and climbed out of the car. I remained glued to my seat. He opened my door.

'Come on, Mo.'

He stroked my cheek, his warm hand kind to me. I took it in my own cold hand, and kissed it. Then I let it go, conscious of the danger of love.

'I'll show you the grave,' he said, 'just so you believe me.'

'I do believe you.' But he was already striding towards the edge of the graveyard where no stones were.

'Where is it?'

He lifted a mass of brambles to reveal the tiny, heart-stopping size of her neglected stone. Her gravest of gravestones.

'This is hers.'

He had to pull away the brambles and ivy to read the inscription.

'I deliberately covered it over again last time – just in case – I don't know why – just cautious.'

It had certainly been completely hidden until he had uncovered it. Even the tiny mound in front was nothing but a bed of nettles and grass.

I can't bear it, I thought. I can't bear to look.

'What does it say?'

He read the words with a flat, numb voice, too grieved to intone what spoke so well for itself.

'The shortest life is best,
The longest sleep most sweet.
Blessed be thy rest,
Until we next shall meet.'

I had to fight to hold on to my objectivity, with her little body lying so close.

'Whose words?'

He looked at me, his eyes narrowing thoughtfully.

'Not Katherine's, surely?'

He shook his head.

'Rolf's?' I ventured bravely.

'My father's words.'

This wasn't an answer, but it wasn't a denial either.

'Very beautiful words,' I said kindly.

He nodded.

In the church, sitting in the front pew, he said:

'I could almost have faith sometimes, just out of necessity, just because the brain collapses under the weight of too much to understand.'

'There's a lot, isn't there?' I mumbled, keen to get started on the 'too much to understand'. I was too curious, too perplexed now, for any further delay.

'It's all right, Mo. I'm coming to it,' he said, reading my thoughts.

He took a deep breath, inhaling the musty air of the church, of the wooden pews and the heavy stone and the damp cold cloth of the cushions and tapestries. Wasn't there also the smell of the huge Bible itself, an old book-bound smell of history?

'You can't lie in a church, can you? Even if you have no faith. The tyranny of childhood wraps its rules round you.'

'He is your father, isn't he?' I said, unable to restrain myself any longer.

He smiled at me and shook his head patiently.

'You've got a lot to learn about therapy, Mo.'

'He is, though, isn't he?'

He nodded.

'He says he is.'

'Don't you believe him?'

'I think so.'

'Why would he lie?'

'I don't know. People do. Don't they?'

I felt that he could see my lies as if they were written on a long list, like an open scroll in front of him.

'Isn't he familiar to you at all?'

'No. I have almost no memory of him. Kittie never spoke of him. No photographs or letters, no belongings, nothing. It was as if he never existed. I remember after Cassie's death, when he left us, Kittie was frantic to find some locket that had his picture in it. But we never did find it. He took everything else.'

The locket. How increasingly important it was. I thought of the man locked in with her. Anton Chekhov's eyes. The likeness was now so obvious, I wondered how I had ever missed it.

'When did he come home?'

'Only very recently.'

'Where from?'

'He went back to India after Cassie's death. Or so he says. He was always in love with a beautiful Indian girl, even when he married Kate – I mean – Kittie. Katherine. It wasn't acceptable to marry Indian women then. Natives. So he married my mother instead, to keep the peace. To keep up with his family, with social expectations, all that bollocks. He was wretched about it. And Kittie was wretched, too, of course. She loved him. After the drowning, he left. He went out and married the Indian girl. Didn't get a divorce. Just married again, under a different name.'

'"Rolf"?'

'That's right. Rolf!' He laughed affectionately. 'Of all the names to choose!'

'So he's been in India ever since then? All those years?'

'In the main.'

He paused, thoughtfully.

'I would go into more detail, only it's – well, it's his life to tell or not, isn't it? I'll fill you in on what's relevant.'

'Fair enough,' I agreed.

And the rest, I schemed, I can get from the horse's mouth.

'I suppose he felt that he'd married a kind of witch,' he said.

'He had, hadn't he?' I quipped.

He glared at me, as if daring me, like an eclipsing sun, to look straight up at him.

'I'm sorry. I'm so sorry. That was a stupid, facetious, flippant thing to say.'

He looked away, accepting my remorse.

'She wasn't a witch to me. Far from it . . . I loved her profoundly. Do you understand? Profoundly.'

'Right.'

'Try to understand,' he said, clearly unimpressed by my response. 'Profound love is profoundly forgiving, Mo.'

'Yes, I believe it is,' I said.

'It enables you to forgive the most vicious acts of revenge. The most violent crimes. Understanding is only part of it. The real key is love.'

'Howard, I don't need a lecture on love. I just need to hear the truth.'

'Quite right. Quite right, Mo.'

'So it was Rolf who told you about Cassie's burial?'

He hesitated, flinching slightly.

'Amongst other things.'

'What is his real name?'

'William.'

'William? How funny.'

'Why?'

'It's my husband's name. Bill.'

'No,' he said categorically, 'William or nothing. Why do you think I was christened Howard? So no one could shorten it. He hates shortened names. Whereas Bill was doubtless christened Bill. Wasn't he?'

'He wasn't, actually, no.'

We fell silent. Unspoken tensions began to pollute the air.

'Have you been married long?' he asked abruptly.

'Ten years. Is that long?'

'Does it feel long?'

I laughed at this. The for ever it had been.

'Sometimes,' I admitted.

I studied the lines of his face.

'Have you ever been married?'

'Mo,' he warned. 'One thing at a time.'

'I want to kiss you,' I said quite out of the blue.

'Don't, would be my advice,' he said.

We were caught unawares for an instant.

'Come on, then,' I said brusquely, breaking the silence like a diver in a still pool of blue. 'Tell me things!'

He smiled, almost laughed at my efforts to resist.

'I will, I will, I will!'

But then he looked at me so longingly that neither of us could say a word.

'You mustn't do this, must you? North.'

'No. I know.'

He stood up and walked over to the altar and waited like a bridegroom there.

If he had ever married, I thought, this was as likely a place as any for him to seal his fate.

'He only told me yesterday what actually happened to Cass.'

Yesterday? I wondered. When, yesterday?

'Does he know?' I asked.

'He knows what happened to her body.'

'And he told you over the telephone, did he?'

'No.' He seemed surprised by my question. 'He told me in person.'

'But you weren't here yesterday.'

'I was.'

'When?'

Had he been that shadow, after all? That frightening threat?

'I came down very late. Or early. In the early hours of the morning, in fact.'

'Funny time to travel.'

'I only found out rather late last night that you weren't at home.'

'So? Does that mean you have to follow me?'

'Yes, I'm afraid it does.'

'Why?'

'Because we're all in danger, Mo. You most particularly.'

'That's reassuring to know. Thanks for the warning before I got involved.'

'I couldn't warn you. I'm sorry.'

'How did you know I'd be down here?'

'I guessed.'

'Am I so transparent?'

'Sometimes.'

'How did you "find out" I wasn't at home? You didn't ask Bill, did you?'

'No, I didn't ask Bill. I drove past your house.'

'And rang the bell? And covered up the peep-hole?'

'No.'

He seemed saddened by my fierce interrogation of him.

'I'm just seeking out the truth, North. Staying objective.'

'I know.' He paused. 'I'll tell you the truth. I came down very late. The old boy was still up, pacing about like a ghost – he was white as a ghost, certainly. He'd had some terrible shock –'

'What shock?'

'I don't know. Somebody had threatened him –'

'Not you?'

'Me? Why me? Threaten my own father?'

'You weren't very fond of him last time you mentioned him, were you? He'd ruined your mother's life, by all accounts.'

'Yes, he had. He did. And he'd be the first to admit it, too,' he almost shouted, the anger shining in his eyes.

'So you found him pacing about . . .' I said calmly, trying to pacify him.

'Yes. I found him pacing about.'

He paused.

'And?' I persisted. 'What then?'

'And. Then. He all but collapsed in my arms.' His face betrayed him, the emotion quivering like lapping water, blown.

'A reunion? Of sorts?' I suggested.

He looked at me as if I understood about as much as an officer in the SS.

'He believed me at last,' he spat at me contemptuously.

'Believed you?' I echoed, as detached as I could be.

'He believed I didn't kill her.'

'Kill who?'

'God, Mo! You're the limit! You're so fucking blunt!'

'You've asked me to be. Please answer the question, North.'

'My mother! Who else? I didn't kill my mother. All right?'

'Well, forgive me, but there was the initial question of Cass's death, too.'

'I didn't kill either of them!' he shouted.

'You're sure of that, are you?'

'Yes, I'm sure of that,' he said, mimicking me.

'Why is it so hard to say, then, if you didn't kill either of them?'

'This is like being in court . . .'

'Answer the question.'

'You'd make a good barrister, Higgs.'

'The question, North.'

'I find it so hard to say, Higgs' – his voice was lethal as steel – 'because they're both fucking dead. I'm suspected of killing them both, so I can't fucking grieve. I've never grieved a fucking thing in my life. It's all in me still. It's ... hard ... to ... say.'

We were silent for a long, long time. My thoughts chased each other about in my head. My feelings rose and fell like a lover's body, up and down. I waited for the whole morass to settle inside me before I dared anything else.

'It's getting dark,' I said finally.

'Figuratively speaking?' he asked.

He was still standing at the altar, waiting for her to arrive. I walked over and took his hand.

'You're going to be all right,' I said. 'You'll have your time to grieve.'

He nodded, not really believing me. Then he wrapped his arms around me, hugging me to him like a piece of flotsam in a shipwrecked sea.

'We've only just started,' he said.

During the drive back, he told me that Cassie's body wasn't in the graveyard at all.

'So where is it?'

'Rolf told me the truth last night.'

'Do we have to go on calling him Rolf?'

'Yes, we do, I'm afraid. Very methodically.'

'Why?'

'Because if he's William, then he's Cassie's father and he's the man who disappeared two weeks after her death – which seemed accidental, but was it? In other words, he was a suspect, too. Primarily because he did disappear. And he still is, all these years later. A suspect.'

'They lie in wait, don't they, these cases?'

'They seem to. The irony is that if he'd stayed in the country, there wouldn't have been an inquiry at all. As it is, what with Katherine's murder and me being a suspect, the case is now open again, like everything else about my family. Open house. Open to scrutiny.'

Open, I thought, like a wound, raw and gaping, the dressing ripped off.

'So what did happen to her body?'

He stopped the car outside the house.

'Apparently,' he began, his face whitening with nausea, 'my mother — my mother dug it up again — after the funeral.'

'Oh, no.' My imagination leapt. 'What did she do with it?'

'She sent it — she wrapped it up and sent it . . .'

'Where? Not to India?'

'That's right. To India. To my father. All wrapped up in sacking and cloth. In a square wooden box.'

'Jesus . . .'

'It was boats in those days. You didn't fly out there. Nor did the packages. So by the time this sweet-smelling gift finally reached him, it stank unimaginably. Of dead, rotting flesh.'

I couldn't find any words.

'He's never recovered from it. Would you? Your own best-loved child?'

As we approached the house from the drive, the old man's face smiled out at us from the kitchen window.

How different he looked to me now. How desperate his smile seemed.

18

The day dragged on, filling up with new wonders.

As I washed up after supper – if the word 'supper' can be used to describe two hard-boiled eggs with burnt toast – the old man suddenly grabbed my arm. Howard was somewhere else in the house and I feared that the old boy was choosing his moment to make a pass at me.

'What are you doing?' I pleaded, as he pulled me towards him.

'Has someone stolen it?' he whispered urgently in my ear.

'Stolen what?'

'The locket!'

If only to prove the impossibility of this, I almost confessed that the locket was in my car, but then I remembered that he had probably searched my car and had failed to find it there. He had no proof that I had it at all.

'What locket do you actually mean?' I asked innocently.

'Tsssh . . .' he hissed at me. 'Be serious. Someone has broken into your car.'

'You broke into it, didn't you? Somehow. At least I assumed you did.'

'I had a look, yes. But someone else has also broken in.'

'What! In this remote place? I don't believe it!'

'And they have smashed the window in –'

'Oh no,' I moaned wearily, thinking of the time and money that it would take to fix.

'Whereas I simply used your key —'

'When did you simply use my key?'

'While you were washing your face.'

'How dare you?'

'Just to see if it was there.'

'And was it there?'

'I couldn't see it,' he admitted, 'but I wondered if you had hidden it very cleverly. You must go and check immediately that it's still there.'

'I don't have a locket to hide anywhere very cleverly. I imagine it's just an ordinary burglary. I assume my suitcase has gone?'

'No, your suitcase is still on the passenger's seat. It has been opened, however. Someone has looked through it very thoroughly.'

The suitcase that Howard had insisted I leave in my car. Why?

'Shit!' I exclaimed, exasperated by this news.

'Howard wants it, of course.'

'Wants what?'

'The locket.'

'Is that who you're suggesting has broken into my car? Howard?'

'No, no. Goodness no. He hasn't the faintest notion that the locket has even been found, let alone hidden away.'

'Why haven't you told him of your suspicions, if you're so convinced I've hidden it from him?'

'Are you serious? Why haven't I told him that you've deliberately deceived him, lied to him? Would that be helpful, do you think?'

'Possibly, wouldn't it?'

He was angry, almost indignant, at my suggestion, and punished me with silence.

'Why do you want this locket so much?' I asked, but he still wouldn't answer. 'So you can give it to Howard yourself? Like a caring father at last? Or so you can destroy the evidence that implicates you in some way?'

He flinched, though at which question, I didn't know. For this very reason a skilled detective would ask only one thing at a time, I rebuked myself.

'He's told you, has he?' asked the old man.

'What?'

'He tells you everything.'

'He's told me you're his father, yes.'

The old man became very grave.

'If you tell anyone —'

'I won't.'

'He thinks you're a veritable safe when it comes to secrets, doesn't he? He trusted your clever twin, for all the good it did.'

The way he said 'clever' somehow highlighted my dull unsubtlety.

'You mean Kate?' I asked, my envy of her undisguised.

His expression grew suddenly stern.

'I don't know who you're talking about,' he said, imploring my discretion with his eyes.

I was reminded of illicit trading, the thickness of thieves, conspiracies.

'Neither do I,' I said complicitly. But he looked doubtful. 'You can't stop me asking questions, Rolf, but I won't answer them to anyone else.'

'What questions?' he asked.

'Were they lovers, then? Howard and Kate?'

'Tssh . . .' was his evasive answer. I thought that this probably meant 'yes'.

'Did she threaten you? Last night?'

'Did Kate threaten me? Why would she threaten me?'

'She wanted the locket, didn't she? Why were you so frightened last night? Who frightened you?'

'Questions are dangerous things –'

'Was Kate here last night?' I demanded.

'Did you see her here last night?' he asked logically.

'I might have done.'

'Do you think you did?'

'Possibly. Yes.'

'Then perhaps you did,' he said, shrugging indifferently.

'She used to come down here,' I said, determined not to let him escape, 'with Howard. Didn't she?'

'Occasionally, yes.'

'And you were living here.'

He didn't answer.

'How come you were living here?' I asked.

'This is my home. I bought this house myself, many years ago.'

'So you came back to England to claim it? Once you knew Katherine was dead?'

'Good heavens, no. What a shocking suggestion.'

He sat down at the kitchen table, as if he no longer trusted his legs.

'Where's Howard gone?' he asked warily.

'I don't know.'

'Check the corridor.'

I did.

'He's not there.'

He relaxed visibly.

'I came back to find them both, that's why I came back. To make my amends. I didn't intend to stay, but I wanted to make my peace.'

'So you turned up here and . . . ?'

'And nobody was here. Eventually I broke in, fearing the worst.'

'The worst?'

'I half-expected to find two rotting corpses here, for some reason . . . But there was nobody at all. A lot of post, addressed to Katherine. Bills, mostly. The various services had all been cut off – the telephone, electricity, gas. Even the water. I was about to report her absence when Howard arrived at the door, with your – with Kate.'

'So you didn't report her absence?'

'We did. Most certainly, we did. But nobody could find her – not for months. When they did eventually find her, of course, she was dead.'

'How awful. For you.'

'For Howard. Awful for Howard. He had finally broken free of her terrible possessiveness, only to be possessed again by this . . . this . . .'

'This what?'

'This – whatever it is. Something possesses him.'

I had the feeling that he knew exactly what it was, but didn't wish to say.

'I'd better check my car, hadn't I?' I asked rhetorically, leaving him alone in the kitchen.

Outside, under a clear moonlit sky, I discovered that the locket had gone.

19

Bill was out when I got back, early the following morning. There was nothing unusual about his being out, and I hadn't warned him of my imminent return, but his absence made me curiously uneasy.

Although I'd left Wiltshire abruptly and with some urgency, once in London I felt immobilized by indecision, like a driver at a junction where several roads beckoned me.

Perhaps I could tell Bill the intrigues I had discovered? But then, he would always take Kate's side. And how should I approach Kate? What if Kate didn't have the locket? How could I investigate anything anyway, with my modest experience, largely acquired vicariously through Bill?

I flicked through the opened mail on the hall table. Brown envelopes mostly. Containing red reminders. It used to be me who took care of the bills, paying them with meticulous regularity and promptness out of our joint account. It was my job. My pathetic contribution to our lives. And I even took pride in my efficiency, routine as it was. It was a symbol of my grasp on reality. A post-stillbirth resolve.

And now? Was this an overt rebuke? Had he planted this evidence of my negligence where no one could miss it? Least of all me.

'Why can't he pay the fucking things himself?' I said out loud.

I kicked the table, ridiculously, as if it were the enemy, in sympathy with Bill. It shuddered in surprise and let fall, amongst other things, an itemized telephone bill.

On picking it up, I glanced over it and noticed several long calls to what I knew was Kate's number. I had hardly phoned Kate in the last three months, and certainly not at any great length. These calls had to be Bill's. In spite of all my suspicions, I still felt betrayed. How I longed to be surprised by him, to discover a true change of heart behind his puffing hot words about saving this marriage of ours. Refreshingly, the discovery troubled me only for an instant.

What troubled me far more was the thought that she might have information about Howard, that she was in some way more intimate with him than I would ever be. Now why should that be worse than Bill betraying me? The thought troubled me so intensely that my whole equilibrium was thrown. Envy and rage surfaced in equal measure inside me. How dare she travel so close to the heart of him? When I was stumbling still, somewhere near the borders of his land?

I paced about in futile agitation before throwing open the french doors into the garden, where I began to attack various overgrown roses with a vicious pair of secateurs. The thorns ripped at my skin in self-defence.

Later, exhausted and somewhat tranquillized by this cathartic butchery, I had the car window replaced by emergency glass. And then I waited for Bill to come home. I waited like a sentinel, checking the time, responding to every sound.

At about seven o'clock I heard a car park outside the house. I jumped to the window to see if it was him. But it wasn't. It was North. The headlights of his motor car switched off like eyes closing wearily. Howard looked at my own small car, and then around him – for Bill's? – and finally up at the house. Then he climbed out and stood on the pavement.

So this is him when he's watching over me, I thought to myself. He can't see me staring straight back. The lights aren't on. He probably thinks I'm out. Or does he think I'm dead?

I opened the front door and shouted to him.

'What on earth are you doing, North?'

He jumped.

'God! Don't do that to me!' He caught his breath. 'I'm keeping an eye on you, what do you think?'

'I'm perfectly all right. I don't need a bloody bodyguard.'

'Are you on your own?'

'Isn't everyone, in the end?' I asked facetiously.

He laughed at this, half-bitterly.

'I mean –' he said in a loud whisper, 'is your – is Bill with you?'

'I don't know where he is.'

We stood looking at each other like teenage sweethearts.

'Come on in,' I said. 'If Hugo doesn't mind waiting.'

'Hugo?'

'Don't you think he's a Hugo?' I said, indicating his car.

'Oh. Him.' He looked at his car as if for the first time. 'Maybe . . . Hugo or – Maurice? Something rather élite and pleased with itself.'

He approached me shyly, one awkward step at a time. On the top step he said:

'Aren't we friends at least?'

'Of course we're friends.'

'I hope so.'

'Of course we are.'

'You mustn't just leave me like that.'

'Leave you?'

'Suddenly you'd just gone, Mo.'

'I had to. Sorry.'

'Why?'

'Because. I did.'

I turned away from him into the house. He followed me, closing the door firmly behind him.

What am I doing? I thought. A feeling of terror rushed through me. What am I doing inviting this suspected unconvicted murderer into my home?

I stood suddenly still, facing him.

Let me at last know the truth, I thought. Even if I die of it. Kate knows, doesn't she? Let me know, too. Let me know more.

'So why am I in such danger that you have to keep this vigil over me?'

'I can't tell you.'

'Why not?'

'Trust me.'

'Trust you? Why? Tell me the truth, please. I need to know the truth.'

He paused, as if thinking about telling me.

'I don't like it that Bill's not here,' he said, looking around him suspiciously.

'*You* don't like it? What about me? I've been betrayed by him for as long as I can remember.' I waited, splitting my sentence in two, for any first reaction from him, before I added, 'He's been having an affair with Kate.'

It was definitely this second statement that pained him so.

'With Kate? Why Kate?' There was a wild look in his eyes. 'What makes you think he's having an affair with Kate?'

'I know,' I said lightly, as if Kate were anyone. Then I picked up the telephone bill, still lying on the hall table, and pointed to her number. 'Kate's. I haven't been calling her.'

He looked down the long list of calls. He made no effort

to disguise his feelings. Perhaps they were too profound. He turned away from me, his arms across him as if clasping an ache in his heart, like an illness in him. He leaned against the wall for support.

'No,' he moaned. 'She can't do that . . .'

'Why can't she?' No response. 'Howard?' I wasn't sure that he could even hear me. 'Why can't she? What is it to you?'

He looked at me, finally, as if I'd only just arrived, as if I'd stolen upon him in the fullness of his grief like some merciless journalist.

'She can't . . .'

'Of course she can,' I said.

I noticed that I was enjoying watching his illusions about her shatter at last. My pleasure shamed me.

'Come and sit down,' I said kindly. I began to pity him, and, with this softening of feeling, I also pitied myself. 'Let's sit down next door,' I said, guiding him into the living-room, on to the sofa.

He sat shivering while I lit the coal-effect gas fire.

'She's unbelievable,' he said.

I sat beside him, holding his hand like a mother comforting a child after his first nightmare.

'She's very important to you, isn't she? Our Kate,' I said, understandingly.

'She's very dangerous.'

'Dangerous? Kate?' This was the last thing I expected him to say. 'I love her,' yes. Or, 'She promised me,' yes. But 'dangerous'? Did she represent the great danger I was in?

'You mean dangerous – to men?' I said, trying to make sense of it.

'Dangerous,' he said, 'to women, Mo.'

His eyes focused on me. I nodded wisely, believing that I understood.

'Sure. I see. I mean, I do see, of course. If she's stolen my husband from me. I see how her –' I was going to say 'charisma' but just couldn't bring myself to – 'how she can easily threaten women like me. The ordinary ones.'

He caressed my cheek with what felt like pity.

'It's OK. I'm used to her showing me up,' I said, laughing self-effacingly.

'You're unique, Mo.'

He leaned towards me – to kiss me? Only in a fraternal way, I was sure, but at that moment a brick – a plain red brick – crashed through the window of the living-room.

'What the fuck . . . ?'

Howard leapt up and closed the curtains fast. He stood rigid, alert, breath held. Finally he exhaled and walked slowly to the other end of the room, where he closed those curtains too.

'What the fuck was that?'

He nodded, as if approving my fear, like a director approving an actor who has finally mastered a scene.

'Now do you believe me?'

'You're not saying that was Kate?'

'I'm not saying anything. I'm saying you're in danger, Mo. Please take care.'

'What should we do?'

'Nothing. Yet. Wait.'

We fell silent. He seemed to be listening for any further threat. I was reminded of the old man on that frightened, frightening night. Had the same danger tyrannized him? Even down to the brick? I remembered the fierce cold draught I had felt in the living-room. But the next morning? There had been no evidence, had there?

186

'Can you hear anything?' he asked.

'No.'

'Good. Neither can I.'

He sat down again.

Was that it? Weren't we going to do something?

'What's going on? Please! You have to tell me.'

He took a deep breath.

'It's not fair, North.'

'Is anything?' he asked rhetorically.

'We usually have it within our power to be a little fairer than life.'

'I love you,' he said, in a way that couldn't possibly mean love as I meant love. 'Your high principles!'

He beamed fondly at me, and then studied the coal-effect fire.

'People's lives hang in the balance every time secrets are revealed.'

This sounded rather melodramatic to me, but I didn't say so. Let him tell it, I thought, as theatrically as he likes, only let him tell it at last.

'But I will tell you,' he said, as if reading my mind.

He narrowed his eyes in concentration, choosing where to begin.

'I've told you I was an adopted child, haven't I?'

'You have.'

'There's no simple way to tell this story, Mo. I always balk at it, like a horse at the last fence – or the last fence but one . . .'

'Have you told many people, then?'

'What was that noise?' he said suddenly, pricking up his ears.

'What noise?'

'I thought I heard a noise . . .'

'I don't think so,' I said.

Pause.

'So, you've told a few people, have you?' I persevered patiently.

'I've told only two people in my whole life. I took forever to find the courage. It's harder every time. Perhaps because the reaction is always so strong, so – disgusted. And the more I esteem a person, the more difficult it is. I fear your opinion immensely, it seems, what with your high principles . . . your right and wrong, black and white. I've been trying to tell you for weeks . . .'

'There's no hurry,' I said, suddenly nervous again of what he might reveal, what crimes he might be answerable for. It has to be murder, I thought. What else could it be? And then I thought, it could be something else. It could be rape, or paedophilia. It could be necrophilia. It could be anything.

'We were lovers, my mother and I.'

But that? No. I hadn't allowed for that.

He wouldn't look at me. He stared ahead of him, straight at the fire. I was glad of this. My face must have betrayed my shock. My bewilderment. Even my contempt. The unutterable revulsion I felt.

My mind ran over this love affair like a dog on a scent seeking out the creature's lair. Her bedroom, the garden, that whole secret house to themselves. I could see them doing it, she seducing him with the sweet reassurances of a mother's love, massaging his virgin muscle into her. Aaah! His ecstasy! His re-entrance into the womb that never bore him. Mother. Body beloved. Those heavenly eyes all over his nakedness. Discovery of her most secret, urgent parts, hungry for him all, every inch of him hers, she whom he loved so profoundly still.

'You're horrified,' he said, finally looking at me. He could read the expression on my face. Blatant as nudity.

'Was it her idea, or yours?'

He didn't answer me.

'Surely it wasn't yours?'

He shook his head, though more in dismay at me than in denial of my words.

'Sorry,' I said. 'I'm just – I'm trying to understand.'

'But you don't, do you? You don't understand.'

I couldn't pretend I did.

'Nobody ever does.'

He turned away again, as if it was he who was disgusted now.

'It's not – it's just not within my experience,' I said, trying not to shame him any further than I had.

'That's apparent, Mo.'

We fell silent, each in our different worlds, our estranged terrains.

'It must have been a lonely secret to bear,' I offered, struggling towards empathy.

'We had each other,' he answered, simply enough.

'But later, as you grew older. Or even just at school?'

'I didn't go to school,' he said.

'Why not?'

'My mother taught me – from an early age. She taught me everything.'

'Yes, evidently she did,' I said, unable to resist the quip.

He glared at me.

'Sorry. You know me.' I tried to laugh it off.

'I'm beginning to know you,' he said soberly.

'Tell me more,' I encouraged him, in a gently inquiring tone.

'She didn't teach me all the way through. By "everything" I just mean the basics, just the three Rs.'

'I see,' I said, trying to sound sincere.

He glanced at me suspiciously before continuing.

'When I was ten – or was I eleven? – she employed a tutor for me. Theo, he was called. Very clever. Handsome, too, well-built, very strong . . . someone to emulate. He was like a surrogate father to me – I was almost in love with him. I longed for him whenever he went away. A crush, you'd call it these days.'

'You had a crush on him?'

'Yes, I did,' he said defensively, 'the same way every adolescent develops a passion for one of his own, before he ventures towards his opposite.'

'Sure,' I said affirmingly, puzzled by the strange coy phrasing he used.

'Then one day in the woods – I must've been about fifteen – I came upon him, or rather, I came upon his backside. It was incredibly white, I remember, and muscular, clenching and releasing, thrusting and mounting, up and down, back and forth. I was mesmerized by the savage rhythm of it. He was fucking my mother. Of course. Who wouldn't? A remote country house, a woman like her, lonely and hungry for love? I hated him from that day forth. He didn't see me. Only my mother saw me. She saw my distress.'

'Sure,' I said, persuading him on.

'She almost – she . . . She seemed to smile at me. Did she? I don't know. All I know is, I suddenly felt this incredible urge for her, this urgent desire burning in my groin. I wanted to do what he was doing to her. Somehow, despite all its horror, its violent savagery, she seemed to be enjoying it. It seemed to be allowed. She allowed it. And she allowed me, invited me to follow, if only because she – she smiled so sweetly at me.'

'Sure,' I said again, not trusting myself with any other words.

'That evening in bed – we'd always shared the same bed, since my father left us . . . That night I – I put her hand on me. I was bigger than I'd ever been. It was a gift – like a gift for her. It was hers. I told her, "It's yours, it's mine for you." And she took it. She received my gift. Rapturously. I mean that. With rapture. She took me.'

'I see,' I said. And I did see. I saw that to take him with rapture was too easily done.

'That was how it began. And how it went on. We lived as lovers. In the end we lived – more or less – as man and wife.'

'You actually married her?'

'I thought I was adopted, Mo.'

'But were you?'

'I don't know. I don't know any more.'

'What's made you doubt it?'

'My father, of course.'

He looked to me for some comfort then.

'Poor Howard,' I said.

But he frowned instantly. Here was the same mood-swing I'd encountered in him before, always when he was at his most vulnerable. His sudden and total frustration with me, like an infant's rage at its mother, when I failed to deliver whatever he needed most from me.

'Don't pity me,' he said. 'I don't want your pity, Higgs.'

'I'm – sorry. I don't mean to . . .'

'I loved her. Profoundly. That's not pitiful.'

'No,' I mollified him.

I thought it was pitiful, though, just as my love for him was pitiful. Love was more often pitiful than noble, I was beginning to believe.

There was another sudden crashing of glass, this time outside.

Howard leapt up again, fingering a crack through the curtains whilst scarcely disturbing them, like a detective in an old black and white film.

'Damn it!' he almost shouted.

'What is it?'

'Someone's smashed the window of your car.'

'What? I don't believe it! Not again!'

'Again?'

'I've just had it fixed. Today.'

'Was it broken before?'

'While I was with you. In Wiltshire. I assumed you knew. Someone broke in.'

'No. I didn't know.'

He sat down again beside me, sighing wearily.

'I assumed the old boy would've said something.'

'He knew, did he?'

'He discovered it.'

'He makes me nervous. There's so much he doesn't say.'

'Like father, like son,' I suggested.

He looked at me, as if admonished by the accusation.

'Yes. Very possibly.' He paused. 'Where was I, then?'

You'd just got to the bit where you first screwed your mum, I heard myself think but, thankfully, not say.

'It makes me so jumpy, this tireless tyranny,' he said.

'It's pretty frightening,' I agreed.

'It's best to ignore it if we can. Not show any fear.' He paused in thought. 'Marriage. That's it. That's where we were. You asked me, while we were in the church, if I'd ever been married.' He paused again, wary of me. 'Well, we did marry, Kittie and I. In Italy. Tuscany. Very secretly.'

This gets worse and worse, I thought. Please, no, they didn't have a child?

'And then, later, after Lizzie, someone else wanted to marry me. Henrietta, she was called. A big sweet girl. She wouldn't leave me alone – kept badgering me. I never loved her, but

Kittie was furious. Frighteningly so. She scared her off by telling her about Cassie — for my own benefit, she said, because I was plagued. Cursed. Because women risked their lives by being drawn to me. She said only she could ever survive me, because she knew the truth. She called it my anger at her.'

'And was it?' I asked nervously, having seen that anger myself.

He paused, thoughtfully.

'When I first met you — at Kate's party — Kittie was still alive. I hadn't seen her for two whole years, but she was still alive. As I later discovered. Certainly I had little reason to think she wasn't. A few days later, just before I asked for your help, she was dead. I asked for your help because I needed to understand. Why was she suddenly dead?'

Despite his methodical delivery, I could tell that he was close to tears, reining them in.

'I needed to know if I'd done it. She couldn't tell me any more. She was dead, dumb-dead. If I had done it, then I'd finally done it to her.'

He was choking on his feelings now. They rose in his throat like vomit.

'They all thought it was me. As you know. But they couldn't detain me. Not enough evidence. They held me overnight — no longer . . . But they're still after me.'

'I sort of assumed they were.'

'And one person in particular is still after me. Tirelessly. She wants her revenge, she's trying to frame me. She'll stop at nothing,' he almost shrieked, the frenzy in his eyes beginning to frighten me. 'I understand it now, you see.'

'Uh-huh,' I said, wishing I did.

'I didn't kill her, I know. I didn't kill anyone. The old boy's explained it to me. Things are clearer than ever. I think I can finally see what's been happening, what the pattern is.'

'The Plague?'

'The Plague! That's right. The Plague. I see how it plays itself out.'

'So Kate is after you? I assume it's Kate.'

He looked at me guardedly.

'Kate is after me, yes.'

So many questions were inside me, pushing for a voice, but I knew from his manner that he had said enough. I suggested instead that he might like something to eat or drink, or he might just like to sleep.

He chose sleep.

'Just for a short while,' he said. 'Just here is fine.'

He was sound asleep in minutes and stayed asleep most of the night. I switched off the lights and kept watch over him.

My own mind was as restless and sleepless as a wild animal's, hunting, or hunted, or both.

20

A sharp winter sky brought an early light to the house. The barren branches of trees were drawn across its blank canvas like dead fingers. The room was thick with confidences. I opened the curtains. The broken window let in the cold air. Howard stirred, but then slumbered on. He seemed to be mine, lying there sweetly asleep like a trusting child.

He pained me. I was part of him now. He had let me in through an open door, where I had stood knocking for weeks. He'd even shown me around. At my own request. And now? I wanted to go home. Like a child at a fun-fair who was hungry for new thrills, the House of Horrors had finally proved too much. But I couldn't leave. I was in too deep. I couldn't get out, even if I wanted to.

I looked around me at the disarray. The shattered glass, the unpaid bills, the pile of rose-cuttings outside. I needed some order again, some ordered ordinariness, if I was going to continue on the strange dark journey ahead.

I woke Howard.

'You'll have to go, I'm afraid.'

'Mmm?'

'Just in case Bill comes back.'

'Yes.' He rubbed his eyes sleepily. 'Yes. Of course.'

'I don't want things to get any more complicated.'

'No.'

Pause.

'Tell me what Kate's trying to do,' I asked.

'Eh? Kate? Do?'

He was still scarcely conscious. I gave him some coffee and swept up the glass. Then I telephoned a glazier. They would fix it straight away, they said. Then I paid a few bills. Before dealing with the rose-cuttings, however, and before the glazier came, I wanted Howard out of the house. I also wanted some questions answered fast.

'Howard –'

'Yes. I'm going,' he said, standing up at once.

He looked at me searchingly, warily.

'It's OK, I'm not about to kill myself,' I said lightly. 'I've just got things to do.'

'I understand,' he said.

Do you? I wondered. Do you understand that, because of you, my life is changing irreversibly?

'Tell me, Howard, if I'm to help you – what does Kate want from you?'

'I – I don't know.'

'Don't lie to me,' I said firmly.

His eyes again focused on me like the lens of a camera. A portrait photographer's eyes, seeing into my soul.

'Revenge. Is what she wants.'

'Why?'

He wouldn't answer.

'What have you done to her? . . . You must tell me, Howard. It's very important that I know.'

'Why? Why on earth should you know?'

I thought of the locket. Shall I tell him? Do I dare?

'You need to know that she's dangerous, Mo. Leave the rest alone.'

'All right, then,' I said, 'if you won't explain your affair with her –' he bristled visibly – 'then at least tell me this: how can she frame you?'

'Because she knows about Cassie –'

'How?'

'Because I told her. How do you think?' he replied irritably.

'Why did you tell her?' I persisted.

'That's not your business, Mo.'

'Very well,' I said impatiently, 'if that's how you feel . . .'

I was filled with furious curiosity. I wanted every detail of their love-affair elaborated upon. He could sense this, I knew.

'It's neither relevant nor safe for you to know about our relationship.'

'If that's how you feel . . .' I repeated.

'That is how I feel,' he replied adamantly.

A long pause.

'So she knows about Cassie's death?'

'Yes. And that I felt some uncertainty. About whether I'd done it or not. If she can produce any evidence that I did do it, that's going to weigh fairly heavily against me in court, in the case of my mother.'

'I thought they regarded each case in isolation?'

'Well, that may be. But if the jury get wind of it – they only need a whisper of it – even if they're told quite clearly to disregard it, they won't. They'll heed it. Wouldn't you?'

'Quite possibly,' I admitted. 'What evidence could she find?'

'I don't know. Probably none. But she could plant it. Or she could find the evidence I need, the evidence that could prove I didn't do it. She's already threatened the old boy, demanding that he tells her if we find anything. She uses the lowest tricks. She's told him she'll expose him for who he really is – for my father – and thus implicate him in the two murders, if he doesn't keep her informed. If she gets hold of any evidence that could help me, she'll destroy it.'

'She wouldn't do that, surely?'

'She would do anything.'

'She would even plant false evidence?'

'Believe me,' he said, 'she would do anything.'

'And what is this evidence you need, to prove your innocence?'

'It's just a locket. My mother used to wear it. I think I mentioned it to you.'

'Yes,' I said, too fast. 'Yes, you did.'

'It was lost during the event of Cassie's death. It just might provide the essential clue. And then again, it might not. But until I find it, who knows?'

I thought of the broken chain. The struggle by the pond.

'Really, above all, I need to prove it to myself. I can't take my father's word for it. I can't take anyone's. I have to see it for myself.'

An uncertain, desperate hope had invaded his eyes.

'I just want to be sure. Or I can't go on living with myself.'

Had I let it go, careless idiot that I was? The one clue that would save him.

'So. She seems to hold your life in her hands.'

'She'd like to. She doesn't yet.'

Oh, but she does, I thought. She does, she does, she does. And it's all my fault.

We both sank into our thoughts as one sinks into quicksand, helplessly.

'What is it you have to do?'

'Sorry?'

He had summoned me back.

'You said you had things to do.'

'Yes, I have. And I don't want you following me. Please?'

'Then where will you be tonight? When it gets dark?'

'I haven't the faintest idea. Not with you, I hope.'

He flinched at this.

'I don't mean it. I just mean – I like to be with you, Howard, I just – I don't want a bodyguard.'

'You need one, Mo.'

'I don't. I can look after myself. And I can certainly defend myself against Kate. I've fought with her often enough.'

He sighed, exasperated.

'God, Mo, are you always this bloody stubborn?'

I thought of Bill's words: 'Be told.'

'Usually,' I said.

'Realize this, then, if you'll realize nothing else: schoolgirl fights aren't Kate's style any more. She doesn't play at this. Look at that brick.'

'What did she do, then, to Rolf?' I asked nervously, studying the brick.

'Enough said, Mo.'

He tweaked my nose and smiled. Then, impulsively, he kissed me full on the mouth, his warm hand caressing my neck.

'I need you.' He said. 'Badly. Be careful. Please.'

He left after that.

21

As soon as the window was fixed, I too left the house. I switched on the burglar alarm, just in case. I also took a small sharp knife.

Waiting at Kate's front door for her to answer the bell, I felt a hollow loneliness, like air, filling me up. I thought about Bill. I wondered if I'd find him there. I minded, at last. Suddenly and furiously. I dreaded the truth about the two of them.

How was it that Kate moved through each loved person in my life and stole them away from me unfailingly? Sooner or later. She was most often there before me, but sometimes after me, and always more emphatically.

When Cliff opened the door, I felt an immediate rush of relief. My ally. My fellow-sufferer. He stood there like a medieval knight, glowing with uncomplicated strength, a shining sword in his hand. He could cut us all free, untangled as he was in this thorny wilderness. He seemed to me, at that helpless moment, to be the answer to everything.

'Mo! You've just caught me. Walked in two minutes ago.'

'I was just — I was after Kate, in fact.'

'Kate?' How surprised he seemed. 'Kate's walked out,' he said. 'I thought you knew that? She's gone.'

'Gone?' I couldn't believe it. 'Where?'

'I don't know,' he said. He was putting the kettle on.

'She's not with Bill, is she?'

'I don't know, Mo,' he said. He searched my face. 'I imagine so.'

I let the news sink in. He put his arms around me, comforting as a big brother's arms. He smelt of clean shirts. I had never stood close enough to Cliff before to enjoy the smell of him. He had always been out of bounds.

'Let me make you some coffee,' he said.

I felt as though I had stepped into someone else's life. It was a curious and unfamiliar sensation. As though everything building up to this moment when I had come to see Kate, with a small knife in my bag, had not in fact happened to me. As though I had come here only to be with Cliff. To be reassured. To be taken in hand, by someone capable and strong.

'How come you're not at work?' I said.

'I've got to pick up the kids.'

'Who's looking after them?'

'I am,' he said. 'That's why I'm not at work.'

'But what about your nanny?'

'It's her day off,' he said.

'Oh, Cliff, I'm so sorry,' I said. 'I'm sorry for both of us.'

He was mixing the coffee beans in the grinder.

'Half-Continental and half-Colombian,' he said mildly, as if he hadn't heard me.

The noise of the grinder prevented any further conversation for a moment. I was glad of this. I watched the back of his neck, his cropped black hair cut sharp against his warm skin. Like Howard's. I could see the muscles of his back push out against his dark blue shirt. A sudden and bewildering desire to make love to him ran like a visitor through me. Was it Howard's story that was breaking down these boundaries for me? Or was it Kate's treachery? Or was it because Howard would not permit my love and it had nowhere else to go? Achingly unfulfilled.

'There's no need to be sorry for me,' said Cliff. 'We've always had an open marriage. It was a deal we made early on. There was always the chance that one of us would leave.'

I was shocked. He said it all so easily. He looked at me calmly.

'We were suffocating each other, Mo. She wanted too much. More than I could give. She wanted to own me. So we worked it through, and that's what we settled for. Open or closed was all she could take. No middle ground. We've kept out of each other's way ever since.'

'What about the kids?'

'They're OK,' he said. 'They never knew.'

'But what about your lovers, then? How did they cope?'

'Differently,' he said. 'Everyone is different.'

'Every lover, you mean?'

'Every person, Mo.'

Pause.

'Did you have many, then?'

'I suppose I've had many lovers in my time,' he said. 'I'm a child of the sixties, remember. It's not such a big deal for me to have sex. Do you want milk?'

I couldn't get the thought out of my mind, the desire for him out of my limbs. I didn't know what to do, where to place myself.

'Darling Mo, where are you?'

'Eh?'

'Milk? Or not milk? Simple question. Simple answer required.'

'Black is lovely,' I said.

He led me into their comfortable living-room, where a new portrait of Kate smiled graciously down at us. As I looked up at it, like a mortal at a god, I was seized by an intense, vehement hatred, such as I had never felt for anyone in my life. How dare she do all that she does and still smile down like a sweet, angelic muse, heavenly to all men? The hideous deceit of her beauty, that concealed such toxicity. How dare she?

'Funny old painting, that,' said Cliff, somewhat irreverently. 'Who did it?'

'That enigmatic character – what's his name? She's known him a couple of years . . . God, what's his name? North? Richard North?'

'Howard?' I said despairingly, but he didn't hear me.

'The guy who's supposed to have killed his own mum . . .'

'Yes. Howard North.'

'That's right. He did it.'

'Is he a painter, then?'

'I don't think so. I don't know what he does. Something in the therapy world. All very intense. He paints for a hobby, I think.'

Howard? My interest in the painting became instantly prurient. How had he seen her, when she sat for him? I looked for clues of their love. Her breasts were visible through her open silk shirt, the nipples firm and erect, as if excited by him. Her expression was fresh and wild, her skin porcelain-pure, her lips slightly parted for the smile – a distant, dreamy smile that deflected from the sinister depths of her chocolate-brown eyes.

'Like it?'

'Not really,' I said, admiring the skill but loathing the subject and all that it implied. So uncomfortably like me.

'I don't either. She looks like a psychopath.'

Cliff was so reassuringly simple. So wholesomely down-to-earth.

'Now if you were up there,' he said, suddenly behind me so that I could feel his breath, 'with your sweet breasts pushing out like that, I'd feel quite differently.'

His breath felt like Howard's breath, warm and soft. I looked round at him in confusion.

'Have I overstepped the mark already?' he asked.

'Possibly,' I said.

'You draw the line. The choice is yours,' he said. He was serious.

I smiled awkwardly and moved away from him. I sat down on the sofa, sipping my delicious coffee. Rich, dark, strong.

'Like it? My brew?'

'Lovely.'

This is Cliff, I told myself. Your old friend Cliff.

'Have I embarrassed you?' he asked.

'I think I've embarrassed myself!' I said, as easily as I could.

'I'm sorry. I just . . .'

He sat down beside me.

'Nobody's fault,' I said.

'You looked – you just look so – hurt.'

He was studying me with a concentration that he usually gave only to work.

'I'm all right,' I said.

'I want you, Mo. I can't help it. Sorry,' he said.

I breathed in his desire as if it were a summer's day. Fresh grass, warm hay, lilac, wisteria. The smell was so sweet. I could feel tears prick my eyes.

'What is it?' he asked softly.

'Nothing.'

'Tell me.'

'It's – it's just things. Things at home.'

'Bill?'

'Yes. Partly Bill.'

He caressed my cheek.

'I know,' he said, and although he almost certainly didn't know, I needed to believe him then. 'I know how it is.'

His hand travelled down to my neck, caressing the tension there.

'Is this OK? If I do this?'

'Do what?'

'Make a little love to you?'

'No, it isn't,' I said, battling with tears, baffled by this unexpected seduction, which I felt I had brought upon myself. 'It's not OK at all.'

'Fair dos,' he said easily, taking his hand away.

And yet the promise of a little love, of physical intimacy, a naked body, warmth, it was so tempting, too. I wanted it too much. I wanted Howard to make love to me.

'It's OK, it's lovely,' I said, closing my eyes.

His lips were warm and soft on mine already. Howard's lips. I kept my eyes closed and let Howard in. His tongue pushed into my mouth, penetrating deep inside, stirring my senses into a hungry need for him, a need for all of him, a need for his need of me, his desire of me.

He took my hand and let it caress his hardness. Howard's hardness. For me. His gift to me, pushing out against the cloth like an arrow poised in its bow, quivering in anticipation of release. I ran my fingers over its round, urgent tip, titillating it.

'Oh, God . . .' he murmured feverishly as I opened him up, his voice low and deep, vibrating through me like love. Like Howard's love.

I bent down over him and took him into my mouth. He moaned helplessly as he thrust himself in and out of me. Then he pulled me up and searched me and found me with his hands. I cried out but he stopped my mouth with a voracious, devouring kiss, one hand still playing below while his other hand climbed up to my breasts, stretching to take both of them at once. Then he kissed my neck, falling on it like a bloodsucker.

'Let me see you,' he said, kneeling down, unpeeling my clothes, layer by layer. He gasped with pleasure, his tongue burning me now, torturing me with the promise of his ultimate entry. I opened my eyes, blurring his features like a soft-focus lens, so that I could only see dark hair.

He laid me on my back so that I could see Kate and Kate could see me and I could think of Howard as I felt the wet round fruit of his love push its way into me. He moved fiercely back and forth, tearing off his shirt and opening mine, taking one breast in his mouth and biting the nipple hard. Howard's desire burst over me like the sun. Warm golden love. I came in waves, shuddering after him.

22

Afterwards, with the weight of his body like a corpse on top of me, I wanted to leave for ever. Leave everything behind. I had trespassed into a cold other world where the senses ruled, while the heart was ridiculed. I felt contaminated. Was it Howard's dark secret that had worked like a fever through me, hot and irrational? A disease of the mind, impelling me forward through obvious boundaries?

Like a refugee fleeing the status quo of my own country, I had come upon the guarded borders of another land, hostile and merciless, but I had crossed them as simply as one crosses a road, briefly hesitant, glancing just fleetingly from right to left and back. I didn't see what was coming at me. Until it was too late.

'What's the time?' asked Cliff, rolling off me like a lazy seal in the sand.

'Twelve-fifteen,' I said stiffly, pulling on my clothes.

'You no joke with me?' he asked, in an accent I had never found funny.

'It's a quarter past twelve,' I confirmed coldly.

'Shit.'

He stood up, dragging his trousers from his ankles to his hips and zipping them up. He bent down over me.

'Sweetheart, you were wonderful. I've wanted to do that to you for as long as I can remember.' His wet lips presumed themselves to be welcome on mine.

'I'm like one of those bastards you hope you only read about who leaves the instant the deed is done, aren't I? But I have got to pick up the kids.'

I could hear him saying this heartless sentence to so many less indifferent women than me, and I felt for them all.

'Did Kate have an affair with North?' I asked plainly, as if it didn't matter to me. I was staring at the portrait again.

'I wouldn't put it past her, would you? She's an anarchist. I mean, it's against the rules, but I shouldn't think she'd care.'

'What rules?'

'Screwing your client. Isn't it?' he asked, but not because he wanted an answer. 'Look – I can't simply ask you to leave now, but could you just lock up after you? You'll work it out,' he said.

He threw me a bunch of keys. Idiot boy.

'Sure,' I said nonchalantly. 'No problem.'

'I won't be back till tea – I promised Sophie we'd see *The Lion King*. Half-day today.'

'Right,' I said.

As if I care, I thought. I never want to see you again.

Did he leave with some idea that I was relieved, not saddened, by his departure?

When the front door slammed shut, I felt like a criminal. A secret agent. A spy. I would find her out. Each secret place would yield itself up to me like an opening shell. Let me catch her. Thief of my heart. Keeper of the Kingdom of the North.

I sat staring at her portrait for some time. What had Cliff said? That Howard painted just for a hobby? That he did 'something in the therapy world' too? Had all my instincts been accurate, then? He knew far more about therapy than I ever would. Dissembler.

There was something else Cliff had revealed about him. What

was it? I focused my mind. Of course! It slammed itself in my face like a prison door, locking me in with the two of them, together for ever, like Sartre's *Huis Clos*.

He had been Kate's client.

Kate's client! Not only mine, but Kate's. Kate's before he was mine, or was he Kate's still? So did she visit him in Chiswick, like a witch-doctor visits the sick, as I had seen her that day, to administer her secret therapy? Had he told her everything, just in the way that he was telling me, and did she love him now, because of it? Or in spite of it? Or both?

What was that noise?

I froze, petrified. Howard's warnings had taken root inside me. Kate was dangerous. I supposed it was just possible that she knew where I was. It was easy enough to guess. Did Howard know too? Had they followed me here together? Was I so obvious and unthinking in this cold twilight world of shadows and snow that my footprints ran away behind me like fickle messengers, reporting my path? Running from, not towards my goal?

I wanted to wash, but even my breath did not dare to move, let alone my body. I hated the feel of Cliff's juice swimming around inside. While I had undeniably complied with his seduction, Bill's 'rape' seemed as nothing now, by comparison. A hot contact of souls, no more. But this? In this contact, or complete lack of it, my soul had died of cold.

Another noise. This time I was sure that someone was there. Someone was on the stairs, creeping towards me. Very quietly.

I felt strangely calm. Almost confident. I waited like a wildcat, as if anticipating my prey, my equal, my match, whoever it was. It could only be Howard or Kate. Or possibly Rolf. Or Katherine's ghost? Whichever one it was, I knew their weaknesses now, all of them. I could fight and win. I reached for my bag and felt the small sharp knife nestling inside the pocket. Its blade felt hard and cold. I fingered the edge and the tip to reassure myself. Lethal, indeed.

The living-room door squeaked a little on its hinges, pushing open gently. I sat rigid. Silent. Alert. Nobody appeared. This move must be an invitation to investigate, one that was intended to catch me suddenly unawares. I had seen the movies. I knew what to do. Don't react. Wait. Be still.

At last I heard the timid miaow of BB, the Burmese cat, and found him at my feet, lashing his tail as he pressed himself against me. My relief was immense, revealing to me the true extent of my fear.

'Hello, Balthazar B! You terrifying animal!'

I picked him up and walked cautiously into the hall, his warm chocolate coat so comforting against my cheek. I stood there listening hard. BB was purring so loudly that any quiet sound would be hidden. I climbed the stairs, slowly and silently. I would make quite sure that I was alone now, that Kate was nowhere to be found, and then I would search the house for the essential clue that I had so foolishly lost. The locket.

As each room proved reassuringly empty, I began to breathe a little more easily. When finally I reached her bedroom – they had always had their separate rooms, Kate and Cliff, for reasons which were now quite clear – I exhaled the last remnants of anxiety.

'Right,' I said aloud, putting BB down again. 'Warn me if you find anything. If anyone comes in. Miaow at them like mad.'

I glanced around her bedroom, wondering whether her big brass bed had supported my husband's frame, or whether they tended to do it somewhere else, somewhere more neutral.

Or do they do it in my bed – our bed – at home, I wondered unwillingly. She would take pleasure in that.

I shuddered. I was in no doubt that she had taken pleasure in Howard up here. I could see them both vividly, like ghosts, their energies imprinting the atmosphere with their naked intensity.

I walked down a flight of stairs into her study, where she practised her therapy with a very select few. It was an airy, impersonal space. A stripped pine floor, lightly varnished. South-eastern sun. Almond-white walls. A colourful kilim rug in the middle of the room and another one on the wall, opposite a huge sash window with twelve panes of glass. Grand, sculptural plants – a palm, a yucca, the familiar swiss-cheese, its larger leaves leering over the desk as though reading each client's notes over Kate's shoulder as she scribbled them down. Two generous, comfortable sofas, face to face either side of the fireplace. Shelves full of books and files. Where was Howard's, then? Locked away somewhere?

I had intended to use the valuable time looking for the locket, but I found myself instead rifling through Kate's files, unashamedly at first, and then more furtively. At last Howard's name caught my eye.

North, H. Age 46. Occupation: Therapist/author.
Family history: Father left home after death of sister when H. aged 5. Brought up by mother. Incest.
Born: India. Nationality: British.
Aims and Objectives: To address problems with own sexuality.

I took a deep breath and sat down at her desk. I flicked through what I already knew, a file full of copious notes that mirrored those I had made. Then suddenly a paragraph jumped out at me:

> Expresses sexual interest in me. Aware of own attraction to client. Hard to separate. Objectivity? Difficult, if not impossible. I ask what is his usual fantasy when sexually interested? 'To take off her clothes,' he says. I ask if she is active or passive in his fantasy? 'Passive,' he says. Is this fantasy designed to render his powerful mother impotent? (Re: incest.) Incapable of seducing him? I ask if she is at least conscious. 'Preferably not,' he says.

I stopped reading, momentarily. The memory of waking in his Chiswick house, in nothing but a dressing-gown, floated back to me. So he had taken advantage of me. Surely not raped me? But certainly he had aroused himself while I was passive to him, his favourite fantasy come true. I had somehow presumed that his arousal had been less calculated – a happy coincidence, not a sought-for event. I read on, with some trepidation now.

> I ask him if sexual interest in me is need to disempower me as the therapist/mother. He says, 'Fuck analysis. Don't interpret me,' which I read as yes.

Typical, I thought. Pig-arrogant.

> We talk about rules. H. hates them. Says, 'How can anyone treat sexual problems except sexually?' Feel excited. Turned on. Ask how he wants to be treated. He says he wants to learn healthy sexual exchange. Ask what's unhealthy for him currently? He says, 'I can't do it. I can only fuck Katherine.'

(His mother. Last had sex with her two months ago. She's now sixty-five). He refuses to see her now, indefinitely. Thinks distance from her will help solve problem. Finds distance v. difficult. Painful. Has he ever had sex with anyone else? 'No.' He is angry at my surprise. I reassure him. Aware I feel v. excited at thought of seducing client.

At least she's honest, I thought. But isn't this sad? And terrible? She can't seduce him. Where's the love in that? She would do the same thing to him all over again by seducing him.

I wanted to cradle Howard in my arms. Protect him. Shelter him from her storm.

A few pages later I found that he had taken off her clothes while she was fully conscious and that she had taken off his. This was seen as progress.

H. stands there with hard-on. He can't move. Standing two feet away from him. Aware I want him. Losing objectivity. Ask him what he wants. 'I want to fuck you,' he says. Not make love. Fuck. Feel doubly turned on. His body is beautiful. I invite him to. I roll a condom over his dick. He pulls it off. Goes soft. 'I can't do it,' he says. Gets dressed. I'm still naked. I tell him I want him. He freaks. 'Where's your professionalism?' he asks. I get dressed. When he's gone, I have to masturbate.

I looked out at the garden, full of their children's toys and swings. Do they play doctors-and-nurses out there, while she plays it in here?

How pathetically reduced in meaning the sexual act seemed to me then. I wondered if I would ever be able to make love again. Or whether I would only have sex, just as I had done that morning with Cliff, in some half-gratifying, half-horrifying rape of the soul. Clandestine squalor.

I read on. There was a great deal more of the same. During almost every session they would try to have reciprocal sex. During one session they both masturbated themselves after a failed attempt to masturbate each other. Howard still couldn't achieve orgasm. On and on it went, almost every week for a year. By the time they started looking for Howard's mother, in the hope that he might be able to resolve his problem by talking it through with her, Kate sounded unimaginably frustrated, beyond what she could comfortably endure. She was obsessed with Howard. She lived in desperate hope of a physical consummation of this obsession, which seemed no longer to regard his needs at all.

I heard BB the cat miaow loudly outside the door. My blood ran cold. What if she was there right now? Waiting? I was trapped. I didn't even have my knife.

I crept to the shelf and replaced Howard's file. Then I stood behind the door, opening it slowly. BB trotted in, rubbing himself against my legs and then against the legs of the desk, purring loudly. I peered through the crack at the hinge-end of the door, but I couldn't see anyone. I waited for BB to venture out again. I figured that he would also rub himself against anyone else's legs the other side of the door. When he did eventually leave the room, however, he simply trotted upstairs towards the bedrooms.

I followed him, snatching the very blunt paper-knife from Kate's desk, as well as a heavy piece of petrified wood that served as a paperweight. I hoped that this could knock a person out without really hurting them.

Again I approached each door with the same absurd terror

that had accompanied my first search through the house, an hour earlier. And again I finished up in Kate's bedroom. It was surely the room most likely to hide the lost clue from view. I intended to search every inch of it.

I put my weapons on the bed where I could easily reach them. Then I shut the door, placing BB outside on the landing, as a sort of lookout. Although such precautions seemed excessive, even neurotic, to me, I felt safer for them. They enabled me to concentrate on the task at hand, which proved increasingly difficult, the less I was able to find.

I began with the obvious places – drawers, boxes, shelves. I even pulled the drawers out altogether to see if anything was taped on to their ends, or hidden behind them. Floorboards came up (the loose ones, at least), pillows and mattresses were examined for recent stitching, I went through the pockets of all her remaining clothes, I checked the ceiling light, the wall-lights, the architrave around the door, the architrave around the windows, the frames of paintings and prints, I checked everything. Short of using a trained sniffer-dog, I couldn't have been more thorough in my search.

But I didn't find the locket. What I did find was very interesting to me, but of no use to North.

I found a book by Neville Hoare, hidden in the mattress. She had cut the outer fabric at the corner seam, and had slipped the book through. Then she had stitched the fabric loosely at the end. The book was his most recent and radical, one that I still hadn't finished reading, called *Beyond the Law*. The subtitle ran: 'Why the individual conscience seeks revenge for a crime which the law fails to recognize as crime.' The word 'revenge' lashed out at me like a brandished knife.

Kate wants revenge, I told myself. That's the exact word he used.

The book was inscribed: 'The law punishes those whom it fails to protect. We must protect those whom it fails to punish. Your secret is safe with me, as mine is with you.' It was signed 'H.N. or N.H. – choose.'

Cryptic though the message was, one thing was certain. Howard North and Neville Hoare were one and the same. The clues had been there all along. But I had missed every one of them.

My heart jumped with a strange kind of joy. I had met him, after all! I had met Neville Hoare! He had turned to me for help!

I sat on the bed with the book in my hand, beaming like an infatuated teenager. I had felt something similar at fifteen, when a lead singer had smiled at me during one of his gigs.

But before I could really grasp the full wonder of my discovery, it happened – far too fast.

I heard a key in the front door. I heard it open, pause, then close. I heard footsteps – a woman's – crisp and firm in the hall. I heard them climb the stairs, fearless steps up flight after flight towards me, pausing only on the floor below to open and close her study door. Then in no time at all I could hear her coming for me. Up the final flight. I could even hear her breath. Everything in the bedroom was upside-down, and she was coming for me. I knew it was Kate. And she knew it was me. Even if she'd had any doubt, my yellow Mini would have convinced her that I was already there, already searching. I only just had time to grab the paperweight before she opened the door.

'I thought I'd find you here.'

She stood quite still, rigid with rage, as her eyes took in the thoroughness of my search.

'Did you find what you were looking for?' she asked, her

face as hard as stone, her mouth a thin line drawn an inch across.

The book was lying beside me, title up.

I couldn't say anything. My mouth was too dry. I held the petrified wood in my fist, my hand hidden under her bedcover. She walked towards me and picked up the book.

'Was this what you were looking for?' she asked, a slight sneer creasing her mouth.

I shook my head.

She must see how terrified I am, I thought. I'm defenceless. She's caught me at my weakest, most open moment of all.

'What do you make of the inscription?' she asked quizzically.

'I don't,' I rasped back.

'Mystifying, isn't it?'

'Quite,' I agreed.

Above all, I wanted her to think me completely ignorant of everything I suspected or knew. I had plenty of my own ideas about what the inscription meant, but I wasn't going to be drawn by her.

'H.N. or N.H. Whose initials are those?'

'Neville Hoare's, I suppose,' I answered pathetically.

'Aren't you clever?' she said, like a sweet mother to a child.

I smiled a feeble smile.

'But not quite as half-intelligent as I know you are,' she jabbed. 'What about H.N.? Whose initials are those?'

'Howard's?' I volunteered.

'Clever girl!' she patronized. 'Very good indeed, Little Molly Brown.'

My childhood nicknames jeered back at me over the years. Little Molly Brown. Scrawny Brawny Brown. Good Golly Miss Molly. Molly Golly Gosh.

'Did he tell you already?'

'What?'

'About being Neville Hoare?'

I shook my head.

'Don't sit there shaking your head like an ornamental dog. If you mean no, say no, slag.'

'No.'

'Why should I believe you?'

'Because it's true.'

'What else is true?' she asked.

That was when she took out the gun. A small revolver, gleaming like a toy.

'What else is true?' she asked again, pointing the gun at me.

'What are you doing?' I yelped. 'Kate!'

'Just like a dog, aren't you? Sniffing around for bones.'

I felt the cold metal nudge my head.

'Talk,' she said.

'Wh— what about?'

'Aren't you cowardly?' She almost laughed. 'I had no idea what a coward you were! All those fights, eh? Scrawny Brawny Brown! I could've slayed you every time! Couldn't I?' she asked, pressing the gun into my temple until it throbbed there.

'Yes,' I acquiesced meekly.

'You're a coward, Mo. Not Howard's type at all. He admires strength, I'm afraid. Fallen for him, haven't you? But he's in love with me. Idiot.'

'I'm not in — I haven't —'

'He laughs at you,' she sneered, cutting me off. 'We laugh at you together, Mo. And Bill does too. We all laugh at you.'

Her spite was nothing new. As a small girl she had wielded extraordinary power with her sharp, evil tongue, her sadistic lies cutting into people's hearts. She was remorseless. I had forgotten this side of Kate, had perhaps even imagined that she had outgrown it, but I wasn't surprised when it reappeared. My worst fears resurfaced, like fleeting visitors.

'Unfortunately, however,' she resumed, satisfied that she had caused me pain, 'I can't return his love. Not any more.'

She paused.

'Aren't you curious?' she asked. 'Don't you long to know why?'

'I suppose so,' I said.

'I'll tell you anyway. Whether you like it or not. He's a murderer. That's why. He killed his own mother, you see. Did he tell you that?' She didn't expect a reply. 'Now I don't think that's nice. I really don't like that sort of behaviour in a man. D'you know what I mean?'

'Mmm,' I mumbled.

'Sorry? Didn't hear you?'

She lifted my chin with the gun so that I was looking at her. She smiled adorably, like her portrait, an angelic Botticelli face radiating love and even compassion for me.

'I said mmm. I do know what you mean.'

'Good. That's good. Little Molly Brown. I'm glad you know what I mean. I don't feel so alone now.'

She dropped my chin again, withdrawing the gun. She crossed her arms, the gun now pointing at some random target in the direction of one of the windows.

If I jump at her now, I thought, and hit her with the paper-weight, the gun will go off over there. It'll hit the window. Someone outside will see the glass break and call the police.

I almost did this, thinking that, with surprise on my side, I was bound to triumph over her, but then I wondered how many bullets were loaded in her gun. I realized that she was unlikely to drop it, and that a second bullet might easily lodge itself somewhere inside me. She'd call it self-defence.

'I wouldn't try anything, Mo.'

'Neither would I,' I said.

She paused indolently.

'Some people like that in a man. That kind of violence. They think it means he's rough – dominant in bed. Women like that, don't they?' She studied my face for a response. 'Don't they, Mo?'

'Do they?' I mumbled sheepishly, thinking of Cliff.

'Whereas, funnily enough, he's very gentle in bed. When eventually you get him there. He likes to be taken. He likes to be seduced.'

'Right,' I said.

'What d'you mean, right? You know this already, do you?'

'No,' I said. 'I'm just – listening.'

'Envious? I liked seducing him. Oh, I seduced him in the end all right. I wonder if that's what tipped the balance for him. He had to kill her then.'

There was some plausibility in this wild theory of hers. It made too much sense now, after what I'd read in her notes. I began to suspect him all over again, in spite of myself. I thought of him standing naked and frustrated in her room. I thought of his need for my objectivity. And hers. His insistence that I did not fall in love with him. Why? Because of what happened when Kate had fallen for him?

It all adds up, I thought. Kate is just a woman scorned, no more dangerous than that. Though that's dangerous enough. He's the killer. Not her. He sees her as dangerous because he can't face the danger in himself. He puts it outside him still, even a clever man like Neville Hoare. Even he projects his violence on to others.

'What are you thinking about?' she demanded.

'I was thinking you were possibly right.'

'About what?'

'About murdering his mother – the reasons –'

'Of course I'm right! It has to be that.'

Her face showed sudden pain. I seized my opportunity.

'You look very sad, Kate.'

Tears filled her eyes and spilled over.

'He's let me down,' she moaned like a wounded animal.

'Sure,' I agreed sympathetically. Possibly he had.

'How dare you pity me!' she bellowed, her mood switching direction like a sweeping punch, impossible to anticipate or avoid.

The gun was at my temple again, this time pressed against it hard. I felt I was suspended from it, a dangling, trembling puppet waiting for her to pull. Or would she release the strings entirely, letting me crumple down as if she had set me free? A sweet act of love, like euthanasia? I stopped breathing. My bowels lurched into spasms of uncontrollable fear.

'I – I need the loo,' I said absurdly.

She sneered at me, my terror pleasuring her like a favourite comedy.

'It's you who's pitiful, Mo!' She laughed mercilessly. 'It's you we're all laughing at, dear!'

She shoved her face in mine. Her chocolate-brown eyes, which always promised heavenly tastes, seemed murky as sewers close up. Did mine too?

'What have you ever done with your miserable, pathetic little life? What tiny thing have you ever achieved? You can't work, you can't breed, you can't cook, you can't even pay your own bills! It's no wonder he's left you, is it? You can't even satisfy your own husband, Mo!'

She'd relinquished the sweeping-punch technique to plunge the knife in, twisting it like a screw, turning it inside me like a torturer.

A host of retaliatory jibes tickled my tongue. I bit my bottom lip so that I could not utter a word. Any word that left me then would have sentenced me to death.

'He's a fabulous lover, I have to admit,' she said.

Pause.

She was waiting. I wanted to scream.

Swap our positions, I thought, and I'd pull the trigger now.

'The best I've ever known. Better than Howard. Just. Easily better than Cliff.' She smiled whimsically.

I swapped lips, biting the top one now. I could taste the blood on my teeth. Waves of nausea washed over me.

I hate her, I thought. I hate her now.

'But you've not had many to compare him with, have you? You didn't know how lucky you were. Poor diddums. Too late now.'

I had the terrible thought that she had done something violent to him.

'Where is he?' I blurted out.

'You mean you care?' she asked in mock-surprise.

'What have you done to him?'

'Oh, dear,' she said ominously. 'What have I done?'

Please be alive, Bill. Please.

'Tell me what you've done,' I said.

'Dear, oh dear, oh me . . .'

I clenched the paperweight. The petrified wood.

'We thought we were getting over you,' she said, explaining her 'mistake' to me. 'We didn't know you cared.'

'We.' How I loathed 'we'.

'What does that mean?'

But she didn't reply. She stared wistfully into the middle distance, like someone with a conscience.

'What does that *mean*, Kate?' I insisted.

My voice betrayed my dread.

She played on this, shaking her head tragically.

'Didn't he – surely he left you a note?' she asked dramatically.

She was the picture of concern, as if wondering, aghast, whether her well-meaning attempt to nurse Bill through what they assumed was my adultery had been a mistake; did I want him, after all?

This isn't my world, I thought. Take me back to the gentle climate I trusted as a child. I never wanted this.

'If he's still alive –' she said – 'and we did discuss the option of suicide quite thoroughly – but if he is still alive, he'll be exploring other women, I hope. We thought that was the obvious route for him – after me.'

I stared at her dumbly, stupefied.

'Are you mad?' I asked.

'You're only a beginner, Mo. You'll learn. You're a scrawny, old-fashioned stick-in-the-mud. All your little prejudices about sex . . .'

'I don't have prejudices, Kate. I have a belief-system.'

'Oh, that,' she said drily. 'I used to have one of those!'

What a world of difference there is, I thought, between Kate's therapy and Steph's. The-Rapist or the therapist. Didn't Bill see that?

'I have a code of ethics, Kate. I wouldn't be without one.'

But even as the words left my bitten lips, I thought of my morning with Cliff. What ethics there? To use another woman's husband, a willing accomplice, admittedly, but a man with whom I could not have, and did not want, any further intimacy. A body, no more. One who had stood in ingloriously, like an understudy in a play, without the slightest chance of any further success. A man incapable of embodying any of the charisma, intelligence or depth that made the true man so irresistible. I had used him, eyes closed, as a poor substitute for the real thing, at a desperate moment.

'That's what he likes about you, isn't it?' she said plainly.

'What?' I asked, shamefaced.

'Your ethical code, you dumb whore. Isn't it?'

'I don't understand.'

'That's what our killer likes about you!' she shouted furiously, enviously, in my face. 'He likes your ethical pontifications, I should think. Your opinionated moral judgements, your anally-retentive moral-high-ground pious high-and-mighty thou-shalt-nots.'

She stared at me triumphantly, as if she had found me out at last. As if I had been dealing in a false currency behind her back. As if I had cheated her of her only prize by some mean, dirty, low-down trick. As if at last she had found a weapon against me, a lie that she could tell, something to dishonour me. In fact, if what she said was true, I had simply played a trump card that she didn't have – a sense of right and wrong, albeit my own – that she would never have now. She had thrown hers away, many years ago. Was I also losing touch with mine? Unbeknownst to myself?

'I always think of Neville Hoare as someone who would deplore anyone with the characteristics you've just described.'

'I'm not talking about Neville bloody Hoare. Who said I was talking about Hoare?'

'Our killer, you said.'

'North's the killer. North's our man. Hoare doesn't exist. All that great liberating crap about the human mind! It's all written by a fictional character! Imagine if they knew! I long for them to know. The greatest, most innovative thinker of our time since Foucault or Freud! And who is he? Fiction-head. Fantasy-brain. Fuck-wit non-existent pervert who can't have sex! Recovering

Catholic boy who for his whole life has wanted to run along the moral tramlines of the Catholic Church. While he was having sex with his own mother! His own bloody mother! Did he tell you that?'

I didn't answer.

'I bet he didn't tell you that, did he? He saves that for the women who can't cope with it.'

'Does he?'

'The women who remind him of her. The possessive ones.'

How she revealed herself at every turn!

'Or should I say the obsessive ones? The ones who've managed perfectly well without needing men, without needing more than the occasional servicing from men. The beautiful ones, who can pick and choose. Those women who aren't afraid to challenge him, who don't just bend over backwards for his body and brains. They're the ones he tells. The ones he can destroy.'

She said this as if the fact that she had been told North's great secret somehow reflected a superiority in her.

'Whereas you, Scrawny Brawny Brown, you don't tax his brain for more than a minute or two. I happen to know that. He likes your simplicity. Your moral straightforwardness. Your naïve view of the world. But you bore him rigid, Mo. Sorry about that. He's just using you. Thinks it'll spice up our sex life somewhat if I get a little jealous of you.'

Her eyes ran over me searchingly, almost with a perverse kind of desire.

'Frankly, he's wrong. Now if he'd chosen someone even half-interesting, even half-enigmatic, with a tiny percentage of real sex-appeal, then possibly, yes, I might've been a little jealous of her. But you? Jealous of you! Well it's silly, isn't it? How could I ever be jealous of someone like you?'

She *was* jealous. There was no doubt about it. Howard had withdrawn his attentions from her and had focused them on me. She hadn't got her own way. She'd lost him. She hadn't conquered him. But she thought I had.

Had I, I asked myself in astonishment. Perhaps I had.

The possibility ran like an electric current through me, excited me, thrilled me. Howard North. Neville Hoare. I even dared myself to think of a future with him. A vibrant, challenging life with a man I truly admired. Admired and desired. Who would need children then?

I thought of Bill, of our ten wretched years of trying to have children, as though nothing else could have made the marriage meaningful. And yet he was a part of me, and I a part of him. We had grown together like two entwined plants. I wondered if our separation would kill us both outright? Even though what we shared was only history. The sudden possibility of really leaving him, not just of losing him defeatedly in exchange for loneliness, but of leaving him behind in exchange for a better love, better life, seemed brutal and shocking, as never before.

'Or is it some part of your body?' she asked suddenly. 'Some secret part of you hidden away in there that I can't see?'

'Sorry?'

'No! It can't be! I've seen your miserable little body often enough,' she sneered. 'There's nothing worth having there.'

Her gun prodded at my chest.

'If I were a man, I'd rape you now,' she said.

'That's nice,' I replied.

'Maybe it's the way you screw.'

She paused. I sensed that she was wondering how she could rape me, how she could somehow experience my love-making.

'What does he want from you?' she screamed, her face red

226

with rage, up against mine. 'What does he want from a barren, sterile hag like you?'

She tore my shirt open and grabbed at my breasts, fresh from her husband's earlier assault. A feeling of revulsion surged through me.

'What are you doing?'

'These! Is it these?' she half-laughed, half-wailed. 'Is it these feeble attempts at fulsomeness he wants? These dry, milkless founts!'

She slapped my breasts contemptuously, degradingly, then pulled at them as if they were dugs – udders to be milked dry . . .

'Get off me,' I said coldly, fingering the heavy wood in my hand.

She stuck the gun in my mouth.

'Or is it that you give good head? Is it because you've got nothing else to offer him, you have to suck him off instead? Like some cheap whore?'

One slight move now and she would pull the trigger. I was sure of it. We were both edging out of control. She needed my fear again, my meek subservience. She had always loved power.

Give it to her, I thought. Pacify her. Let her think she has control of me.

I closed my eyes, the gun deep in my mouth.

If she thrusts it any further down my throat, I'll retch, I thought.

'I'll have to kill you anyway now,' she said nonchalantly.

I didn't believe her but I looked at her pleadingly, none the less.

'Well, I've told you Howard's secret now, haven't I? And that's unethical.'

I tried to speak through the gun. She withdrew it from my mouth.

'What?' she ordered. 'What did you say?'

'He'd told me already,' I said.

'Told you what?'

'His secret.'

'Which one?' A brief pause. 'Answer the question, you disgusting hag.'

'The secret about his mother. And him.'

She looked at me in disbelief.

'*You?*' She seemed almost revolted. 'He told you?'

I nodded meekly.

'I hate you,' she said, lifting her gun to my head.

She said it in a way that I believed. A matter-of-fact way. Her finger moved on the trigger. I hit the gun from her hand but it didn't fall. It shot the mattress. Her arm moved again, as if for a second aim. I took her wrist with one hand so that I could control her aim. With my other hand, while she scrambled to break free of my grip, I hit her with the petrified wood. She dropped the gun and shielded her head with both hands. She was suddenly unsteady on her feet. There was blood running slowly through her fingers. She stumbled backwards, her head cracking on the wall as she fell against it. She slid down the wall until she was sort of crouching. She moaned with the pain. I picked up the gun.

'Kate?'

She moaned again. I wanted to see the wound, to see that it was real, serious, deep, before I would help her. I feared that she was deceiving me, that she would wait until I was close to her, then grab the gun and shoot.

'Let me see,' I said, pointing the gun at her. 'Take your hands away from your head.'

She ignored me.

'For God's sake!' I shouted, panicking now.

She moaned again.

'Are you all right?' I asked urgently. 'Shall I call an ambulance?'

She didn't respond. Instead she took her hands away from her head to look at the blood.

'I'll call an ambulance,' I said, as soon as I saw.

We waited in silence, in limbo, like two astronauts floating in space. I felt helpless. Powerless. Lost in shock.

How do I explain? I wondered. The room looked like the aftermath of a burglary. They will ask us what happened. What will she say? And who will they believe? Who would I believe?

I wiped the gun with the bedcover, regretting that I'd picked it up. If only her fingerprints alone had been all over it, I could have argued a case. But now? What evidence did I have now? I knew she would frame me somehow. Just as she was trying to frame North. This TV personality's word against mine? And in her own home?

When the ambulance arrived, I let the crew in. She explained that I had threatened to kill her. That's how it happened. I was a murderer.

'Would I call you,' I said, 'if I wanted her dead?'

They said that I'd better accompany her. I thought so too.

After various examinations, they helped her to her feet. I followed behind, my tail between my legs like a dog.

Kate was still wearing her coat, I noticed, although it was a little bloody by then. It wasn't a coat I'd seen her wear before. It was an elegant coat. Well-cut. I thought I'd seen it somewhere before, on somebody else.

I probably have, I told myself. What does it matter?

But it troubled me. I knew it was significant, somehow.

'You'll have to ride in front, love,' somebody said to me.

It was only when we passed a couple of drunks, staggering down the middle of the road, that I remembered. I remembered the tramp in Bloomsbury. And I remembered the coat, sweeping past me towards her as if to help, and then sweeping on. Leaving her bloody and dead. Kate's coat.

Who would believe me now?

23

She was soon unconscious, thankfully. I was safe from her lies until she came round again. Assuming that she would.

Would she? I wondered. Suppose she dies?

A wild panic seized me.

Suppose I've killed her? I thought.

I followed the stretcher as they wheeled her past reception, turning left through swing-doors, half-way down a corridor that seemed to have no end, which seemed to beckon me on and on down its shiny, slippery surface of blue.

'Would you mind waiting outside, madam?' a male nurse ordered me.

'Of course.' I paused. 'Not,' I corrected myself: 'Of course not. Do I have to make a statement or anything?'

'Do you?' he replied.

'It was an accident,' I said.

'If you need to make a statement, madam, you'd better telephone the police. I'll ask reception. They'll do it for you.'

What had I said?

'I don't think I do,' I said.

'Perhaps someone has called them already?' he asked.

'Not to my knowledge,' I said.

'None of the ambulance crew?'

'Not to my knowledge,' I said. But perhaps they had.

'You'd better wait in reception, madam,' he said coldly, reaching for the telephone.

I waited in reception obediently. It was only a very short time before two policemen came in and made an inquiry at the desk, while a car flashed its blue lights outside. I couldn't hear what they said, but they were directed down the same long corridor and turned off through the same swing-doors.

Then Howard came in. He walked directly towards me and sat down at my side. He hardly moved his lips.

'I'll follow you,' he whispered. 'Just walk out very calmly. Turn left. Wait by the car, as inconspicuously as possible. I'll be right behind you.'

I obeyed, without any hesitation. I trusted him, I realized, implicitly.

He drove very fast, down back roads I'd never seen, until we were careering along the M1 motorway, due north.

'Where are we going?' I asked, finally.

'Scotland. It's rather an obvious route. But it's the fastest. I'm counting on their inefficiency.'

'Why Scotland?'

'It's a good place to hide.'

'How do you know?'

'I don't. I'm guessing.

Pause.

'Is this really the right thing to do?' I asked.

'Are you serious?'

'It looks so suspicious, doesn't it?'

'I'll tell you what looks suspicious,' he barked. 'You going in there. Cliff coming out. You staying in. Kate going in. Kate coming out dripping with blood, carried off in an ambulance. You following. Witnesses galore.'

I let this sequence of images sink in.

'I take it you followed me after all. Despite what I'd said?'

I demanded crossly, ashamed of anything else he might have seen.

'What were you going to do? Give yourself up? Expect justice?' he asked in disbelief.

'Watch your speed,' I said, seeing a police car ahead.

He dropped back abruptly, into the middle lane.

The day felt unreal. Something to wake up from. A movie. A book. A dream. Something that should end, leaving me thankful for my mediocre life.

'They'll call it attempted murder, Mo.' He issued the statement like a kindly lawyer, trying to persuade himself of my innocence.

'It wasn't,' I said, 'attempted murder.'

'What was it, then?'

'Self-defence.'

'Was it the gun she threatened you with? I thought I heard a shot.'

'What do you mean, was it the gun?'

'She threatened the old boy with a gun and a knife.'

I thought of the knife in my bag, still sitting on the sofa of Kate's living-room. How would that look to anyone investigating the case?

'Yes. It was the gun. She was about to pull the trigger. That's the only reason I –'

'Did you touch the gun?'

'Yes, I did.'

'Higgs . . .' He sighed, shaking his head.

'I wiped it afterwards.'

'Worse still. Everything points to you. She's not stupid, Mo.'

'But she's mad! You should've heard some of the things she was saying!'

'Do you think they'd believe you?'

'It's the truth,' I said, simply.

But no. I didn't think they'd believe me. And the terror of not being believed shot through me like a bullet.

'Bill will believe me, won't he?'

'Will he?' Howard asked, unconvinced. 'Wasn't he having an affair with her? While you were off playing with a suspected murderer?'

'But he's my husband.'

I was aware of the ridiculousness of this statement, and yet it felt like such a good reason for his trust.

Is there no such thing as justice, after all, I asked myself. At best, I should be cosseted now, counselled out of my shock, protected, reassured. At worst, I should be released after various court hearings, while Kate should receive two life sentences. For attempted murder and murder itself.

'What did your mother look like when she died?' I asked. 'Was she – poor?'

'My mother?' He glanced at me in surprise, before his eyes returned to the road ahead. 'She looked like a – like wax.'

'I mean, what was she wearing, what was her hair like, what –'

'Yes, she was poor,' he said. 'She looked like someone who had lived on the streets for two years.' He sounded sorry, as if it were his fault.

'Had she?'

'In all likelihood. Her fellow cardboard-box dwellers said she'd been looking for me. She came to London for the day and never went back.'

'So she looked – what? Like a tramp?'

'I suppose you might say that,' he conceded. 'She looked like Katherine to me. Only she was dead. And her eyes had gone. She was blind.'

Everything fell into place.

'You didn't kill her, did you?' It was more of a statement than a question.

'You tell me,' he said.

'I know you didn't.'

He smiled. A smile of relief? That someone else believed him at last?

'I think I know how you must have felt, all this time,' I said.

'You'll know soon,' he confirmed.

I saw the days ahead, the knowing days. They stretched before me like the long, beckoning hospital corridor, unremittingly bleak.

'Kate killed her, didn't she?' I said, out of the blue.

He shrugged.

'Didn't she?' I wanted her crime admitted, at least. I knew that he knew.

He wouldn't answer me. I thought of his inscription in Kate's book. That 'secret' of hers, 'safe' with him. Why wouldn't he tell me the truth?

'Why didn't Katherine just – just go to your house? She must have known where you lived?' I asked.

'Nobody knew. I'd only recently moved.'

'But surely you –'

'Surely what?' he snapped, cutting me off.

'I suppose that, being Neville Hoare, you –'

'Who told you that?' he snapped again, the car swerving slightly.

'I guessed. I found a book of Kate's,' I admitted. 'The initials –'

'I see,' he said coldly.

We both fell silent, estranged. We drove on for another half-hour without saying a word.

Finally he spoke.

'She didn't have my address because – because I was trying to break free of her. And Kate had suggested that I spend less time with her. Or in fact no time with her. But I failed to explain to her why. I just – I just stopped visiting. After forty-six years of being there almost all the time.' He paused. 'It must have been very painful for her.'

Somehow I didn't care very much any more about Howard's woes. I had too many of my own. If I could have done anything then to turn back the clock, to have my chance again, I would have done it. I would have loved my ordinary, mediocre, unsuccessful life more than anything. I would have loved to eat and sleep and garden and shop and be lonely and row.

'You remember our first session?' he said, pulling me back to the present.

'How could I forget it?' I said.

'Do you remember my face had been slightly rearranged?'

'Yes. You were very stubborn about not telling me why.'

'I hit Kate.'

Of course. Her swollen cheek. So he was responsible for that. It was all tied in together, just I had suspected. But so what? It was too late now.

'I hit her because I thought she'd killed my mother. And she, being Kate, fearless and feminist, hit me back.'

'I see,' I said, no longer interested, since there was nothing I could do about it now. There was nothing I could do about anything now.

'I picked up your passport, by the way,' he said. 'You might need it.'

'My passport?'

'I'm afraid I had to break in through your french doors.'

'Why?' I asked stupidly.

'To get it.'

'When?'

'When I saw the ambulance. And Kate. I thought it would be sensible.'

'You're like a minder,' I said.

I didn't want to be with him, I realized. I blamed him. I felt that he had lured me away from my dead life into a fatal trap. And now I couldn't escape. My freedom was gone. *My freedom.*

'Will I see Bill again?'

'Do you want to?'

'Of course I do.'

'Then you will.'

'How will he know where I am?'

'I'll tell him.'

'Promise me,' I said desperately.

'I promise you,' he said kindly, hearing the wretchedness in my voice. A wretchedness that he knew only too well. The great big loss of love.

We stayed the night in a remote hotel. Or perhaps it was a bed and breakfast – I didn't know. I did know that it was miles from anywhere. We checked in as Mr and Mrs Andrews and I dreamt of Gainsborough's painting all night long.

The beds stood four feet apart. We slept fully dressed. I felt no fear. I didn't know whether this was because I felt safe, or whether it was just that I didn't care any more.

In the morning Howard brought a large breakfast up to the room for me. He refused a hot, buttered bread roll.

'I've eaten,' he said.

He stood at the window, staring out over the snow on the moors.

'It's a beautiful view,' I said.

'Yes,' he agreed dreamily, then added more resolutely, 'I'm going for a drive – see if I can find somewhere.'

'Find somewhere?'

'To stay. Keep a low profile, won't you? News is already out.'

When he went, I wondered if he'd ever come back. Probably not, I thought. Too dangerous.

I sat on the window-seat of our heavy-panelled room and gazed at the snow all day. The bleak relentlessness of the rolling moors seemed to insist on a warm inner life, since no comfort could be had without; the climate seemed to reject my frail humanity. God help me, I thought. What warmth can I hope to find inside me now?

I remembered the dream I had, that last night of love with Bill. The unbearable cold. The rules I didn't understand. The punishing.

What had I done?

I was asleep when Howard returned, my head against the window like a dog waiting stubbornly for a walk.

'Any joy?' I asked, feeling a little joy myself on seeing him again.

'Possibly,' he said.

He was uncommunicative. He kept his head bowed low, as though weighed down by too much thought. Worry. Gravitas.

'Anything I can do?'

'Cut your hair. Sound Scottish. Change,' he said. 'Be someone else.'

We stayed in the same hotel for another two nights. I didn't leave our room once. I didn't dare. Not for anything.

Howard helped me to cut my hair, holding mirrors at difficult angles so that I could see. By the time we'd finished, I looked like a boy. An urchin. The mousey-brown tufts stood away from my narrow face in shock.

We practised my Scottish dialect whenever we spoke. I was forbidden the use of my native tongue. Howard was as pedantic as Higgins in Shaw's *Pygmalion*. We created a history and an occupation for me, a new name, an introverted personality, a way of walking, of dressing, of writing, of everything. A whole new identity. Howard even bought me a pair of spectacles, which I found too obvious by far, but with which he was so delighted that I finally acquiesced. They were a dark tortoise-shell which made me look very stern, and they were very round. The overall effect was of a thin, startled, rather angry owl.

We laughed at me a lot. The laughter of the lost. Partners in crime.

'Why are you doing this for me?'

'Scottish!' he ordered.

'Why are yer doing this fer mee?' I asked Scottishly.

'Doowin' . . .' he corrected.

'Why are yer doowin' this fer mee?'

'Nay bad, lass! Nay bad at all!' he exclaimed triumphantly.

But he didn't answer the question. On reflection I realized that his reasons were self-evident. He was a man obsessed with ideals. Ideologies. His own set of rules. His truth, which denied accepted morality. And his truth, or story, spilled into mine. In protecting me from the judgement of others, he was protecting himself. He was a man who stood outside the law. He was Neville Hoare.

We left in the early hours of the third morning so that no one would see us. Or me. Howard wouldn't tell me what news was out, whether my photograph had been printed anywhere, or even whether anyone knew that he was on the run with me. Instead he simply cultivated in me an immense enthusiasm for my role as Urchin-Wonder of the North. So that I'd convince, fearlessly.

I was conscious that I was surrendering my will entirely to his direction, but I had no other choice. Without his faith in me, his humour and kindness and love, I'd have surrendered to the law at once. I lacked his strength.

Our next stop was a monastery on the Isle of Iona. A haven of gentleness. A place to die.

We took a boat via the Isle of Mull and earned our keep at the monastery by occasional labours of love. Ordinary, pleasurable chores like cooking, cleaning, tilling the soil, pruning fruit-trees, fixing a leaking roof, clearing paths through the snow. Summer would be the busy time there, when crops were tended and harvested for food.

I would have stayed there a lifetime, sheltering from the blizzard that roared through my days, but Howard allowed us a fortnight and no more.

'They'll start asking questions soon.'

'We can answer them,' I said.

'How? With lies?' He respected the truth in curious ways. 'We must seem like innocent civilians, just enjoying a fortnight's retreat.'

We left the following day, back on the boat, eating smoked mussels with plastic forks from polystyrene trays.

Loch Tay was our destination. I was reading the map. A cottage was vacant there which Howard had rented for me. The contracts had been exchanged, unbeknownst to me, two days previously. Howard had arranged for us to have access before all the paperwork was done. We drove via Perth to pick up the keys.

'How much is it?' I asked, bewildered by gratitude.

'Very little. It's only very basic, Mo.'

And although it was 'only very basic', the view was breathtaking. The two front rooms of the cottage, both the bedroom

240

and living-room, looked straight out over the water – an enormous expanse of fresh, deep blue that harboured the blowing sails of boats – yellows, reds, whites, greens – surrounded by mountainous slopes of woodland and grass.

I opened the window and breathed in the air.

'It smells of the sea!' I said joyfully.

Howard grinned, indulging my childish glee.

'The garden has a couple of fruit-trees, an apple and a pear, I think, which doubtless need pruning soon –'

'Lovely,' I said.

'Then there's a clematis, a honeysuckle, and countless roses, I'm afraid. Can't abide them, myself.'

I thought of the garden at his mother's house.

'Too much of a good thing . . .' I said.

'Possibly,' he agreed. He seemed glad of my intuitive response.

We were caught suddenly in a startling web of desire, like two unsuspecting flies.

He reached out a hand. I took it willingly. He drew me towards him, wrapping his arms around me like two big angel's wings. He breathed in my aroma and sighed, as once he had breathed in Richmond Park's heavenly scent. He kissed me tentatively, like a shy boy, stroking my short tufts of hair with his big warm hand. Then he stood away from me a little, holding me at arm's length, smiling peacefully.

'I knew I was right about you,' he said, but wouldn't explain what he meant.

Instead he set about lighting the fire, while I explored the territory, standing a good ten minutes in each particular space: the two bedrooms, the kitchen, the bathroom, and finally the garden, rolling down the hill towards Loch Tay.

Perhaps I've died, I thought, and this is my afterlife.

In the evening we cooked some potatoes from the monastery, and ate them with a jar of mayonnaise and a packet of cold ham. Then we opened a cheap bottle of wine, sitting by the fire, close as lovers might be.

'I'll have to leave you tomorrow,' he said. 'First thing. Before they start looking for my car.'

Don't go, I thought. This is my paradise and you are my angel, my Gabriel, guardian Gabriel angel, who carries me on wings away from birds of prey.

We lay naked under our coats by the fire on the floor and caressed our longing limbs. I slept, and dreamt of *The Water Babies*. When I woke we were at love, in love, in the middle of love, in the making of the middle of love. Sweet love, like penetrating songs, like an angel's high notes or like the pealing of bells through our surrendering cells. Then we slept, then loved again, and so on in the same sweet way until the break of day.

Who am I now, I wondered. Nobody I know.

Stripped of the fabric of my life, those threads that wove a place for me in other people's days, I felt free. Just when I thought that freedom was gone, that my life was dead, I felt more alive and free than ever before. The cluttering constraints of my old reality were shed from me as easily as clothes. I was free of guilt, free of grief, free of duty and show.

Blessed. Free to begin again. Resurrected in love.

24

In the morning a memory came back to me very clearly. Had it returned in an effort to make sense of things? I remembered the day we got the news about the shooting.

Bill was in South Africa. We'd only been married two months. At the door there were two police officers, in uniform. They made me go over to Kate's, where Cliff could look after us, before they would say anything. Kate wasn't famous then. She made us all some fresh coffee and we sat in the kitchen. I had the sense that the two officers didn't know how to begin. Obviously something was wrong, but I didn't know what. I thought it might be something insignificant, to do with our being twins, to do with one of us being mistaken for the other. It was a common occurrence for us. Maybe Kate had been shop-lifting again and someone had spotted her. She used to enjoy shop-lifting as a teenager. She always loved the challenge of getting away with it. Maybe she hadn't, this time.

She smiled conspiratorially at me. A 'here we go again' smile. We were more equal then. A day in the life of twins. Who had done what, this time?

'I'm afraid your parents are dead,' said the WPC.

What I remembered most clearly about this moment was Kate's face. The way it crumpled, like tissue-paper. The way it folded in on itself. As if it were a mask disintegrating. The mask of life. I felt I was watching mortality take place in a split second, as if standing outside time. I was watching Kate die.

But then she was resurrected. Beneath the mask was someone I had longed to find again. Someone I had known and loved. Someone to whom I belonged, and who belonged to me. Not just my own flesh and blood, but my own soul. Someone to keep and never to lose again.

Like everything else between us, she got there first. She understood before I did what the WPC had said.

'How?' she said.

'How?' I echoed, hearing the sentence consciously at last: *I'm afraid your parents are dead.*

Playing it back like a telephone message, and hearing it clearly now, I, too, understood what the policewoman said. I didn't believe it, but I understood what she was trying to say. I explained to her that it wasn't possible.

'Our parents are on holiday,' I said.

'I'm sorry, but they've been killed.'

I tried to explain to her as patiently as I could that our parents couldn't possibly have been killed since they were in South America. On holiday.

'What do you mean, they've been killed?' asked Kate, cutting through me.

'I'm sorry to say – they were in the wrong place at the wrong time,' the other police officer said. He thought he was better than his colleague at breaking difficult news, and he took over now. 'There was a shoot-out today at the airport in Buenos Aires.'

'Well, that's where they are,' I said, beginning to feel just a little uneasy now.

'That's right, miss, that's where they were.'

'Are,' I corrected. 'That's where they are.'

'Mo, will you just *shut up*!' Kate shouted at me.

The tears were rolling down her face like oceans of grief.

When I saw them I realized. I looked at the police officers.

'What happened?' I asked in a sudden half-voice, the other half out of control like the music on a cassette just before it is chewed up.

'They were in the way,' he said, 'caught in the cross-fire, I'm sorry to say. Between some drug-dealers and the police.'

I thought of them 'in the way'. I thought of their faces. I thought of them dropping their suitcases and wrapping themselves in each other's arms. And then I thought: they wouldn't even have known that they were going to die.

Kate was howling now.

'Who was the first to go?' I asked. I wanted the facts.

'They shot your mother first.'

I thought of her slipping out of Dada's arms. I thought of him trying to hold her up, trying to hold her alive, trying not to let her go. Trying not to be without her for as long as possible. I thought of the continuing cross-fire. I thought of Mama's body, bleeding on the ground.

'How quickly afterwards did they get my father?' I asked.

'They . . . well, he – when he knew your mother was dead, he – well, he ran towards them, into the gunfire.'

'What are you saying?' blurted Kate through her tears.

'He ran towards them,' repeated the officer. 'He screamed at them.'

'So? Wouldn't you?' she asked.

'So they shot him.' He looked squarely at Kate. 'I'm sorry,' he said.

I thought of Dada running towards them. I thought of him shouting at them. I thought of the look in his eyes. I thought of him turning back to see the blood on Mama's clothes and shouting at them again, asking them to look at her, to see what they had done. I thought of the bullet in his chest, of his legs buckling under him. I thought of him struggling to walk. I thought of him collapsing on the ground. Did he get back to Mama? Did he reach her in time? I tried to imagine that he did, but I couldn't quite see it. I couldn't quite think of any more.

'I can't tell you how sorry we are,' said the WPC. 'I wish we had some other kind of news to tell you.'

'Amen!' shouted Kate. 'Get out of my house now, will you?'

Her face was red with tears and it was clear that she blamed them.

'The trouble with your laws,' she said, 'is they do more harm than good.'

Epilogue

It is visitors' day today. I've come back to wait in my cell. Bill was due to arrive at two, but he's late. As usual. He never used to be late for appointments. But then, I never used to be a prisoner. Free people don't notice lateness so much. They can walk away and do something else.

Kate is dead now. After a long coma.

Howard is a prisoner too. Kate planted the evidence in his house on her last visit there (the same day that I saw her from my car). A knife. She got his fingerprints on the knife that killed Katherine. Howard says that she must have left it lying on his desk when he went to answer the door. I wish I hadn't knocked. Afterwards, she told the police about a knife that she had seen in his house. He only found it after she had gone. He didn't recognize it, so he picked it up to look at it, and put it down again.

He got a life-sentence for that.

In his last letter, over a month ago now, he said that he felt relieved in some ways to be a prisoner. 'Kate wanted the same power over me that Katherine had,' he said, 'but I could never give it to her. I've only ever made love to one other woman in my life,' he said, 'and that was you. As for the Plague,' he said, 'it is inside me. I have infected every woman who has ever loved me. I've turned each one into a killer. If a woman loves me, she is doomed. And, God help her, if I want her to love me, she will.'

Being famous, Neville Hoare's trial got a lot of publicity. So did mine, because mine was linked with his, and because Kate was famous too, but, relatively speaking, my trial hid in the shadow of his like a timid child in its mother's skirts. He gets a lot of post because of his fame, so he doesn't write as often as I would like. I miss him.

His father visits sometimes. He is trying to prove our innocence, which is nice of him, but he's not getting very far. I try not to pin too much hope on him, because he is old now and likely to die before any real progress is made. But I like to be believed.

Bill thinks I'm guilty. When he visits, we sit in silence for almost all of the time. And the time is so short. There is a look of such bewilderment in his eyes that I don't know where to begin.

The Official
Arsenal
Book of Records

First published in 2013

Copyright © Carlton Books Limited 2013

A CIP catalogue record for this book is available from the British Library.

Carlton Books Limited, 20 Mortimer Street, London W1T 3JW

ISBN: 978-1-78097-336-4

Editor: Martin Corteel
Art Director: Darren Jordan
Picture Research: Paul Langan
Production: Rachel Burgess

Printed in Dubai

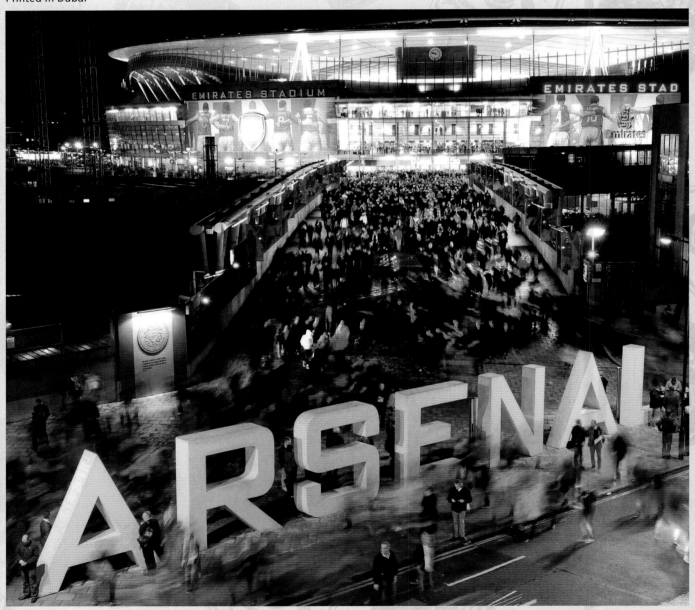

ABOVE & RIGHT: Emirates Stadium, which opened in 2006.

The Official
Arsenal
Book of Records

Iain Spragg

CARLTON
BOOKS

Contents

ALL PICTURES, FROM LEFT TO RIGHT: Patrick Vieira with the FA Cup in 2005; Arsene Wenger; celebrations after winning the 1994 European Cup Winners' Cup; Ted Drake in action in 1935; Thierry Henry during the 2005–06 season; David O'Leary with the Division One trophy in 1991; Tony Adams lifts the Premier League trophy.

Introduction

One of the most famous and successful sides in English football, Arsenal is a club with a proud and illustrious history. From embryonic days as Royal Arsenal in south-east London in the 1880s to the modern era and life at the magnificent Emirates, the Gunners have been synonymous with both style and silverware.

Founded by workers at the Royal Arsenal factory in Woolwich back in 1886, the Gunners turned professional five years later and in September 1893 the Club broke new ground when it played its first-ever game in the Football League, a 2–2 draw with Newcastle United at the Manor Ground in the old Second Division.

It was the beginning of a remarkable footballing story and, in the 120 years since the Club began its transformation from fledgling league newcomers to one of the biggest clubs in Europe, Arsenal have lifted trophies with a reassuring regularity.

The 1930 FA Cup was the first to grace the Highbury trophy cabinet and 12 months later they were crowned Division One champions for the first time. Since then the Gunners have amassed 25 more major honours, including a record three League and FA Cup doubles, to underline the Club's pedigree as an undisputed thoroughbred of the English game.

Many of football's most legendary players and managers have forged their reputations with Arsenal and from the early days of Herbert Chapman and Cliff Bastin in the 1930s, Bertie Mee and Frank McLintock in the 1970s, through George Graham and Tony Adams in the 1980s and 1990s and Arsene Wenger and the Invincibles in the Premier League era, the Gunners have always been a major force.

This book charts the collective and individual achievements of those who have pulled on the famous red and white shirt since 1893, and is the most comprehensive guide available to the Club's player and team records and managerial milestones.

The book also celebrates the most iconic players and coaches to have been associated with the Gunners over more than a century of domestic and European titles and triumphs, providing a definitive and invaluable guide to the rise of one of football's greatest and most popular teams.

RIGHT: Arsene Wenger celebrates winning the 2003–04 Premier League title on the pitch at Highbury.

PART 1
Team Records

Over the years the Gunners have boasted countless outstanding individual players but football remains a team game and this opening chapter is all about the greatest collective achievements in the Club's long and glorious history.

Including matches played in the Premier League, the Football League, FA and League Cups and Europe, the section details the Club's all-time team records from 1893 to the present day.

From their dazzling 26–1 demolition of a hapless Paris XI side in a friendly early in the 20th century to their biggest-ever success in the League Cup in 1979, Arsenal have regularly raised the bar in front of goal and all their biggest wins are included in the pages that follow.

This chapter also focuses on the side's longest unbeaten sequences in all competitions, their fantastic winning streaks, highest points totals in a single season and the team's best defensive campaigns as the Gunners have emerged as a powerhouse in English football.

Triumph, however, cannot come without the occasional tear – so there are also details of Arsenal's worst-ever defeats in both league and cup competition, as well as the side's longest runs without tasting victory and the Gunners' worst campaigns in terms of goals conceded and points amassed.

ABOVE: Bertie Mee in 1971 with the Division One trophy and FA Cup – the famous double.

RIGHT: Frank McLintock captained the Gunners to the double in 1970–71.

OPPOSITE: The Arsenal team parade the FA Cup and Division One trophy through the streets of Islington.

All-Time Records

In this section the focus is on the Gunners' most comprehensive wins and defeats in the Football League, FA Cup and League Cup, as well as the side's friendly fixtures. The Club's longest victorious streaks, losing sequences and most prolonged series of draws are also included.

BELOW: Michael Thomas (right) scores in injury time at Anfield to win the 1988–89 Division One title.

All-Time Records – Biggest Wins

ABOVE: Striker Alan Sunderland scored 92 goals in 281 appearances for the Gunners.

PARISIANS HUMBLED

Arsenal's recent French connection – since Arsene Wenger's arrival in London in 1996 – is well documented. But more than a century ago there was a distinct lack of Anglo-French camaraderie when the Gunners faced a Paris XI at the Manor Ground in Plumstead.

The 1904 match was no more than a friendly, with the Gunners fielding a team bolstered by reserve players. But the Parisians clearly didn't travel well and Arsenal romped to a stunning 26–1 triumph, the most comprehensive victory in the Club's history.

Arsenal were 8–1 to the good at half-time but really cut loose in the second 45 minutes with 18 more strikes – and legend has it that the French side's only goal came when Gunners goalkeeper Jimmy Ashcroft took pity on the hapless visitors, kicked the ball to the opposition and allowed them to score.

Inside-forward Robert Watson was top scorer with seven, but his exploits were not enough to secure a long-term future with the Club. In July the following year he was sold to Leeds United after making just 10 competitive appearances for the Gunners.

ASHFORD ANNIHILATED

The FA Cup has proved a happy hunting ground for Arsenal over the years and back in October 1893 the competition pitted the Gunners against Ashford United in the first qualifying round.

To describe the contest as one-sided would be an understatement. When the final whistle sounded – much to the delight of the beleaguered Ashford players – Arsenal had found the back of the net a dozen times for a record-breaking 12–0 victory.

The game produced two hat-trick heroes with Scottish inside-forward James Henderson and English inside-left Arthur Elliott each recording a treble.

LEFT: Jack Lambert was a major part of Arsenal's record win against Grimsby Town in the 1930–31 season.

◀ GRIMSBY TOWN DEMOLISHED

The old First Division was the pinnacle of English league football before the birth of the Premier League, and Arsenal's record triumph in the division came in the 1930–31 campaign when Grimsby Town were the visitors to Highbury.

Record signing David Jack did the damage with a superb four-goal salvo, while Jack Lambert scored a hat-trick and at full-time the Gunners were 9–1 winners.

▲ SEVENTH HEAVEN

The Gunners may not have lifted the League Cup in 1979–80 but it was the season in which they posted their biggest-ever win in the competition – a resounding 7–0 victory over Leeds United in September 1979.

A week earlier the first leg of the second-round tie at Elland Road had finished 1–1 but the 35,133 supporters who packed Highbury seven days later for the return match did not have to endure any second-leg nerves as the home side ran riot.

Striker Alan Sunderland led the way with a hat-trick while Liam Brady twice scored from the penalty spot and Terry Neill's team marched effortlessly into the next round.

LOUGHBOROUGH ROUT

The advent of the 20th century saw Arsenal playing in the old Second Division and in March 1900 they entertained Loughborough Town in the capital in a clash that would see the Gunners rewrite the record books.

Loughborough were in the midst of a financial crisis so severe that most of their first team had already been sold to try to balance the books. Arsenal even had to help the club with their travel costs to get to London.

The Gunners' generosity, however, did not extend to the pitch. Harry Bradshaw's side mercilessly put Loughborough to the sword, running out 12–0 winners to register the Club's biggest-ever victory in league football.

Yorkshireman Ralph Gaudie helped himself to a hat-trick, a haul that saw the prolific centre-forward finish as Arsenal's top scorer that season, with 15 goals in 25 league appearances.

▶ DRAKE DOMINANT IN BIRMINGHAM

Home advantage can often prove decisive but Arsenal made a mockery of that theory in December 1935 when they played Aston Villa at Villa Park, racing to a 7–1 success and the Club's largest-ever league victory on the road courtesy of seven goals from Gunners legend Ted Drake.

RIGHT: Ted Drake made history with his superb seven-goal salvo against Aston Villa.

▲ GUNNERS AT THE LANE

The Second World War played havoc with the football calendar, but despite the widespread disruption there were still some friendly games on offer to distract people from the hostilities.

One such match saw Arsenal play Clapton Orient. Bizarrely, the game took place at White Hart Lane, but the unfamiliar surroundings obviously didn't unsettle the Gunners players and they stormed to a 15–2 win.

The undisputed Man of the Match was Leslie Compton, who was a centre-half by trade but, pressed into emergency service as a centre-forward on the day, scored 10 of the 15 goals.

Sadly, as the game was not classed a competitive fixture, his remarkable tally could not be included in his official career statistics and when he left Arsenal in 1952, his record amounted to a rather more modest six goals in 273 appearances.

ABOVE: Leslie Compton reached double figures in a friendly against Clapton Orient in a match played at White Hart Lane during the Second World War.

ARSENAL'S FOOTBALL LEAGUE RECORD 1893–1913

Division Two

	P	W	D	L	F	A	PTS	POS
1893–94	28	12	4	12	52	55	28	9th
1894–95	30	14	6	10	75	58	34	8th
1895–96	30	14	4	12	59	42	32	7th
1896–97	30	13	4	13	68	70	30	10th
1897–98	30	16	5	9	69	49	37	5th
1898–99	34	18	5	11	72	41	41	7th
1899–1900	34	16	4	14	61	43	36	8th
1900–01	34	15	6	13	39	35	36	7th
1901–02	34	18	6	10	50	26	42	4th
1902–03	34	20	8	6	66	30	48	3rd
1903–04	34	21	7	6	91	22	49	2nd

Division One

	P	W	D	L	F	A	PTS	POS
1904–05	34	12	9	13	36	40	33	10th
1905–06	38	15	7	16	62	64	37	12th
1906–07	38	20	4	14	66	59	44	7th
1907–08	38	12	12	14	51	63	36	15th
1908–09	38	14	10	14	52	49	38	6th
1909–10	38	11	9	18	37	67	31	18th
1910–11	38	13	12	13	41	49	38	10th
1911–12	38	15	8	15	55	59	38	10th
1912–13	38	3	12	23	26	74	18	20th

All-Time Records – Biggest Defeats

AGONY AT THE ATHLETIC GROUND

The Gunners may have enjoyed their record Football League victory against Loughborough Town in March 1900 – a 12–0 success – but it was against the same opposition nearly four years earlier that the Club also suffered its most humbling league defeat.

The old Second Division clash in December 1896 was held at the home side's Athletic Ground and it was to prove a truly miserable 90 minutes for the visitors as Loughborough scored eight times without reply. The final 8–0 scoreline, however, could have been even worse for Arsenal were it not for the referee disallowing two further goals for the home side.

"The Arsenal never gave up," read the match report in the local Loughborough newspaper, "the forwards exerting themselves to the end. Their half-backs were pretty good and so were the forwards, but the backs were weak and the custodian had scarcely any chance with the shots that scored."

The most dejected of the Gunners XI must surely have been the custodian in question – Arthur Talbot, who was playing only his second league game for the Club. Three more league appearances followed but, with memories still fresh from the eight-goal demolition, Talbot was released at the end of the season.

At least the travelling Arsenal support had reason to be more cheerful, however, when it was announced the Club would refund the cost of their match tickets as a gesture of apology for the team's performance.

SIX-GOAL MISERY

Arsenal's exploits in the FA Cup have provided many golden moments in the Club's history but on three separate occasions the team has fallen to record 6–0 defeats in the game's oldest knockout competition.

The first came in the third round in January 1893 when they were ambushed by Sunderland at Newcastle Road. They succumbed to the same scoreline six years later at the same stage of the tournament at home against Derby County.

The Club's most recent 6–0 FA Cup reverse was also in the third round when West Ham United proved too strong at Upton Park in January 1946.

▶ CUP MAULING

Arsene Wenger is renowned for fielding experimental sides in the League Cup but his decision to name what was effectively a reserve team for a fourth-round meeting with Chelsea at Highbury in 1998 was not his finest hour.

The visitors had established a slender 1–0 advantage at the break courtesy of a Frank Leboeuf penalty, but the Gunners' second-half fightback failed to materialize as Chelsea took complete control with a brace from Gianluca Vialli, a Nelson Vivas own goal and a fifth from Gus Poyet to inflict Arsenal's heaviest-ever defeat in the competition.

RIGHT: The Gunners suffered a shock 5–0 defeat against Chelsea in the 1998–99 League Cup.

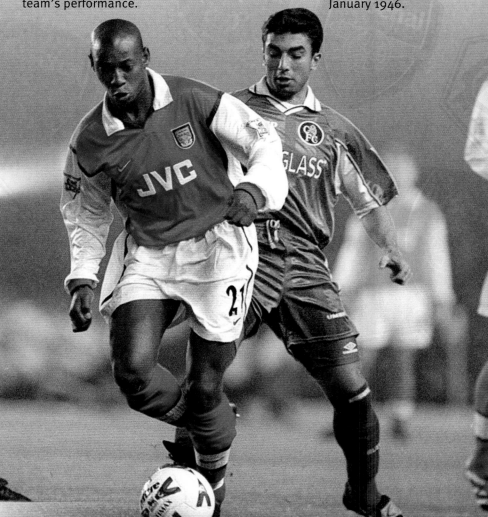

▲ LIVERPOOL VICTORIOUS
Arsenal and Liverpool have produced some epic encounters over the decades but the Division Two clash between the two in October 1893 was one to forget, from the Gunners' perspective, with the game at the Manor Ground finishing 5–0 to the Merseysiders. It remains Arsenal's joint worst league defeat at home.

ABOVE: Arsenal take on Liverpool during the 1905–06 season.

TERRIERS TRIUMPHANT
The Gunners were ever-present in the old First Division between 1919 and 1992 and while the Club's 73-year unbroken stay in the top-flight brought 10 title triumphs, there were also setbacks.

Perhaps the most sobering was when they faced defending champions Huddersfield Town at Highbury in February 1925 and found themselves on the wrong end of a 5–0 scoreline – the Club's worst top-flight defeat at home.

The Terriers went on to win the league that year for a second successive season, but Arsenal had their revenge at Highbury 14 months later in the shape of a 3–1 victory.

LEAKY DEFENCE
Arsenal are no strangers to scoring seven but they have also conceded seven away from home in the league four times in their history.

They suffered their first 7–0 reverse against Blackburn Rovers at Ewood Park in October 1909 and their defence was again breached seven times without reply at the Hawthorns against West Bromwich Albion in October 1922.

Newcastle United emerged 7–0 winners against the Gunners at St James' Park three years later while the Club's most recent seven-goal demolition came against West Ham United at the Boleyn Ground in March 1927.

ARSENAL'S FOOTBALL LEAGUE RECORD 1913–39
Division Two

	P	W	D	L	F	A	PTS	POS
1913–14	38	20	9	9	54	38	49	3rd
1914–15	38	19	5	14	69	41	43	5th

Division One

	P	W	D	L	F	A	PTS	POS
1919–20	42	15	12	15	56	58	42	10th
1920–21	42	15	14	13	59	63	44	9th
1921–22	42	15	7	20	47	56	37	17th
1922–23	42	16	10	16	61	62	42	11th
1923–24	42	12	9	21	40	63	33	19th
1924–25	42	14	5	23	46	58	33	20th
1925–26	42	22	8	12	87	63	52	2nd
1926–27	42	17	9	16	77	86	43	11th
1927–28	42	13	15	14	82	86	41	10th
1928–29	42	16	13	13	77	72	45	9th
1929–30	42	14	11	17	78	66	39	14th
1930–31	42	28	10	4	127	59	66	1st
1931–32	42	22	10	10	90	48	54	2nd
1932–33	42	25	8	9	118	61	58	1st
1933–34	42	25	9	8	75	47	59	1st
1934–35	42	23	12	7	115	46	58	1st
1935–36	42	15	15	12	78	48	45	6th
1936–37	42	18	16	8	80	49	52	3rd
1937–38	42	21	10	11	77	44	52	1st
1938–39	42	19	9	14	55	41	47	5th

All-Time Records – Winning Sequences

BELOW: Michael Thomas celebrates after scoring, this time against Everton, during the 1987–88 campaign.

▶ FOURTEEN VICTORIES

The ability to string together a sustained sequence of victories is the hallmark of a great side and during the 1987–88 season the Gunners proved their pedigree with 14 wins in succession to set a new Club record.

The incredible run began in mid-September when an Alan Smith goal gave Arsenal a 1–0 victory over Nottingham Forest at the City Ground in the old First Division. Wimbledon were despatched 3–0 at Highbury the following Saturday and, when Doncaster were defeated by the same scoreline in a second-round, first-leg League Cup clash at Belle Vue, George Graham's side were gathering momentum.

RIGHT: Frank Stapleton spent seven seasons at Highbury and was part of the 1979 FA Cup-winning side

West Ham, Charlton, Doncaster and Oxford United were all beaten before Arsenal faced arch-rivals Tottenham at White Hart Lane in mid-October. There, courtesy of goals from Michael Thomas and David Rocastle, the Gunners came away with a priceless 2–1 victory and an eighth win in eight.

Defeats of Derby, Bournemouth in the League Cup, Newcastle, Chelsea and Norwich followed and the superb run climaxed with a fourth-round League Cup clash with Stoke at Highbury in November. Goals from David O'Leary, Rocastle and Kevin Richardson sealed the 3–0 triumph that set the new milestone.

The sequence featured 10 Division One wins and four in the early stages of the League Cup, also making it Arsenal's most successful series of Football League victories.

◀ ON THE ROAD

A win away from home is a precious commodity and in 1977 the Gunners went away from Highbury in the First Division six times in succession and each time returned to north London with the points.

The record run began after a 2–0 victory over Bristol City at Ashton Gate on 22 October and continued in early November when goals from Graham Rix and Malcolm Macdonald at Old Trafford gave the Gunners a 2–1 win against Manchester United.

Newcastle United were overcome by the same scoreline at St James' Park before the Gunners enjoyed a slice of luck against Middlesbrough at Ayresome Park when an own-goal settled the contest in Arsenal's favour.

Two Frank Stapleton goals against Coventry at Highfield Road made it five from five and the side set a new Club record of six successive league wins on the road two days after Christmas when Liam Brady, Alan Sunderland and Macdonald were on target in a 3–1 triumph over West Bromwich Albion at the Hawthorns.

MARVELLOUS MANOR GROUND

Arsenal were in sensational form in 1903–04. As well as winning their first eight games, the side also registered 15 league wins on the bounce at home for the Club's most-successful-ever sequence in the Football League.

The first four wins came in the initial eight-match run and, although that came to an end, the Gunners remained indomitable at the old Manor Ground in Plumstead and reeled off 11 more victories between November 1903 and April 1904.

The all-conquering run saw Arsenal score 67 times and concede just four times. Of the 15 defeated sides, only Bradford (4–1), Stockport (5–2) and Glossop (2–1) were able to find the back of the Gunners' net.

BELOW: Malcolm Macdonald scored 57 times for the Gunners during his three-season spell with the Club.

ARSENAL'S FOOTBALL LEAGUE RECORD 1946–59
Division One

	P	W	D	L	F	A	PTS	POS
1946–47	42	16	9	17	72	70	41	13th
1947–48	42	23	13	6	81	32	59	1st
1948–49	42	18	13	11	74	44	49	5th
1949–50	42	19	11	12	79	55	49	6th
1950–51	42	19	9	14	73	56	47	5th
1951–52	42	21	11	10	80	61	53	3rd
1952–53	42	21	12	9	97	64	54	1st
1953–54	42	15	13	14	75	73	43	12th
1954–55	42	17	9	16	69	63	43	9th
1955–56	42	18	10	14	60	61	46	5th
1956–57	42	21	8	13	85	69	50	5th
1957–58	42	16	7	19	73	85	39	12th
1958–59	42	21	8	13	88	68	50	3rd

▼ RECORD START TO NEW SEASON

The 1903–04 season saw Arsenal finish as Division Two runners-up to Preston North End and earn promotion to the top-flight of English football for the first time. But manager Harry Bradshaw may have been disappointed not to have won the title after the sensational start his side made to their campaign.

The Gunners began the season with a 3–0 win over Blackpool at the Manor Ground in September thanks to a brace from the prolific Bill Gooing – and in their next four league games they beat Gainsborough, Burton United, Bristol City and Manchester United without conceding a goal.

In October the Arsenal defence was finally breached when they faced Glossop away from home but another brace from Gooing was enough to seal a 3–1 victory. The unbeaten run continued a fortnight later after a 3–2 win against Port Vale at the Athletic Ground.

The side made it eight from eight just 48 hours later when they demolished Leicester Fosse 8–0 in London courtesy of a hat-trick from Irish inside-forward Tommy Shanks. Although the run finally came to an end at the end of October when Barnsley ran out 2–1 winners at Oakwell, the sequence remains the Gunners' most successful start to a Football League season in terms of victories.

In total, Arsenal conceded just three goals and scored 35 during their irresistible spell with Gooing top-scoring with nine.

ABOVE: Arsenal's 1903–04 promotion winning team, who won their first eight games of the season, a Club record in terms of victories.

All-Time Records – Undefeated Records

HOME SWEET HOME

Highbury was famous as a fortress for the Gunners but its predecessor – the Manor Ground in Plumstead – was also an intimidating venue for visiting teams. It was here that Arsenal set a Club record of 33 home games unbeaten in the Football League at the start of the 20th century.

The streak started in November 1902 when Manchester City were beaten 1–0 in the old Division Two and by the time Aston Villa lost 1–0 in Plumstead in October 1904, courtesy of a Bill Gooing goal, Arsenal had strung together a sensational 33 home league games without defeat. The Gunners completed the entire 1903–04 season without losing at the Manor Ground to earn promotion to the old First Division for the first time, but the step up in standard was to ultimately end the sequence when they faced Nottingham Forest and were 3–0 losers.

The run featured 28 wins in 33 fixtures and the side kept a total of 23 clean sheets. More remarkably, however, Arsenal scored a grand total of 105 goals in the process and only let in 11.

BRILLIANT BACK FOUR

By definition, a clean sheet means a team cannot lose, and unsurprisingly the Arsenal Club record in the Football League for not conceding at home was set during the side's 33-match unbeaten record.

Their first clean sheet was recorded in April of the 1902–03 campaign when Chesterfield were beaten 3–0. By the time the same opposition was demolished 6–0 at the same venue in November of the 1903–04 season, the Gunners had gone eight games at the Manor Ground without their defence being breached.

LEFT: The Arsenal team of 1903–04. They never lost at the Manor Ground that season.

BELOW: Sweden midfielder Anders Limpar was part of Arsenal's 13-game unbeaten away run.

LUCKY THIRTEEN

The Gunners' unbeaten streak that spanned the 1989–90 and 1990–91 seasons also saw the side set a new Club record of 13 Football League games away from home without defeat.

The 2–2 stalemate with Norwich at Carrow Road in May 1990 was the catalyst, and over the next nine months Arsenal travelled 12 more times in the league and each time came home with at least a point.

The highlight of the run was a 1–0 victory over Manchester United at Old Trafford in October, thanks to an Anders Limpar goal, while the final game in the sequence saw the side held to a goalless draw by Spurs at White Hart Lane before a defeat by Chelsea at Stamford Bridge.

GRAHAM'S SIDE SPARKLE

George Graham's Arsenal were crowned Division One champions at the end of a dominant 1990–91 campaign and it was little surprise the Scot's team walked away with the silverware after a superb season in which they registered a Club-record 26-match unbeaten run in the Football League.

The sequence actually began in 1989–90 when the Gunners beat Millwall and Southampton and drew with Norwich in their final three fixtures of the campaign. They picked up where they had left off in August in 1990–91 with a convincing 3–0 victory over Wimbledon at Highbury. Arsenal were now firmly in their stride and in their next 13 matches they collected 31 from a possible 39 points to set the pace.

In early December, the team faced defending champions Liverpool at Highbury but any fears that the sequence might come to an abrupt end were dispelled with a resounding 3–0 win, the goals coming from Lee Dixon, Alan Smith and Paul Merson.

Three successive draws against Luton, Wimbledon and Aston Villa followed before the Gunners returned to winning ways – and when Everton were beaten in north London in January, courtesy of a Merson strike, the streak had reached an incredible 26 matches featuring 17 wins.

A 2–1 defeat in the London derby with Chelsea at Stamford Bridge a fortnight later was the end of the fairytale, but the sequence provided enough of a platform for Arsenal to dethrone Liverpool as champions by seven clear points.

ABOVE: George Graham's 1990–91 side were unbeaten in 26 games.

ABOVE: Paul Merson scored 16 times for the Gunners in the 1990–91 campaign.

CHAMPIONS ELECT

The Club's best-ever start to a Football League campaign in terms of unbeaten matches also came in the 1990–91 season as Arsenal posted a Club-record 23 games before they found themselves on the losing side.

It began with the 3–0 victory away to Wimbledon in August and climaxed with a 1–0 win at Highbury over Everton in January.

The streak featured three games in which the team hit four goals against the opposition. The first was the 4–1 mauling of Chelsea in September while a Smith brace and further goals from Merson and Limpar saw Southampton despatched 4–0 in November. In December Sheffield United were beaten at Highbury by the same scoreline, courtesy of another brace from Smith.

The Gunners won 15 of the 23 matches, scoring 42 goals and conceding just 10. They also kept 15 clean sheets, including six in a row from early October, and a 2–0 victory against Norwich, to mid-November and the side's demolition of Southampton.

ARSENAL'S FOOTBALL LEAGUE RECORD 1959–79
Division One

	P	W	D	L	F	A	PTS	POS
1959–60	42	15	9	18	68	80	39	13th
1960–61	42	15	11	16	77	85	41	11th
1961–62	42	16	11	15	71	72	43	10th
1962–63	42	18	10	14	86	77	46	7th
1963–64	42	17	11	14	90	82	45	8th
1964–65	42	17	7	18	69	75	41	13th
1965–66	42	12	13	17	62	75	37	14th
1966–67	42	16	14	12	58	47	46	7th
1967–68	42	17	10	15	60	56	44	9th
1968–69	42	22	12	8	56	27	56	4th
1969–70	42	12	18	12	51	49	42	12th
1970–71	42	29	7	6	71	29	65	1st
1971–72	42	22	8	12	58	40	52	5th
1972–73	42	23	11	8	57	43	57	2nd
1973–74	42	14	14	14	49	51	42	10th
1974–75	42	13	11	18	47	49	37	16th
1975–76	42	13	10	19	47	53	36	17th
1976–77	42	16	11	15	64	59	43	8th
1977–78	42	21	10	11	60	37	52	5th
1978–79	42	17	14	11	61	48	48	7th

All-Time Records – Miscellaneous

TWO-POINT MILESTONE

The three-points-for-a-win system was adopted by the Football League in 1981. But in the era of a modest two points for a victory, Arsenal set an enduring Club record in the 1930–31 season with an impressive tally of 66 from 42 games.

The Gunners won 28 times in the old First Division to claim the title for the first time and were beaten just four times, finishing with a goal difference of plus 68 and seven points clear of runners-up Aston Villa.

RELEGATION FORM

The 1912–13 season was one to forget in Arsenal history, with the team setting two unwanted records – lowest points tally and fewest goals scored – in the same campaign.

Unsurprisingly the side were relegated after struggling to just three wins in 38 league games and amassing a mere 18 points over the course of what proved to be a miserable season.

The Gunners scored just 26 times in the process, with 11 goals coming at the Manor Ground and 15 on the road.

ABOVE: Arsenal were in prolific form in the 1930–31 season, registering well over a century of league goals – a record.

RIGHT: John Barnwell scored 24 times in 151 appearances for the Club.

 RECORD GOAL TALLY

The 1930–31 campaign was a remarkable season for Arsenal and, as well as registering a record 66-point haul, the team scored an incredible 127 league goals.

It's a milestone that is yet to be eclipsed and saw the Gunners average more than three goals per game en route to the silverware.

The highlights of the all-conquering season included a 7–1 thrashing of Blackpool, a 9–1 demolition of Grimsby courtesy of a four-goal salvo from David Jack, and a 5–0 victory against Bolton at Highbury on the final day of the season.

In total, the team scored 60 goals in their 21 away games that season – which is another record for the Club.

 SIX SUCCESSIVE STALEMATES

Draws are far from rare in football and in the 1960–61 season Arsenal registered a Club-record six successive stalemates between March and April.

The frustrating run began when the Gunners were held 2–2 by Aston Villa in Birmingham and continued a week later with a goalless draw against Blackburn Rovers at Highbury.

The team's clash with Manchester United at Old Trafford seven days later ended 1–1 and the subsequent London derby with West Ham then failed to produce a goal. A 2–2 draw with Fulham at Craven Cottage made it five games without a positive result and the first game in April for the Club ended 1–1 against Bolton at Burnden Park.

The Arsenal faithful were probably beginning to despair of ever seeing the team triumph again but they finally returned to winning ways just 48 hours after the Bolton stalemate with a 4–2 victory over Fulham at Highbury, the goals coming from John Barnwell (2) and Jackie Henderson (2).

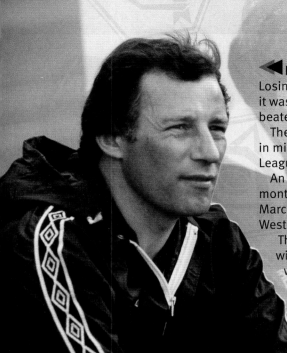

LOSING STREAK

Losing matches is a habit that teams can sometimes find difficult to break and it was certainly the case for Arsenal during the 1976–77 season when they were beaten in eight consecutive games, the worst sequence in the Club's history.

The unwelcome run in what was Terry Neill's first season as manager began in mid-February when they were beaten 1–0 by Manchester City at Maine Road. League defeats followed, to Middlesbrough (3–0) and West Ham (3–2) .

An FA Cup tie against Middlesbrough at Ayresome Park at the end of the month failed to relieve the pressure, ending in a 4–1 loss for the visitors, while March was equally disappointing with losses to Everton (2–1), Ipswich (4–1), West Brom (2–1) and Queens Park Rangers (2–1).

The demoralizing series of results eventually came to an end with a 1–1 draw with Stoke at the Victoria Ground while Arsenal finally returned to winning ways in April when they beat Leicester 3–0 at Highbury thanks to a brace from centre-half David O'Leary.

LEFT: Terry Neill was Arsenal manager between 1976 and 1983. He did not get off to winning ways but soon steered the Gunners back to form.

FIRST LEAGUE SUCCESS

Arsenal may have been founded in 1886 but it was not until the 1893–94 season that the Gunners first sampled league football when the Club became the first southern side to play in the old Second Division.

The team began the historic campaign with a 2–2 draw against Newcastle United followed by a 3–2 defeat away to Notts County. But two days later – on 11 September 1893 – the Gunners despatched Walsall 4–0 courtesy of a hat-trick from Joseph Heath for the Club's first-ever league victory.

 DREADFUL DEFENDING

Marshalled by the likes of Tony Adams, Lee Dixon and Nigel Winterburn, the Arsenal defence was famously miserly in the 1980s and 1990s but the same couldn't be said of the Gunners' back four in the 1926–27 Division One season when they conceded a record 86 times in 42 games.

The damage was done away from Highbury with 56 goals coming in their 21 matches on the road.

Arsenal, however, did not learn their lesson and in the 1927–28 campaign the side again let in 86 goals.

ABOVE: The Gunners side that played Cardiff in the 1927 FA Cup final with manager Herbert Chapman front right.

ARSENAL'S FOOTBALL LEAGUE RECORD 1979–92
Division One

	P	W	D	L	F	A	PTS	POS
1979–80	42	18	17	7	52	36	52	4th
1980–81	42	19	15	8	61	45	53	3rd
1981–82	42	20	11	11	48	37	71	5th
1982–83	42	16	10	16	58	56	58	10th
1983–84	42	18	9	15	74	60	63	6th
1984–85	42	19	9	14	60	47	66	7th
1985–86	42	20	9	13	49	47	69	7th
1986–87	42	20	10	12	58	35	70	4th
1987–88	40	18	12	10	58	39	66	6th
1988–89	38	22	10	6	73	36	76	1st
1989–90	38	18	8	12	54	38	62	4th
1990–91	38	24	13	1	74	18	83	1st
1991–92	42	19	15	8	81	46	72	4th

Premier League Records

The start of the Premier League in 1992–93 began a new chapter in Arsenal's history and this section details the Club's most significant records and feats in the competition, as well as reviewing the phenomenal performance of Arsene Wenger's fabled Invincibles side during the famous 2003–04 campaign.

ABOVE: Arsenal celebrate at Highbury after claiming the Premier League title for a third time in 2003–04.

Premier League Records – Biggest Wins

▼ TOFFEES TORN APART

Since the old First Division underwent a radical overhaul in the summer of 1992, re-emerging as the Premier League, Arsenal have continued their proud record as ever-present in the top-flight – and their biggest victory in the rebranded division came in May 2005 when Everton were spectacularly swept aside at Highbury.

The Gunners' record-setting 7–0 triumph was built on the genius of Dutch striker Dennis Bergkamp, whose sublime touch and vision set up goals for Robin van Persie and Robert Pires inside the opening 12 minutes in north London. Bergkamp was pivotal once again as Patrick Vieira scored the third on 37 minutes and at half-time the match was already over as a genuine contest.

Arsenal, however, were far from finished yet. A second from Pires and an Edu penalty compounded Everton's misery before Bergkamp helped himself to the goal his performance so richly deserved to make it six. Substitute Mathieu Flamini rubbed even more salt into the wound five minutes from time, and at the final whistle the Gunners were literally in seventh heaven.

It was an irresistible but not unique performance from Arsene Wenger's side and just eight months later they repeated the feat when Middlesbrough came to Highbury in January 2006.

Bergkamp had been Everton's tormentor-in-chief the previous season but this time it was Thierry Henry who stole the show with a

RIGHT: Edu celebrates after scoring from the spot in a 7–0 demolition of Everton at Highbury in 2005.

devastating hat-trick as Boro were hit for seven.

The prolific Frenchman opened his account with a stunning early volley, clinically broke clear for his second on the half-hour and completed his treble midway through the second half with another characteristically cool finish.

Philippe Senderos, Pires, Gilberto Silva and Alexander Hleb were the Gunners' other scorers but – with his third goal taking him to 150 in the league and in the process equalling Cliff Bastin's tally for the Club – the day undoubtedly belonged to Henry.

RIGHT: Ian Wright was the Gunners' top scorer in the 1992–93 season with 30 goals.

▲ WRIGHT ON TARGET

The first Premier League season of 1992–93 saw the Gunners average less than a goal per game but, despite their relatively modest haul in front of goal, the team did twice record 3–0 victories in that inaugural campaign – against Coventry City and Crystal Palace.

Arsenal hit three against the Sky Blues at Highbury in November through Ian Wright, Alan Smith and Kevin Campbell, and repeated the trick in May in north London against the Eagles with goals from Wright and Campbell again and a third from substitute Paul Dickov.

DERBY DELIGHT

The first north London league derby against Tottenham was played back in December 1909 – a 1–0 victory for Arsenal – and since the start of the Premier League the Gunners have scored five against their old rivals three separate times.

Their first five-star performance against Spurs was in November 2004 when a pulsating game at White Hart Lane was settled by a Robert Pires goal on 81 minutes as the visitors emerged 5–4 winners.

There were five more for the Emirates faithful to cheer in February 2012 when Arsene Wenger's side recovered from going 2–0 down to record a sensational 5–2 win. And in November the same year the Gunners again ran riot at home in another 5–2 triumph over their London neighbours.

HEAVYWEIGHT BATTLE

Arsenal and Manchester United are the two most successful sides in Premier League history in terms of overall victories. In 42 clashes with the Old Trafford side since 1992, the Gunners' most comprehensive win came in September 1998 when they despatched the Red Devils 3–0 at Highbury.

Arsene Wenger's side had already beaten United 3–0 in the Charity Shield at Wembley in August and they inflicted the same scoreline on the Manchester side a little over a month later with goals from Tony Adams, Nicolas Anelka and substitute Freddie Ljungberg.

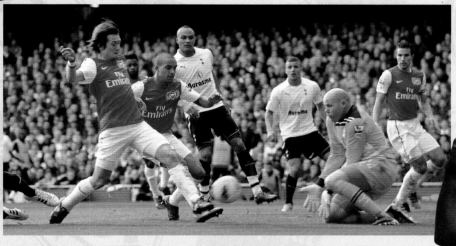

ABOVE: Tomas Rosicky scores in the 5–2 romp against Tottenham at Emirates in February 2012. At one point the Gunners were 2–0 down before scoring five in a row.

RIGHT: Patrick Vieira was on target for the Gunners in the 6–1 victory over Middlesbrough at the Riverside.

ARSENAL'S PREMIER LEAGUE RECORD

	P	W	D	L	F	A	PTS	POS
1992–93	42	15	11	16	40	38	56	10th
1993–94	42	18	17	7	53	28	71	4th
1994–95	42	13	12	17	52	49	51	12th
1995–96	38	17	12	9	49	32	63	5th
1996–97	38	19	11	8	62	32	68	3rd
1997–98	38	23	9	6	68	33	78	1st
1998–99	38	22	12	4	59	17	78	2nd
1999–2000	38	22	7	9	73	43	73	2nd
2000–01	38	20	10	8	68	38	70	2nd
2001–02	38	26	9	3	79	36	87	1st
2002–03	38	23	9	6	85	42	78	2nd
2003–04	38	26	12	0	73	26	90	1st
2004–05	38	25	8	5	87	36	83	2nd
2005–06	38	25	7	8	57	25	82	3rd
2006–07	38	19	11	8	63	35	68	4th
2007–08	38	24	11	3	74	31	83	3rd
2008–09	38	20	12	6	68	37	72	4th
2009–10	38	23	6	9	83	41	75	3rd
2010–11	38	19	11	8	72	43	68	4th
2011–12	38	21	7	10	74	49	70	3rd
2012–13	38	21	10	7	72	37	73	4th

MIDDLESBROUGH MAULED

Arsenal's heaviest victory away from home in the Premier League dates back to April 1999 when they headed north to face Middlesbrough at the Riverside Stadium.

The tone of the match was set in the third minute when Nicolas Anelka was hauled down in the area and Marc Overmars converted the resulting penalty. Anelka himself added a second on 38 minutes, and when Man of the Match Kanu produced a sublime solo effort in first-half injury-time the Gunners were already out of sight.

Patrick Vieira made it 4–0 on the hour before Kanu and then Anelka helped themselves to a second apiece. Although Alun Armstrong scored a late goal for the home side, it was no more than a consolation effort as Arsenal recorded a 6–1 triumph – their biggest win on the road since 1935 and Boro's worst defeat at home in the 100 years since they turned professional.

Premier League Records – Biggest Defeats

SKY BLUES TAKE THREE POINTS

The opening day of a new season is a chance to set the tone for the rest of the year but Arsenal's 1993–94 campaign got off to the worst possible start when they were beaten 3–0 by Coventry City at Highbury.

A Micky Quinn hat-trick condemned the Gunners to their worst-ever first-day defeat in the Premier League – but it's worth noting that the side recovered from the shock result to finish the season with the division's most miserly defence, conceding just 28 goals in 42 games.

END-OF-SEASON BLUES

Arsenal finished the 1999–2000 Premier League season as runners-up but as the campaign drew to a close in May, the Gunners were preoccupied with preparations for their UEFA Cup final showdown with Galatasaray rather than gathering league points.

The last league game against Newcastle United at St James' Park fell just three days before the final and an under-strength Gunners side proved no match for the Magpies on home soil, falling to a 4–2 defeat despite goals from Kanu and Stefan Malz.

It remains the Club's biggest last-day defeat in the Premier League.

RIGHT: The Gunners' 1999–2000 Premier League season ended in defeat at Newcastle.

 DERBY DEFEAT

The Premier League era has seen Arsenal dominate Tottenham in terms of results and the Lilywhites won just once at Highbury before the Gunners bid a fond farewell to the stadium in 2006.

That rare victory came in May 1993 in the final league game of the season and owed much to George Graham's decision to rest key players ahead of the FA Cup final against Sheffield Wednesday at Wembley just four days later.

Tottenham took a two-goal lead through Teddy Sheringham and John Hendry and although Paul Dickov reduced the arrears early in the second half, a second from Hendry was enough to give the visitors a 3–1 win and their biggest – and only – Premier League success at Highbury.

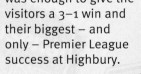

ABOVE: George Graham's Arsenal side faced Tottenham 11 times at Highbury during his managerial reign.

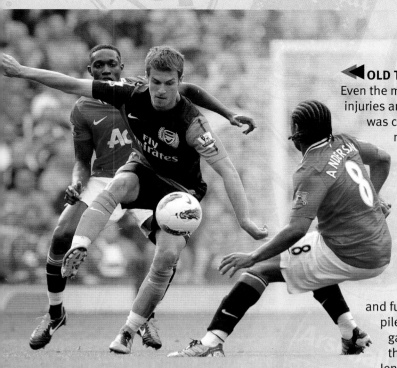

◀ OLD TRAFFORD NIGHTMARE

Even the most accomplished managers are powerless when injuries and suspensions ravage their squad and Arsene Wenger was certainly left stony-faced when he was forced to field a makeshift XI against Manchester United at Old Trafford in August 2011. The game ended in a sobering 8–2 defeat, Arsenal's record Premier League reverse and the Club's heaviest loss for 115 years.

Danny Welbeck opened the scoring for the home side on 22 minutes but the writing was on the wall for the Gunners when Robin van Persie's penalty was saved moments later. Theo Walcott did breach the home defence in first-half injury-time but at the break United were 3–1 ahead.

Wayne Rooney completed his hat-trick after the break and further goals from Ashley Young, Nani and Park Ji-Sung piled on the misery. Van Persie's 74th-minute effort briefly gave the travelling Arsenal fans something to celebrate but their temporary delight quickly turned to despair when Carl Jenkinson was sent off for a second bookable offence.

ABOVE: Aaron Ramsey in action against Manchester United at Old Trafford, where Arsenal suffered their worst loss for 115 years.

BELOW: Mikael Silvestre battles with Didier Drogba at Emirates, a match that ended in a 4–1 home loss.

ELLAND ROAD ROUT

The inaugural season of Premier League football was not a vintage one in Arsenal's history and the low point of the campaign came in November 1992 when they faced Leeds United at Elland Road.

The Gunners were unbeaten in their previous 15 meetings in all competitions against the Yorkshire side but, despite holding the reigning Division One champions to a goalless first-half, they were overrun after the break with goals from Chris Fairclough, Lee Chapman and Gary McAllister condemning the visitors to a 3–0 loss and their biggest defeat of the 1992–93 season.

◀ CAPITAL CLASH

Highbury and latterly Emirates have proved daunting destinations for visiting teams in the Premier League down the years, but home advantage deserted Arsenal in May 2009 when Chelsea made the short journey from SW6 to N5.

It was only the third time the two London sides had met at Emirates in the league and for the first time it was the Blues who took all three points after a 4–1 triumph, a result which remains the Gunners' worst loss at home since the Premier League began.

ARSENAL PREMIER LEAGUE RECORDS

Most Individual Goals In A Season 30 – Robin van Persie (2011–12), Thierry Henry (2003–04)

Most Team Goals In A Season 85 – 2002–03

Fewest Goals Conceded In A Season 17 – 1998–99

Most Goals Conceded In A Season 49 – 1994–95, 2011–12

Highest Points Total 90 – 2003–04

Lowest Points Total 56 – 1992–93

Most Victories In A Season 26 – 2001–02, 2003–04

Fewest Victories In A Season 13 – 1994–95

Biggest Victory 7–0 v Everton (May 2005), 7–0 v Middlesbrough (January 2006)

Biggest Defeat 8–2 v Manchester United (August 2011)

Premier League Records – The Invincibles

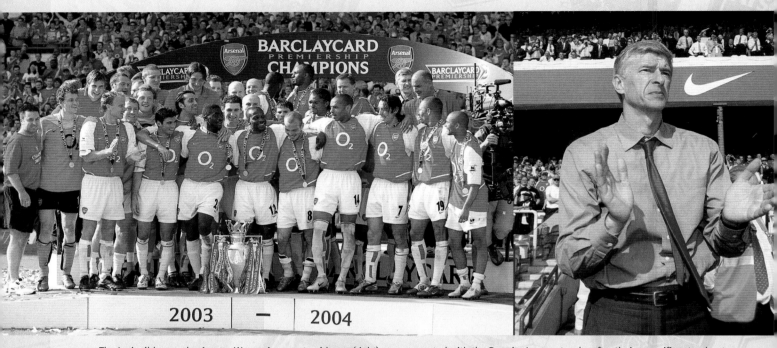

2003 — 2004

ABOVE: The Invincibles, under Arsene Wenger's expert guidance (right), are presented with the Premier League trophy after their magnificent unbeaten campaign, which lasted nearly 18 months.

 THE LONG RUN

The 7th of May 2003 was a special day in the history of Arsenal Football Club. The Gunners may have been licking their wounds after surrendering their Premier League crown to Manchester United just three days earlier, but the Highbury faithful were still in good voice as a Jermaine Pennant hat-trick inspired a 6–1 demolition of Southampton.

Little did Arsene Wenger or the 38,000-strong crowd that day realize that the result was the beginning of an unprecedented, undefeated Premier League run that would last 17-and-a-half unbelievable months, span 49 glorious games and comprehensively rewrite the record books.

No wonder the all-conquering side became known as "The Invincibles", such was their complete dominance.

The destruction of the Saints was Arsenal's penultimate league game of the 2002–03 campaign. They followed it up with a 4–0 win over Sunderland on Wearside and, as the summer break beckoned – albeit not before the small matter of an FA Cup final triumph over Southampton at Wembley – thoughts turned to recapturing their Premier League title in the following season. They were to achieve their target in truly devastating style.

The new season in mid-August began with the visit of Everton to Highbury and goals from Thierry Henry and Robert Pires in a 2–1 success ensured the momentum of May's back-to-back victories did not evaporate. Three more wins and a draw followed but in late September the Gunners' embryonic record was nearly lost as the side headed north to face Manchester United in the "Battle of Old Trafford".

Controversies in previous meetings between the two sides ensured the match was another ill-tempered, fractious affair. There were seven yellow cards in total and a red for Patrick Vieira in the 80th minute, but a goal looked a remote possibility until United were awarded a penalty in the final minute and Dutch striker Ruud van Nistelrooy stepped forward to take it. Unexpectedly, he crashed his effort against the crossbar and Arsenal's unbeaten sequence remained intact.

It was now eight games and counting. Buoyed by their escape at Old Trafford, the Gunners marched on. The 20th game in the run saw Wolves despatched 3–0 at Highbury, the 30th finished with a 2–0 victory over Bolton at the Reebok Stadium while the 36th ended with a 2–2 draw with Tottenham at White Hart Lane, a result which confirmed the Club were champions once again.

The final fixture of the Premier League season brought Leicester City to Highbury but the script did not feature the Foxes taking a first-half lead through former Gunner Paul Dickov. Wenger's side, however, were not to be denied and a goal from Henry – his 30th league strike in 37 appearances – plus a second from Vieira completed a 2–1 win and ensured the side completed the campaign with a phenomenal unbeaten record.

Arsenal became the first side since Preston in 1888–89 to win the league without suffering a single defeat. But while North End had played a modest 22 games over a century ago, the Gunners had remained unbeaten over the course of 38 fixtures, extending their overall streak to 40.

German goalkeeper Jens Lehmann was the only player to feature in all 38 matches while Henry and Kolo Toure (37 appearances), Pires (36) and Sol Campbell (35) were the other mainstays of perhaps the greatest side ever to grace Highbury.

There was of course more to come. The 2004–05 season kicked-off with a comprehensive 4–1 victory over Everton at Goodison and two-and-a-half weeks later the side broke yet another record when they demolished Blackburn at Highbury, in the process eclipsing Nottingham Forest's 26-year-old record of 42 league games unbeaten.

Five more victories and a 2–2 stalemate with Bolton followed and the sequence was now an unparalleled 49 Premier League matches since Arsenal had last tasted defeat.

On Sunday 24 October 2004, the run came to an end. The side headed to Old Trafford once again but this time van Nistelrooy was on target from the penalty spot as Manchester United overcame the visitors 2–0 and the Gunners were finally beaten.

The statistics of the team's sensational sequence barely tell the full story of their achievement. The 49 games yielded 36 victories and 13 draws, they scored 112 goals and conceded just 35 and they claimed the 2003–04 Premier League title by 11 clear points from second-place Chelsea.

Many believe the amazing exploits of Wenger's "Invincibles" between May 2003 and October 2004 will never be surpassed. Whatever happens, the team's place in the history books is assured.

BELOW: Thierry Henry top scored for Arsenal with 30 goals in 37 Premier League appearances.

THE INVINCIBLES' RECORD RUN

2002/2003
1. Arsenal 6-1 Southampton (7 May, 2003)
2. Sunderland 0-4 Arsenal

2003/2004
3. Arsenal 2-1 Everton
4. Middlesbro 0-4 Arsenal
5. Arsenal 2-0 Aston Villa
6. Man City 1-2 Arsenal
7. Arsenal 1-1 Portsmouth
8. Man Utd 0-0 Arsenal
9. Arsenal 3-2 Newcastle
10. Liverpool 1-2 Arsenal
11. Arsenal 2-1 Chelsea
12. Charlton 1-1 Arsenal
13. Leeds 1-4 Arsenal
14. Arsenal 2-1 Tottenham
15. Birmingham 0-3 Arsenal
16. Arsenal 0-0 Fulham
17. Leicester 1-1 Arsenal
18. Arsenal 1-0 Blackburn
19. Bolton 1-1 Arsenal
20. Arsenal 3-0 Wolves
21. Southampton 0-1 Arsenal
22. Everton 1-1 Arsenal
23. Arsenal 4-1 Middlesbro
24. Aston Villa 0-2 Arsenal
25. Arsenal 2-1 Man City
26. Wolves 1-3 Arsenal
27. Arsenal 2-0 Southampton
28. Chelsea 1-2 Arsenal
29. Arsenal 2-1 Charlton
30. Blackburn 0-2 Arsenal
31. Arsenal 2-1 Bolton
32. Arsenal 1-1 Man Utd
33. Arsenal 4-2 Liverpool
34. Newcastle 0-0 Arsenal
35. Arsenal 5-0 Leeds
36. Tottenham 2-2 Arsenal
37. Arsenal 0-0 Birmingham
38. Portsmouth 1-1 Arsenal
39. Fulham 0-1 Arsenal
40. Arsenal 2-1 Leicester

2004/2005
41. Everton 1-4 Arsenal
42. Arsenal 5-3 Middlesbro
43. Arsenal 3-0 Blackburn
44. Norwich 1-4 Arsenal
45. Fulham 0-3 Arsenal
46. Arsenal 2-2 Bolton
47. Man City 0-1 Arsenal
48. Arsenal 4-0 Charlton
49. Arsenal 3-1 Aston Villa (16 September, 2004)

Premier League Records – Other Undefeated Records

ABOVE: David Seaman kept five consecutive clean sheets away from home in 1997.

◀ AWESOME AWAY FORM

Going away from home in the Premier League is a challenge for any side but in 1997 Arsenal left north London five times in succession without letting in a goal.

A goalless draw at Elland Road against Leeds in February was the catalyst for the sequence and the Gunners followed it up with a hard-fought 0–0 draw with old rivals Spurs at White Hart Lane. A 2–0 win over Everton at Goodison, a 2–0 triumph against Southampton at The Dell and a 3–0 mauling of Chelsea at Stamford Bridge followed, and it was not until Dion Dublin beat David Seaman at Highfield Road in April in a 1–1 draw that Arsenal allowed the home side to score.

STRONGEST START

Arsenal's best-ever start to a Premier League season in terms of not conceding a goal came in 2012–13 when the Gunners went a Club-record 315 minutes of play before the defence was finally breached.

The side began the campaign with a goalless draw against Sunderland at Emirates and kept another clean sheet in their second game after a scoreless draw with Stoke at the Britannia Stadium.

A 2–0 victory over Liverpool at Anfield a week later extended the run and it was not until Danny Fox beat Wojciech Szczesny on the stroke of half-time in the Gunners' 6–1 demolition of Southampton that the side allowed the opposition to score.

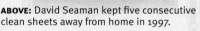

LEFT: Manuel Almunia was a hard man to beat during the 2008–09 campaign.

◀ IMMACULATE ALMUNIA

Keeping clean sheets is a guaranteed way to avoid defeat and Arsenal went a record eight Premier League games unbeaten at Emirates in 2008–09 without conceding a single goal.

The impeccable run began on 28 December 2008 with a 1–0 victory over Portsmouth in London and through January, February and March, Bolton, West Ham, Sunderland, Fulham, Blackburn, Manchester City and Middlesbrough were all unable to find a way past the Arsenal defence.

Spanish goalkeeper Manuel Almunia was in goal for all eight matches but made way for Lukasz Fabianksi for the clash with Chelsea at Emirates in May, a game which the Gunners lost 4–1 to bring their impressive streak to an end.

TITLE TRIUMPH

The Gunners were crowned Premier League champions for the first time in 1997–98, edging out Manchester United by a single point, and the success of the side was built on two superb but separate unbeaten sequences over the course of the season.

Arsenal's initial 12-match streak began on the opening day of the campaign with a 1–1 draw with Leeds United at Elland Road after an Ian Wright goal. It was to be 11 more games before Arsene Wenger's side were finally toppled, losing 3–0 at Derby County in early November.

The initial burst had confirmed Arsenal as genuine title contenders but it was the side's subsequent 18-match unbeaten streak that secured the silverware.

Their second sequence began on Boxing Day with a 2–1 win over Leicester City at Highbury and they went all the way through to May before tasting defeat again.

The highlight of the run came in March when the team travelled to Old Trafford to face Manchester United and came away with three crucial points courtesy of Marc Overmars' goal. Although a heavy 4–0 loss to Liverpool at Anfield brought things to an abrupt halt, the Gunners had already done enough to lift the Premier League trophy.

SEVEN-MATCH SEQUENCE

The inaugural 1992–93 Premier League season was far from Arsenal's best but the Gunners signalled that they would become a force to be reckoned with in the future with a seven-match unbeaten run in the new league.

It started in September with a goalless draw against Sheffield United at Bramall Lane and over the next two months Manchester City, Chelsea, Nottingham Forest, Everton, Crystal Palace and Coventry all failed to prevent the Gunners taking at least a point.

WENGER MASTERMINDS SUPERB STREAK

The record-breaking achievements of Arsene Wenger's "Invincibles" are well documented but the Arsenal side of 2007–08 and 2008–09 was almost as difficult to beat. Between April and December 2007, the team strung together an impressive 22-match unbeaten run.

A goalless draw with Newcastle at St James' Park was the start and in their final six fixtures of the 2007–08 campaign, the Gunners recorded three wins and three draws.

They continued their fine form at the start of 2008–09 with a 2–1 opening-day win over Fulham at Emirates, with goals from Robin van Persie from the spot and Alexander Hleb and extended the streak for another 14 games, culminating in a 1–1 draw with Newcastle in the north-east.

Middlesbrough's 2–1 win at the Riverside four days later stopped the superb sequence – but not before the Gunners had collected 50 points from a possible 66.

LEFT: Robin van Persie in action against Fulham at the start of the 2008–09 season.

ABOVE: Ian Wright was on target 10 times in 24 Premier League games in 1997–98.

LONGEST UNBEATEN SEQUENCES SEASON-BY-SEASON

1992–93 – 7 games	
1993–94 – 19	
1994–95 – 5	
1995–96 – 7	
1996–97 – 10	
1997–98 – 18	
1998–99 – 19	
1999–2000 – 9	
2000–01 – 12	
2001–02 – 21	
2002–03 – 12	
2003–04 – 38	
2004–05 – 12	
2005–06 – 6	
2006–07 – 7	
2007–08 – 15	
2008–09 – 21	
2009–10 – 10	
2010–11 – 16	
2011–12 – 8	
2012–13 – 10	

Premier League Records – Miscellaneous

ABOVE: Freddie Ljungberg scored 72 times in 328 games for the Club.

◄ SCORING SEQUENCE

The aim of football is essentially simple – get the ball by any legal means into the back of the net. It's a message that hasn't fundamentally changed since the game was invented and Arsenal certainly took heed between May 2001 and November 2002 when they scored in an incredible 55 consecutive Premier League games, a milestone that has yet to be surpassed by any other club.

It was on 19 May in the final fixture of the 2000–01 season that the Gunners began their prolific streak, with goals from Ashley Cole and Freddie Ljungberg in their 3–2 defeat to Southampton in the final-ever league game at The Dell.

The summer break did not dampen the side's attacking instincts and they kicked off the 2001–02 campaign with a 4–0 demolition of Middlesbrough at the Riverside. The goals continued to flow and by the end of the season the remarkable run in front of goal stood at 39 games.

Another summer of inactivity again failed to stem the flood of goals. The opening-day fixture in 2002–03 saw Birmingham despatched 2–0 at Highbury with strikes from Sylvain Wiltord and Thierry Henry – and the side continued the amazing sequence through to the end of November when a brace from Henry and a third from Robert Pires sealed a 3–1 triumph over Aston Villa in north London.

Arsenal finally drew a blank in a 2–0 loss to Manchester United at Old Trafford in December but the loss took none of the sheen off the side's unprecedented, record-breaking 55-match run in which they netted 116 times and lost just eight times.

► CITY SCALPED

Every club has another team they relish playing and, since the start of the Premier League, Manchester City have undoubtedly been the Gunners' opposition of choice.

Between August 1994 and January 2005, they beat City in 11 consecutive matches to set a new Premier League record and leave the Mancunians thoroughly sick of the sight of Arsenal.

The run began with a 3–0 win at Highbury on the opening day of the 1994–95 season and climaxed more than 10 years later when the Gunners won 1–0 at Eastlands with a Freddie Ljungberg strike.

The sequence yielded 30 goals and is the longest winning run for one side over another in Premier League history.

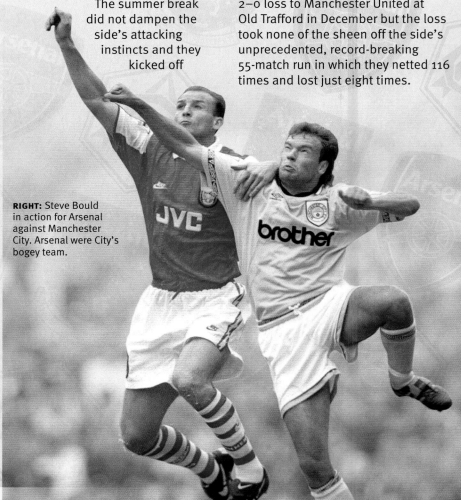

RIGHT: Steve Bould in action for Arsenal against Manchester City. Arsenal were City's bogey team.

CLEAN SHEET RECORD

The Arsenal defence was incredibly miserly during the 1998–99 season. The Gunners may have missed out on the title by a single point, but the back four could certainly be proud of their collective efforts after conceding just 17 goals in 38 games.

Remarkably, only one side managed to score more than one goal in a league match against Arsene Wenger's team – Aston Villa in their 3–2 win at Villa Park in December – and in total the Gunners kept 23 clean sheets during the campaign.

To put the Club-record feat into context, champions Manchester United conceded 37 times that season while the next meanest defence belonged to Chelsea with 30 goals scored against the Blues.

BELOW: David Seaman was part of one of the meanest-ever defences during the 1998–99 Premier League season.

POINTS MILESTONE

The Gunners' record points haul in the Premier League era was achieved en route to the title in 2003–04, with "The Invincibles" collecting a total of 90 from a possible 114.

They achieved the tally as the division's top scorers (with 73) and the league's tightest defence, conceding just 26 times in their 38 matches.

FANTASTIC FIGHTBACKS

The ability to fight back after going behind in a match is the mark of a team with real character – and the Gunners proved their battling characteristics in 2012 when they took all three points in four successive Premier League fixtures despite conceding the first goal.

The Club-record rearguard action began in February when they fell behind to a 70th-minute James McClean goal at Sunderland but Aaron Ramsey equalized five minutes later before Thierry Henry, playing the final game of his loan spell from the New York Red Bulls, scored an injury-time winner.

Two weeks later the Gunners faced Tottenham and Emirates was temporarily silenced as Spurs took a two-goal, first-half lead. Despair, however, quickly turned to delight as a five-goal salvo, including a late Theo Walcott brace, turned things around and Arsene Wenger's side marched to a famous 5–2 victory.

A trip to Anfield to play Liverpool in early March saw the Gunners fall behind again, albeit to a Laurent Koscielny own goal, but Robin van Persie was on hand to rescue his side, netting the winner in injury-time.

There was another late, late show against Newcastle later in the month. Hatem Ben Arfa put the Magpies in front at Emirates only for van Persie to equal moments later but, as the match headed into the fifth minute of injury-time, it seemed another miraculous recovery was beyond Arsenal. Cue defender Thomas Vermaelen and a dramatic last-gasp winner.

RIGHT: Thierry Henry scores a dramatic injury-time winner at the Stadium of Light in 2012.

FA Cup & League Cup Records

Arsenal have lifted the FA Cup 10 times since their first triumph at Wembley in 1930 and have won the League Cup twice – and the next 10 pages are packed with all the team's notable milestones in English football's two major domestic knockout competitions.

LEFT: Alan Sunderland celebrates his dramatic winning goal in the 1979 FA Cup final against Manchester United.

BELOW LEFT: Paul Merson races away after scoring against Sheffield Wednesday in the 1993 League Cup final.

BELOW: Patrick Vieira lifts the 2005 FA Cup after Arsenal overcame Manchester United.

RIGHT: Charlie George scores the winning goal in the 1971 FA Cup final against Liverpool.

FA Cup & League Cup Records – Winners

DRAKE NETS WINNER

The 1935–36 season saw Arsenal begin the campaign as the reigning Division One champions and although the team were unable to successfully defend their title – finishing sixth behind winners Sunderland – they did end the year on a high with victory in the FA Cup final.

The Club's second success in the final came against Sheffield United, courtesy of the only goal of the match from Ted Drake in the second half at Wembley.

The match was notable as it was the first time Arsenal players wore the Club's iconic red and white shirts in the final, having walked out in all-red tops in their three previous Wembley appearances.

▶ FIRST TROPHY TRIUMPH

The Gunners first sampled the unique atmosphere of an FA Cup final in 1927 when they were beaten 1–0 by Cardiff City in front of a crowd of 91,206 at Wembley. Three years later skipper Tom Parker, a survivor of the previous clash, was finally lifting the famous trophy after Arsenal beat Huddersfield.

After drawing a blank against Cardiff, Scottish inside-forward Alex James made history with his 16th-minute strike against the Terriers to become the first Arsenal player to score in an FA Cup final while Jack Lambert doubled the lead for Herbert Chapman's side two minutes from time to seal a milestone 2–0 victory.

The side's 2–0 triumph was also the Club's first-ever piece of major silverware, 39 years after the Gunners had turned professional.

RIGHT: The Gunners in action in the 1927 FA Cup final against Cardiff.

▶ JENSEN MAKES HISTORY

The Gunners' first six FA Cup triumphs were achieved exclusively with sides featuring British and Irish players but that all changed in 1993 when John Jensen became the first foreigner to play for the Club in a final.

The Danish midfielder signed for Arsenal from Brondby in the summer of 1992 and less than 12 months later found himself part of the team that drew 1–1 with Sheffield Wednesday at Wembley after extra-time.

Jensen was also part of the starting XI that beat the Owls 2–1 in the rematch five days later, the first time the Gunners had found themselves involved in a replay.

RIGHT: John Jensen was part of the Arsenal side that beat Sheffield Wednesday in the 1993 FA Cup final at Wembley.

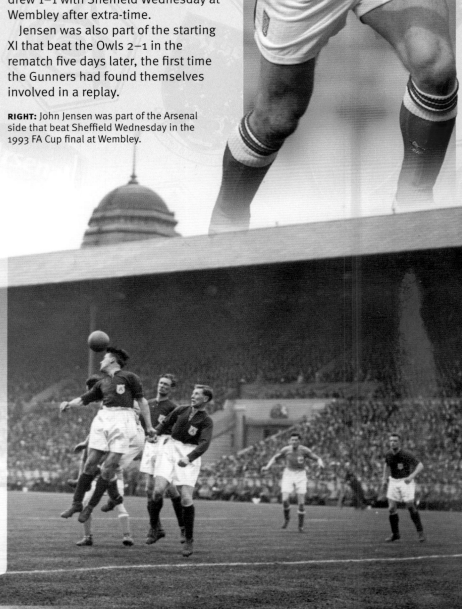

NICHOLAS' WEMBLEY HEROICS

George Graham won six major trophies during his nine-year reign as Arsenal manager. His first silverware at Highbury came in the shape of the 1987 League Cup after his side triumphed over Liverpool in front of a 96,000-strong crowd at Wembley.

Appointed to succeed Don Howe in May 1986, Graham made an immediate impact as Arsenal cruised effortlessly through the early rounds of the competition before drawing old rivals Tottenham in the semi-finals.

Spurs won the first leg at Highbury 1–0 thanks to a Clive Allen goal but the Gunners responded by winning the return leg at White Hart Lane 2–1 courtesy of strikes from Viv Anderson and Niall Quinn, to make the tie 2–2 on aggregate.

A replay was required as away goals did not count double. So a coin was tossed to decide the venue for the rematch and the two teams headed to White Hart Lane once again to settle the issue.

Another Allen goal gave the home side the early advantage but Arsenal were plotting a dramatic denouement and strikes from Ian Allinson and David Rocastle in the final eight minutes booked the Gunners' place at Wembley.

The final also saw Graham's side forced to stage a late fightback after Ian Rush opened the scoring for Liverpool in the 23rd minute. Charlie Nicholas equalized seven minutes later but the two teams were locked at 1–1 until late in the second half and injury-time beckoned.

Nicholas, however, had other ideas and his second goal, in the 83rd minute, gave Arsenal a famous 2–1 win. It was the Club's first League Cup triumph and went some way to erasing the painful memories of defeat in the finals of 1968 and 1969.

ABOVE: Charlie Nicholas was Arsenal's hero in the 1987 League Cup final.

BELOW: Marc Overmars celebrates after scoring the Gunners' first goal in the 2–0 defeat of Newcastle in the 1998 FA Cup final.

ARSENAL'S FA CUP RECORD 1889–1915

1889–90 – Fourth Qualifying Round (Lost 5–1, Swifts)

1890–91 – First Round (Lost 2–1, Derby County)

1891–92 – First Round (Lost 5–1, Small Heath)

1892–93 – First Round (Lost 1–0, Sunderland)

1893–94 – First Round (Lost 2–1, Sheffield Wednesday)

1894–95 – First Round (Lost 1–0, Bolton Wanderers)

1895–96 – First Round (Lost 6–1, Burnley)

1896–97 – Fifth Qualifying Round (Lost 4–2, Millwall)

1897–98 – First Round (Lost 3–1, Burnley)

1898–99 – First Round (Lost 6–0, Derby County)

1899–1900 – Third Qualifying Round (Lost 1–0, New Brompton)

1900–01 – Second Round (Lost 1–0, West Bromwich Albion)

1901–02 – First Round (Lost 2–0, Newcastle United)

1902–03 – First Round (Lost 3–1, Sheffield United)

1903–04 – Second Round (Lost 2–0, Manchester City)

1904–05 – First Round (Lost 1–0, Bristol City)

1905–06 – Semi-Finals (Lost 2–0, Newcastle United)

1906–07 – Semi-Finals (Lost 3–1, Sheffield Wednesday)

1907–08 – First Round (Lost 4–1, Hull City)

1908–09 – Second Round (Lost 1–0, Millwall)

1909–10 – Second Round (Lost 5–0, Everton)

1910–11 – Second Round (Lost 1–0, Swindon Town)

1911–12 – First Round (Lost 1–0, Bolton Wanderers)

1912–13 – Second Round (Lost 4–1 Liverpool)

1913–14 – First Round (Lost 2–0, Bradford Park Avenue)

1914–15 – Second Round (Lost 1–0, Chelsea)

DUTCH DELIGHT

Jensen paved the way for Arsenal's foreign legion in the FA Cup. Five years after his landmark appearance at Wembley, Marc Overmars picked up the baton when he became the first non-British or Irish player to score for the Club in a final.

The Dutch winger was on target midway through the first half in 1998 as the Gunners beat Newcastle United 2–0 to lift the trophy for a seventh time.

Ironically, Arsenal's second goal came courtesy of French striker Nicolas Anelka, 46 minutes after Overmars' opener, but it was too late to earn a place in the record books.

The victory also saw the Gunners complete the fabled league and cup double for the second time, the first Club in the history of the English game to achieve the feat twice.

► LEWIS'S RECORD DOUBLE

In total Arsenal have appeared in 17 FA Cup finals since first making it to Wembley in 1927. Including the 1993 replay against Sheffield Wednesday, the Gunners have scored 20 times in the showpiece game of the English domestic season.

There have been 14 different scorers for the Club but Reg Lewis remains the only player to have found the back of the net twice in the final.

His unique achievement came in 1950 when Arsenal faced Liverpool at Wembley and his 18th and 63rd-minute strikes ensured the Gunners were champions for a third time.

Ian Wright and Freddie Ljungberg both also boast two FA Cup final goals on their CVs but their efforts came in separate games.

▼ SUCCESSFUL TROPHY DEFENCE

Only seven sides have recorded back-to-back triumphs in the FA Cup in the long and illustrious history of the competition, and Arsenal joined the exclusive club in May 2003 when they overcame Southampton at the Millennium Stadium.

The game was settled by a solitary Robert Pires goal in the first half in Cardiff to secure the trophy for a ninth time and in the process lift the Gunners to second outright in the all-time winners' list above Tottenham.

ABOVE: Reg Lewis made history with his double against Liverpool in the 1950 FA Cup final.

LJUNGBERG ON TARGET AGAIN

The 2002 FA Cup pitted the Gunners against Chelsea in an all-London final and history was made when Freddie Ljungberg found the back of the net in Arsenal's 2–0 victory at Wembley.

The Swedish midfielder was on target in the 2001 final defeat to Liverpool and when he scored in the 80th minute against Chelsea, following up Ray Parlour's 70th-minute strike, he became the first player to score in successive finals since Tottenham's Bobby Smith 40 years earlier.

Days later the Gunners beat Manchester United 1–0 at Old Trafford courtesy of a Sylvain Wiltord goal to win the Premier League title and in the process draw level with Manchester United on three league and cup doubles.

LEFT: Robert Pires' goal proved pivotal against Southampton at the Millennium Stadium in 2003.

MORROW DENIES OWLS

The Gunners' second success in the League Cup came in 1993 when Graham steered his side to the final for a second time in five years, lining up against Sheffield Wednesday at Wembley in April.

As they had in 1987, Arsenal went behind in the match when John Harkes beat David Seaman after only eight minutes, but the revival began when Man of the Match Paul Merson was on target 12 minutes later.

The two teams went in at the break level but it was Graham's team who were to emerge 2–1 winners at the final whistle thanks to a rare Steve Morrow goal in the second half.

Captain Tony Adams proudly climbed the famous Wembley steps to collect the trophy and, while the silverware was handled with due care and attention, he was less careful when he hoisted Morrow above his shoulders in the post-match celebrations, dropping his team-mate and breaking his arm.

PENALTY SHOOTOUT

Arsenal's first nine successes in the FA Cup saw the side score at least once in the final, albeit in extra-time in 1971 against Liverpool, but the sequence came to an end in 2005 when they faced Manchester United.

The two sides failed to muster a goal in open play but it was the Gunners who held their nerve in the penalty shootout as Lauren, Freddie Ljungberg, Robin van Persie, Ashley Cole and Patrick Vieira were all on target from the spot to clinch a 10th win.

RIGHT: Steve Morrow scored the winner at Wembley in the 1993 League Cup final.

ECSTASY IN EXTRA-TIME

A repeat of the 1950 final, the 1971 showdown between Arsenal and Liverpool at Wembley in May made history – both as the first final featuring the Gunners to go to extra-time and as the climax of the Club's first-ever league and cup double.

The match was goalless in the opening 90 minutes but the goals suddenly flowed in extra-time. Steve Heighway gave Liverpool the lead but substitute Eddie Kelly – the first replacement to feature in a final for the Gunners – equalized before Charlie George hit the winner in the 111th minute of the contest.

Arsenal had wrapped up the Division One title five days earlier courtesy of a 1–0 victory against Tottenham at White Hart Lane, making the success against Liverpool the Club's maiden double.

BELOW: The 1971 FA Cup final was the second leg of the Club's famous double.

ARSENAL'S FA CUP RECORD 1919–50

1919–20 – Second Round (Lost 1–0, Bristol City)
1920–21 – First Round (Lost 2–0, QPR)
1921–22 – Quarter-Finals (Lost 2–1, Preston North End)
1922–23 – First Round (Lost 4–1, Liverpool)
1923–24 – Second Round (Lost 1–0, Cardiff City)
1924–25 – First Round (Lost 1–0, West Ham United)
1925–26 – Quarter-Finals (Lost 2–1, Swansea City)
1926–27 – Runners-Up (Lost 1–0, Cardiff City)
1927–28 – Semi-Finals (Lost 1–0, Blackburn Rovers)
1928–29 – Quarter-Finals (Lost 1–0, Aston Villa)
1929–30 – Winners (Won 2–0, Huddersfield Town)
1930–31 – Fourth Round (Lost 2–1, Chelsea)
1931–32 – Runners-Up (Lost 2–1, Newcastle United)
1932–33 – Third Round (Lost 2–0, Walsall)
1933–34 – Quarter-Finals (Lost 2–1, Aston Villa)
1934–35 – Quarter-Finals (Lost 2–1, Sheffield Wednesday)
1935–36 – Winners (Won 1–0, Sheffield United)
1936–37 – Quarter-Finals (Lost 3–1, West Bromwich Albion)
1937–38 – Fifth Round (Lost 1–0, Preston North End)
1938–39 – Third Round (Lost 2–1, Chelsea)
1945–46 – Third Round (Lost 6–1, West Ham)
1946–47 – Third Round (Lost 2–0, Chelsea)
1947–48 – Third Round (Lost 1–0, Bradford Park Avenue)
1948–49 – Fourth Round (Lost 1–0, Derby County)
1949–50 – Winners (Won 2–0, Liverpool)

FA Cup & League Cup Records – Sequences

▼ **RECORD UNBEATEN RUN**

Arsenal are one of the most successful sides in FA Cup history. Between January 1979 and May 1980, the Gunners set an incredible Club record of 21 consecutive games in the competition without suffering defeat.

The phenomenal run began when the team were drawn in the third round against Sheffield Wednesday. The initial clash at Hillsborough ended 1–1 but it was an era in which replays were unlimited and it would require a remarkable four more meetings between the two teams to pick a winner.

The first replay ended 1–1, the second 2–2 and the third 3–3, and it was only in the fourth rerun of the original tie that Arsenal finally emerged victorious courtesy of goals from Frank Stapleton and Steve Gatting.

BELOW: Terry Neill's side enjoyed huge success in the FA Cup

RIGHT: Liam Brady on the ball during the 1980 FA Cup semi-final against Liverpool.

Notts County and Nottingham Forest were both despatched without the need for a second match but the sixth-round clash with Southampton in March did go to a replay which the Gunners eventually won 2–0.

Arsenal saw off Wolves comfortably in the semi-final and their entertaining 3–2 victory over Manchester United in the final at Wembley took their unbeaten run in the FA Cup to 11 games.

Replays were the name of the game again the following season as the Gunners battled their way through to another final.

It took the side 180 minutes to overcome Cardiff in the third round in January and, although Brighton were beaten in the fourth round inside 90 minutes, it was a two-legged affair against Bolton in the next phase.

Watford fell 2–1 to Arsenal in the last eight but another epic, replay-laden contest awaited the team in the form of Liverpool in the semi-finals. The first clash was goalless while the

first and second replays finished 1–1 and it was only in the fourth game between the two that the Gunners did the business with a 1–0 win thanks to Brian Talbot's solitary goal.

Terry Neill's side were to lose the final to West Ham just nine days later, but their 21-match unbeaten sequence remains a record subsequent Arsenal teams have been unable to surpass or equal.

SEMI-FINAL SUCCESS

Between 2001 and 2005, the Gunners reached five successive FA Cup semi-finals, the most consistent run of reaching the last four in the Club's history.

Only their 2004 meeting with Manchester United at Villa Park, a narrow 1–0 defeat, failed to yield an appearance in the final itself.

Arsenal had previously battled through to the semis in three consecutive seasons twice, reaching the last four in 1971, 1972 and 1973 and again from 1978 to 1980.

▲ READING ROMP

Arsenal's phenomenal 7–5 victory over Reading in the fourth round of the League Cup in October 2012 set a new record for the highest aggregate score in the competition – but the match also saw the Gunners record another piece of football history.

The result booked them a place in the quarter-finals of the League Cup for a 10th consecutive season, a record that no other side can equal.

EARLY CUP PITFALLS

The Gunners' first foray in the FA Cup came in the 1889–90 campaign but, initially at least, the side struggled to come to terms with the competition and for 11 successive seasons they failed to get beyond the first round proper.

Arsenal's debut in the tournament in 1889 saw the team progress past Lyndhurst, Norwich Thorpe and Crusaders in the preliminary stages but a 5–1 defeat to Swifts in the fourth qualifying round saw the Gunners denied a first-round fixture.

The following six seasons all saw the team feature in the first round but victory proved frustratingly elusive as Derby, Birmingham, Sunderland, Sheffield Wednesday, Burton and Burnley all proved too great an obstacle.

Millwall beat Arsenal 4–2 in qualifying in 1897 and there was further disappointment for the Gunners over the next three years.

The unwanted losing streak finally came to an end in 1901 when they faced Blackburn at the Manor Ground and goals from James Tennant and Thomas Low earned the home side an overdue 2–0 win and a place in the second round for the first time.

The team lost 1–0 to West Bromwich Albion in the next round, but – although it would be 29 years before they lifted the FA Cup for the first time – they had broken the habit of falling at the first hurdle.

ABOVE: Marouane Chamakh scored twice in extra-time in Arsenal's record 7–5 win over Reading in the League Cup in 2012.

ARSENAL'S FA CUP RECORD 1950–80

1950–51 – Fifth Round (Lost 1–0, Manchester United)

1951–52 – Runners-Up (Lost 1–0, Newcastle United)

1952–53 – Quarter-Finals (Lost 2–1, Blackpool)

1953–54 – Fourth Round (Lost 2–1, Norwich City)

1954–55 – Fourth Round (Lost 1–0, Wolverhampton Wanderers)

1955–56 – Quarter-Finals (Lost 3–1, Birmingham City)

1956–57 – Quarter-Finals (Lost 2–1, West Bromich Albion)

1957–58 – Third Round (Lost 3–1, Northampton Town)

1958–59 – Fifth Round (Lost 3–0, Sheffield United)

1959–60 – Third Round (Lost 2–0, Rotherham United)

1960–61 – Third Round (Lost 2–1, Sunderland)

1961–62 – Fourth Round (Lost 1–0, Manchester United)

1962–63 – Fifth Round (Lost 2–1, Liverpool)

1963–64 – Fifth Round (Lost 1–0, Liverpool)

1964–65 – Fourth Round (Lost 2–1, Peterborough United)

1965–66 – Third Round (Lost 3–0, Blackburn Rovers)

1966–67 – Fifth Round (Lost 1–0, Birmingham City)

1967–68 – Fifth Round (Lost 2–1, Birmingham City)

1968–69 – Fifth Round (Lost 1–0, West Bromwich Albion)

1969–70 – Third Round (Lost 3–2 Blackpool)

1970–71 – Winners (Won 2–1 aet, Liverpool)

1971–72 – Runners-Up (Lost 1–0, Leeds United)

1972–73 – Semi-Finals (Lost 2–1, Sunderland)

1973–74 – Fourth Round (Lost 2–0, Aston Villa)

1974–75 – Quarter-Finals (Lost 2–0, West Ham United)

1975–76 – Third Round (Lost 3–0, Wolverhampton Wanderers)

1976–77 – Fifth Round (Lost 4–1, Middlesbrough)

1977–78 – Runners-Up (Lost 1–0, Ipswich Town)

1978–79 – Winners (Won 3–2, Manchester United)

1979–80 – Runners-Up (Lost 1–0, West Ham United)

Other Domestic Cup Competitions

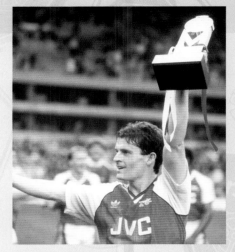

BARBOUR'S FINAL BRACE

Before turning professional in 1891, the amateurs of Arsenal used to compete in the Kent Senior Cup and won the inaugural competition in 1890. The Gunners faced Thanet Wanderers in March and claimed the trophy courtesy of goals from Humphrey Barbour (2) and Harry Offer.

Two weeks later Arsenal were celebrating more cup glory after beating Old Westminsters 3–1 in the final of the London Charity Cup, a competition that was finally disbanded in 1975, with the goals coming from Offer, W.E. Fry and Albert Christmas.

 EMIRATES EXCELLENCE

Since 2007 Arsenal have been fine-tuning their preparations for each new campaign at the two-day-long Emirates Cup and the Gunners have lifted the trophy three times in five attempts.

The side's first success was in 2007 when victories over Paris Saint-Germain and Inter Milan gave them the silverware and they were victorious once again in 2009 after beating Rangers and Atletico Madrid. Arsenal made it a hat-trick of wins 12 months later after drawing with AC Milan and overcoming Rangers.

The team's biggest victory since the start of the Emirates Cup came in 2009 when goals from Jack Wilshere (2) and Croatia striker Eduardo gave Arsene Wenger's side a 3–0 win. There was no Emirates Cup in 2012 as it clashed with the London Olympics.

CAPITAL CUP

Although the Club no longer enters a side, Arsenal were crowned the London Senior Cup champions back in 1891 after beating a St Bartholomew's Hospital XI 6–0 in the final.

The Gunners had lost to Old Westminsters in the final 12 months earlier – their only other appearance in the showpiece – but made amends against Bartholomew's with the goals coming from David Gloak, Humphrey Barbour (2), Harry Offer, Peter Connolly and W.E. Fry.

ABOVE: The Gunners were triumphant over Manchester United at Villa Park in 1988.

▲ **CENTENARY CELEBRATIONS**

The Mercantile Credit Centenary Trophy was a one-off tournament staged in 1988 to celebrate the centenary of the Football League. After battling through to the final, Arsenal became champions by beating Manchester United 2–1 in front of 22,182 supporters at Villa Park.

George Graham's side overcame Queens Park Rangers 2–0 in the quarter-finals before knocking out Liverpool 2–1 in the last four.

The final between two of the heavyweights of English football saw Paul Davis and Michael Thomas on target for the Gunners while Clayton Blackmore scored for United.

BELOW: Jack Wilshere in action against Rangers in Emirates Cup in 2009.

THE NEXT GENERATION

Arsenal are the second most successful side in the history of the FA Youth Cup, lifting the trophy a total of seven times since its inception in 1953.

The Gunners' Under-18 side first won the competition in 1966 after beating Sunderland 5–2 on aggregate over two legs – with a team that featured future Arsenal legend Pat Rice.

Five years later the team were champions again after a 2–0 triumph against Norwich City and the trophy returned to Highbury in 1988, 1994, 2000 and 2001.

The Club's most recent success came in 2009 when a young Arsenal side demolished Liverpool 6–2 over two games.

The Gunners' most comprehensive aggregate success, however, was in 2001 when the team, including Jack Wilshere and Emmanuel Frimpong, overcame Blackburn Rovers 6–3 on aggregate, winning the first leg at home 5–0 before a 3–1 defeat in the return game.

▼ CITY DEMOLISHED

The Community Shield, the traditional season-opening game between the top-flight league and FA Cup winners, has seen Arsenal lift the trophy 11 times outright, as well as sharing the silverware in 1991 with Tottenham after a goalless draw at Wembley.

The side's biggest victory in the competition, however, came in 1934 when the Gunners faced Manchester City at Highbury, tearing the visitors' defence to shreds with goals from Ralph Birkett, Jimmy Marshall, Ted Drake and Cliff Bastin in a 4–0 triumph.

Fourteen years later Arsenal were in Community Shield action once again, beating Manchester United 4–3 at Highbury thanks to a brace from Reg Lewis to register the Club's biggest aggregate score in the competition.

BELOW: Cliff Bastin's Arsenal career spanned 17 glorious years during which he scored 178 goals.

RIGHT: The Club's young players have lifted the FA Youth Cup seven times.

ARSENAL'S FA CUP RECORD 1980–2013

1980–81 – Third Round (Lost 2–0, Everton)
1981–82 – Third Round (Lost 1–0, Tottenham Hotspur)
1982–83 – Semi-Finals (Lost 2–1, Manchester United)
1983–84 – Third Round (Lost 3–2, Middlesbrough)
1984–85 – Fourth Round (Lost 1–0, York City)
1985–86 – Fifth Round (Lost 3–0, Luton Town)
1986–87 – Quarter-Finals (Lost 3–1, Watford)
1987–88 – Quarter-Finals (Lost 2–1, Nottingham Forest)
1988–89 – Third Round (Lost 1–0, West Ham United)
1989–90 – Fourth Round (Lost 2–0, QPR)
1990–91 – Semi-Finals (Lost 3–1, Tottenham Hotspur)
1991–92 – Third Round (Lost 2–1, Wrexham)
1992–93 – Winners (Won 2–1 aet, Sheffield Wednesday)
1993–94 – Fourth Round (Lost 3–1 aet, Bolton Wanderers)
1994–95 – Third Round (Lost 2–0, Millwall)
1995–96 – Third Round (Lost 1–0, Sheffield United)
1996–97 – Fourth Round (Lost 1–0, Leeds United)
1997–98 – Winners (Won 2–0, Newcastle United)
1998–99 – Semi-Finals (Lost 2–1, Manchester United)
1999–2000 – Fourth Round (Lost 6–5 on penalties, Leicester City)
2000–01 – Runners-Up (Lost 2–1, Liverpool)
2001–02 – Winners (Won 2–0, Chelsea)
2002–03 – Winners (Won 1–0, Southampton)
2003–04 – Semi-Finals (Lost 1–0, Manchester United)
2004–05 – Winners (Won 5–4 on penalties, Manchester United)
2005–06 – Fourth Round (Lost 1–0, Bolton Wanderers)
2006–07 – Fifth Round (Lost 1–0, Blackburn Rovers)
2007–08 – Fifth Round (Lost 4–0, Manchester United)
2008–09 – Semi-Finals (Lost 2–1, Chelsea)
2009–10 – Fourth Round (Lost 3–1, Stoke City)
2010–11 – Quarter-Finals (Lost 2–0, Manchester United)
2011–12 – Fifth Round (Lost 2–0, Sunderland)
2012–13 – Fifth Round (Lost 1–0, Blackburn Rovers)

FA Cup & League Cup Records – Miscellaneous

ABOVE: Robert Pires was a seven-time winner for Arsenal.

▲ SEVEN WINNER'S MEDALS

Arsenal legend Robert Pires won an amazing seven winners' medals during his stay with the Gunners. The France midfielder won three FA Cups (2002, 2003 and 2005) and two FA Community Shields (2002 and 2004) as well as his two Premier League winner's medals in 2001–02 and 2003–04.

O'LEARY'S CUP MILESTONE

Irishman David O'Leary holds the Arsenal Club record for appearances in both the FA Cup and League Cup, playing 70 times in each competition.

The centre-half made his League Cup debut in September 1975 in a 2–2 draw with Everton at Goodison and sampled the FA Cup for the first time four months later as part of the Gunners side beaten 3–0 by Wolverhampton Wanderers at Molineux.

During his 18-year Highbury career, O'Leary won the FA Cup twice and the League Cup twice.

▼ CUP DOUBLE

Arsenal made history in 1993 when they became the first Club ever to claim an FA Cup and League Cup double, beating Sheffield Wednesday in both finals.

The first instalment of the famous feat came in mid-April when the Gunners beat the Owls 2–1 at Wembley in the League Cup final courtesy of goals from Paul Merson and Steve Morrow. The two sides were back in north London a month later for the FA Cup final rematch.

The game went into extra-time after Ian Wright had opened the scoring only for David Hirst to equalize after the break and, with neither side able to make the breakthrough in the additional 30 minutes of play, a replay was required. Five days later they reconvened at Wembley.

Wright again opened the scoring, Wednesday again levelled in the second half (through Chris Waddle) and the game again headed into extra-time. But this time George Graham's side did score as Andy Linighan hit the winner in the penultimate minute and the Gunners had completed an unprecedented cup double.

LEFT: Andy Linighan heads the winning goal in the 1993 FA Cup final replay against Sheffield Wednesday.

CUP MARATHON

1979–80 saw Arsenal playing 18 times in the FA Cup and League Cup.

The Club played seven times to lose in the fifth round of the League Cup then added 11 fixtures in the FA Cup where they needed a replay to get past Cardiff City then two games to knock out Bolton. But it was the epic semi-final with Liverpool that really ratcheted up the number of games.

The first meeting finished goalless while the first and second replays ended 1–1 and it was only Brian Talbot's goal in the fourth meeting that could separate the two teams.

The Gunners lost the resulting final 1–0 to West Ham, the 18th domestic cup game in what was a record-breaking campaign.

MADJESKI MASSACRE

Arsenal's incredible 7–5 victory over Reading in the last 16 of the 2012–13 League Cup was the highest aggregate score in the history of the competition.

The record-breaking meeting in October saw the Gunners leak four unanswered goals in the first half before Theo Walcott scored to spark an unbelievable fightback just before the break.

Arsene Wenger's side emerged for the second half transformed and further strikes from Olivier Giroud, Laurent Koscielny and a last-minute second from Walcott levelled the scores at 4–4 and sent the match into extra-time.

Marouane Chamakh made it 5–4 before Reading rallied with a Pavel Pogrebnyak equalizer. But the drama was far from over, as Walcott and Chamakh both scored in the last minute to seal an improbable and record-breaking 7–5 triumph.

ARSENAL'S LEAGUE CUP RECORD 1966–2013

1966–67 – Third Round (Lost 3–1, West Ham United)
1967–68 – Runners-Up (Lost 1–0, Leeds United)
1968–69 – Runners-Up (Lost 3–1 aet, Swindon Town)
1969–70 – Third Round (Lost 1–0, Everton)
1970–71 – Fourth Round (Lost 2–0, Crystal Palace)
1971–72 – Fourth Round (Lost 2–0, Sheffield United)
1972–73 – Quarter-Finals (Lost 3–0, Norwich City)
1973–74 – Second Round (Lost 1–0, Tranmere Rovers)
1974–75 – Second Round (Lost 2–1 Leicester City)
1975–76 – Second Round (Lost 1–0, Everton)
1976–77 – Quarter-Finals (Lost 4–1, Middlesbrough)
1977–78 – Semi-Finals (Lost 2–1 on aggregate, Liverpool)
1978–79 – Second Round (Lost 3–1, Rotherham United)
1979–80 – Quarter-Finals (Lost 4–3, Swindon Town)
1980–81 – Fourth Round (Lost 1–0, Tottenham Hotspur)
1981–82 – Fourth Round (Lost 3–0, Liverpool)
1982–83 – Semi-Finals (Lost 6–3 on aggregate, Manchester United)
1983–84 – Fourth Round (Lost 2–1, Walsall)
1984–85 – Third Round (Lost 3–2, Oxford United)
1985–86 – Quarter-Finals (Lost 2–1, Aston Villa)
1986–87 – Winners (Won 2–1, Liverpool)
1987–88 – Runners-Up (Lost 3–2, Luton Town)
1988–89 – Third Round (Lost 3–1, Liverpool)
1989–90 – Fourth Round (Lost 3–1, Oldham Athletic)
1990–91 – Fourth Round (Lost 6–2, Manchester United)
1991–92 – Third Round (Lost 1–0, Coventry City)

1992–93 – Winners (Won 2–1, Sheffield Wednesday)
1993–94 – Fourth Round (Lost 1–0, Aston Villa)
1994–95 – Quarter-Finals (Lost 1–0, Liverpool)
1995–96 – Semi-Finals (Lost on away goals after 2–2 aggregate draw, Aston Villa)
1996–97 – Fourth Round (Lost 4–2, Liverpool)
1997–98 – Semi-Finals (Lost 4–3 on aggregate, Chelsea)
1998–99 – Fourth Round (Lost 5–0, Chelsea)
1999–2000 – Fourth Round (Lost 3–1 on penalties, Middlesbrough)
2000–01 – Third Round (Lost 2–1, Ipswich Town)
2001–02 – Quarter-Finals (Lost 4–0, Blackburn Rovers)
2002–03 – Third Round (Lost 3–2, Sunderland)
2003–04 – Semi-Finals (Lost 3–1 on aggregate, Middlesbrough)
2004–05 – Quarter-Finals (Lost 1–0, Manchester United)
2005–06 – Semi-Finals (Lost on away goals after 2–2 aggregate draw, Wigan Athletic)
2006–07 – Runners-Up (Lost 2–1 aet, Chelsea)
2007–08 – Semi-Finals (Lost 6–2 on aggregate, Tottenham Hotspur)
2008–09 – Quarter-Finals (Lost 2–0, Burnley)
2009–10 – Quarter-Finals (Lost 3–0, Manchester City)
2010–11 – Runners-Up (Lost 2–1, Birmingham City)
2011–12 – Fifth Round (Lost 1–0, Manchester City)
2012–13 – Quarter-Finals (Lost 3–2 on penalties, Bradford City)

FIVE-GOAL THRILLER

The League Cup abandoned its old two-legged format for the final in the 1966–67 season. Since the showpiece game became a one-off affair, Arsenal jointly hold the record for the highest aggregate scoreline.

They equalled the record in 1988 when they played Luton Town at Wembley. Brian Stein gave the Hatters a shock early lead but second-half goals from Martin Hayes and Alan Smith appeared to give the Gunners the upper hand – only for Danny Wilson and Stein again in the final minute to snatch a dramatic 3–2 victory.

The five-goal tally equalled the record set in the finals of 1967 and 1979, as well as the 1977 replay.

BELOW: Martin Hayes scores for the Gunners to draw level with Luton Town in the 1988 League Cup final. The game did not go the Gunners' way however, as Luton snatched a late winner.

RIGHT: Herbert Chapman, seen here in his playing days at Northampton Town, led Arsenal to their highest-ever winning scoreline in the FA Cup, 11–1 against Darwen in 1932.

HAT-TRICK DOUBLE

The Gunners' biggest-ever win (12–0) in the FA Cup came against Ashford United in 1893 in the first qualifying round but the Club's heaviest victory in the competition proper came in January 1932 when they played Lancashire side Darwen.

The first-round clash at Highbury was nothing if not one-sided and, thanks to four goals from Cliff Bastin and a David Jack hat-trick, Herbert Chapman's side raced to a crushing 11–1 victory.

European Records

The Gunners first experienced European football during the 1963–64 season when they played in the Inter-Cities Fairs Cup and since that debut the Club has been a regular in Continental competition. This section is dedicated to all of Arsenal's greatest European achievements, as well as some of the team's inevitable disappointments.

BELOW: The Gunners famously lifted the UEFA Cup Winners' Cup in 1994.

RIGHT: Alan Smith celebrates after scoring the winner in the final against Parma in Copenhagen.

European Records –
Biggest Wins

WRIGHT'S SEVEN-GOAL SALVO

Arsenal's first-ever competitive match in Europe was also one of the Club's biggest-ever wins.

The match came away from home against Danish side Stævnet in September 1963 in the first round of the Inter-Cities Fairs Cup, a forerunner of the UEFA Cup, and produced eight goals.

Billy Wright's side scored seven of them courtesy of hat-tricks from Geoff Strong and Joe Baker ... and the Gunners' European history had begun.

▼ PRAGUE'S EMIRATES EMBARRASSMENT

The Gunners have enjoyed some glorious European nights at Emirates but perhaps none more memorable than their clash with Slavia Prague in the group stages of the Champions League in October 2007. Arsenal were irresistible going forward, slicing through the Czech defence at will for a European Club-record 7–0 victory.

The writing was on the wall for the visitors after just five minutes when Cesc Fabregas hit a superb curling shot from the edge of the area and things went from bad to worse for Slavia midway through the first half when David Hubacek inadvertently poked the ball into his own net.

Theo Walcott made it 3–0 to Arsene Wenger's side before the break and the match was already over. The Gunners, however, were far from finished and the 60,000-strong crowd were treated to four more goals in the second half as Alexander Hleb, Walcott, Fabregas and Nicklas Bendtner piled on the misery.

▼ SUPERB IN THE SAN SIRO

Arsenal's biggest win away from home in the Champions League came in the group stages of the 2003–04 competition, a magnificent 5–1 triumph over Inter Milan at the San Siro on 25 November 2003.

The Italian giants had beaten the Gunners 3–0 at Highbury two months earlier and Arsene Wenger's team clearly had revenge on their minds.

Thierry Henry began the rout midway through the first half. Christian Vieri briefly equalized for the Italians before Freddie Ljungberg restored the advantage and Henry made it three with a stunning individual effort.

In the 86th minute, Edu grabbed the fourth and Robert Pires rubbed salt into the wound in injury-time with the fifth.

ABOVE RIGHT: Henry was twice on target as Inter Milan were humbled in the San Siro.

RIGHT: Walcott ripped the Slavia defence to shreds in the 2007–08 Champions League.

RIGHT: It was seventh heaven for Arsenal as they demolished Standard Liege in Belgium in 1993.

▶ SEVEN IN BELGIUM

The 7–0 annihilation of Slavia Prague is Arsenal's biggest Champions League win and equalled the Club's previous record European success, a 7–0 demolition of Standard Liege in the 1993–94 Cup Winners' Cup.

The Gunners qualified for the competition after their win over Sheffield Wednesday in the replay of the 1993 FA Cup final and lined up against the Belgians in the second leg of their second-round clash in the wake of a 3–0 victory in the first match.

Manager George Graham rested striker Ian Wright, one booking away from a suspension, but his side were no less potent in attack in the Stade Maurice Dufrasne, scoring seven unanswered goals on Belgian soil.

The 7–0 win was set up as early as the third minute when Alan Smith converted Paul Merson's inviting cross. Tony Adams, Ian Selley, Kevin Campbell (2), Merson and substitute Eddie McGoldrick all helped themselves and Arsenal went through to the third round with a 10–0 aggregate scoreline.

The victory clearly had a morale-boosting effect and the Gunners went on to win the Cup Winners' Cup after beating Parma in the final.

ARSENAL'S CHAMPIONS LEAGUE RECORD

1998–99 – Group Stage
1999–2000 – First Group Stage
2000–01 – Quarter-Finals (Lost on away goals after 2–2 aggregate draw, Valencia)
2001–02 – Second Group Stage
2002–03 – Second Group Stage
2003–04 – Quarter-Finals (Lost 3–2 on aggregate, Chelsea)
2004–05 – Last 16 (Lost 3–2 on aggregate, Bayern Munich)
2005–06 – Runners-Up (Lost 2–1, Barcelona)
2006–07 – Last 16 (Lost 2–1 on aggregate, PSV Eindhoven)
2007–08 – Quarter-Finals (Lost 4–3 on aggregate, Liverpool)
2008–09 – Semi-Finals (Lost 4–1 on aggregate, Manchester United)
2009–10 – Last 16 (Lost 6–3 on aggregate, Barcelona)
2010–11 – Last 16 (Lost 4–3 on aggregate, Barcelona)
2011–12 – Last 16 (Lost 4–3 on aggregate, AC Milan)
2012–13 – Last 16 (Lost on away goals after 3–3 aggregate draw, Bayern Munich)

◀ DEPORTIVO CRUSHED

Spain is the most successful European country in terms of trophies won, but the Gunners have claimed a Spanish scalp 10 times in the Club's history.

The team's most emphatic victory over La Liga opposition was in March 2000 when Deportivo La Coruna came to Highbury for the first leg of a UEFA Cup fourth-round clash.

Arsene Wenger gambled by leaving Tony Adams, Ray Parlour and Kanu on the bench. But his side still proved too powerful for the Spanish visitors as Lee Dixon, Thierry Henry (2), Kanu from the bench and Dennis Bergkamp all scored in a 5–1 romp.

WEMBLEY ADVENTURE

Between 1998 and 2000 Arsenal relocated to Wembley. When they qualified for the Champions League for the first time, during their temporary residency at the home of English football, their biggest win came against Swedish side AIK.

The two teams met in the group stages in September 1999 and Freddie Ljungberg opened the scoring after 28 minutes. The visitors equalized but the Gunners registered a record 3–1 Wembley win courtesy of injury-time goals from Thierry Henry and Davor Suker.

LEFT: Lee Dixon was on the score sheet as Spanish side Deportivo La Coruna were thumped 5–1 at Highbury in 2000.

European Records – Biggest Defeats

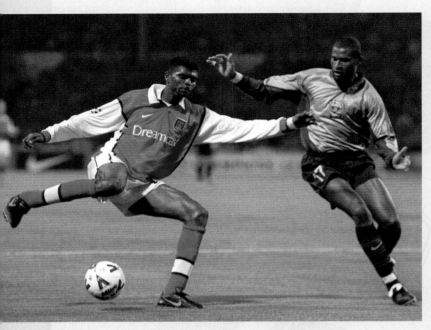

ABOVE: The Gunners were far from their best against Barcelona at Wembley in October 1999.

FOUR UP FOR BARCELONA

Arsenal relocated to Wembley for European nights during the 1989–99 and 1999–2000 seasons and in the six games they played at the home of the England team, the Gunners were beaten three times. The worst defeat was a 4–2 loss to Barcelona in the group phases in October 1999.

Rivaldo and Luis Enrique put the Spanish ahead and although Dennis Bergkamp pulled one back before half-time, Barcelona stretched their lead through Luis Figo and Phillip Cocu after the break and Marc Overmars' 84th-minute strike was no more than a consolation.

ITALIAN WOE

Arsenal played three seasons in the old Cup Winners' Cup, lifting the trophy in 1994 and finishing as runners-up in 1980 and 1995. In total the side lost just twice in the now defunct tournament, suffering their biggest defeat – a 3–2 reverse – against Sampdoria in Italy at the semi-final stage in April 1995.

MILAN HIT FOUR

Arsenal were beaten just twice in the Champions League during the 2011–12 campaign and the second of those defeats proved to be the Gunners' heaviest loss in the revamped competition.

The opposition were Italian giants AC Milan at the San Siro in February in the last 16 of the tournament. Arsene Wenger's side found themselves trailing after just 15 minutes when Kevin-Prince Boateng struck a superb long-range effort. A brace from Brazilian Robinho either side of half-time did further damage while a late penalty from Swedish striker Zlatan Ibrahimovic condemned Arsenal to a 4–0 defeat and their biggest-ever Champions League failure.

The Gunners took revenge three weeks later in the second leg at Highbury with a 3–0 triumph – but it was not enough to earn the side a quarter-final place.

LEFT: AC Milan were too strong for Arsene Wenger's side in Italy in February 2012.

PORTUGUESE PITFALL

Before the introduction of the Champions League in 1992–93, Arsenal enjoyed two seasons of European Cup football, in 1971–72 and then again in 1991–92. In 10 fixtures, the team was beaten four times and the heaviest of those was a 3–1 extra time loss to Portuguese side Benfica at Highbury in November 1991.

INTER-CITIES DISAPPOINTMENT

Arsenal's first three seasons of European football came in the Inter-Cities Fairs Cup and in 24 outings in the competition, they suffered defeat just six times.

The team's debut campaign in 1963–64 saw Billy Wright's team beaten 3–1 by Standard Liege seven days before Christmas and the Gunners equalled that record Inter-Cities reverse during their 1969–70 campaign, losing 3–1 to Anderlecht in April.

SPARTAK SMASH GUNNERS

The Club's largest loss in any competitive European match came in the UEFA Cup in 1982–83. Arsenal faced Spartak Moscow at Highbury in September and, having lost the first leg in Russia a fortnight earlier, Terry Neill's team desperately needed to win the rematch.

Unfortunately things didn't go according to plan as the visitors smashed five goals past goalkeeper George Wood. Lee Chapman and a Spartak own-goal briefly gave the Highbury faithful something to cheer, but at full-time the Gunners had been beaten 5–2.

► IRRESISTIBLE INTER

The Gunners' biggest reverse at home in the Champions League also came against a team from Milan but this time it was Inter who inflicted it.

The game at Emirates came in September 2003 in the opening fixture of the group stages and the home side found themselves on the back foot on 22 minutes when Julio Ricardo Cruz opened the scoring.

Three minutes later Andy van der Meyde doubled the advantage and when Thierry Henry had a penalty superbly saved by Francesco Toldo, the writing was on the wall. Obafemi Martins added Inter Milan's third before the break and, although there were no further goals in the second half, the Gunners crashed to their biggest home defeat in the competition.

RIGHT: Messi singlehandedly knocked Arsenal out of the 2009–10 Champions League.

► MESSI MAULS ARSENAL

The Gunners reached the knockout stages of the Champions League for a fourth successive season in 2009–10 but their involvement in the tournament came to an unceremonious end after they were beaten 4–1 by Barcelona in the Nou Camp.

The two teams locked horns in Spain just six days after a 2–2 draw at Emirates in the first leg of their quarter-final encounter and when Nicklas Bendtner scored, after just 18 minutes, Arsenal were dreaming of a place in the last four.

They hadn't, however, reckoned with the genius of Lionel Messi who transformed the tie with a first-half hat-trick and a fourth after the break to seal a 4–1 triumph and condemn the Gunners to their worst loss in the knockout stages of the Champions League.

BELOW: Freddie Ljungberg was unable to stop the Gunners losing 3–0 to Inter at Highbury in 2003.

ARSENAL'S EUROPEAN CUP RECORD

1971–72 – Quarter-Finals (Lost 3–1 on aggregate, Ajax)

1991–92 – Second Round (Lost 4–2 on aggregate, Benfica)

European Records – Champions

▶ MEE MAKES HISTORY

Arsenal's first taste of European glory came in the 1969–70 season when Bertie Mee's side entered the Inter-Cities Fairs Cup and, despite their inexperience of Continental football and a side exclusively featuring English and Scottish players, battled through all the way to the final.

The Gunners had little problem despatching Irish opponents Glentoran 3–1 on aggregate in the first round and a 3–0 victory over two games against Portuguese side Sporting Lisbon, next up, eased the team into round three.

French club Rouen stood in the way of a place in the quarter-finals and, after a goalless draw in the first leg at Highbury, Arsenal were heavily indebted to a goal from Jon Sammels at the Stade Robert Diochon in January to ease the team into the last eight.

Romanian side FCM Bacau proved no match for the Gunners in the quarter-finals, losing 9–2 on aggregate, and in their debut campaign Mee's team found themselves in the semi-finals.

Ajax, who were to lift the European Cup just 12 months later, lined up against Arsenal in the last four but were swept aside in the first leg at Highbury as goals from Sammels and Charlie George (2) secured a priceless 3–0 win. The Dutch side exacted a degree of revenge in Amsterdam in the second leg with a 1–0 success seven days later but it was not enough to prevent the Gunners reaching the final.

Belgian club Anderlecht, 2–1 aggregate winners over Inter Milan in the semis, were the only remaining hurdle but Arsenal's prospects of silverware looked bleak after the first leg in the Constant Vanden Stock Stadium as the home side recorded a 3–1 victory. Ray Kennedy grabbed a late 82nd-minute consolation but the Gunners knew they still needed a vastly improved performance in the return match at Highbury.

An early goal to settle the nerves was top of the agenda in north London in late April and Eddie Kelly provided it after 25 minutes. John Radford levelled the tie on aggregate midway through the second half and just a minute later Sammels settled the issue with his sixth goal of the campaign.

Ajax had no reply and, 84 years after the Club was founded, Arsenal were lifting a European trophy.

RIGHT: Manager Bertie Mee secured Arsenal's first ever European trophy in 1970.

BELOW: George Armstrong celebrates Jon Sammels' winning goal against Anderlecht in the 1970 Inter Cities Fairs Cup final.

SMITH STRIKE SEALS SILVERWARE

The Gunners' triumph over Sheffield Wednesday in the 1993 FA Cup final at Wembley earned the Club a place in the Cup Winners' Cup the following season, the second time the Gunners had entered the competition.

The team were drawn against Danish side Odense in the first round. After a 2–1 victory in the first leg away from home courtesy of goals from Ian Wright and Paul Merson, George Graham's team ground out a 1–1 draw at Highbury to progress.

The second round saw the Gunners face Standard Liege but the Belgians were simply outclassed in both legs, losing 3–0 at Highbury before slumping to a one-sided 7–0 defeat at their Stade Maurice Dufrasne in early November as six different players got on the score sheet.

Italy's Torino were the quarter-final opponents and the Serie A outfit provided a far sterner test of Arsenal's credentials. The first leg in Turin finished goalless and the tie was only finally settled at Highbury when captain Tony Adams became an unlikely hero with the only goal of the match on 66 minutes.

The semi-final against Paris Saint-Germain was equally tense. A Wright goal earned the Gunners a 1–1 draw in Paris and, although Kevin Campbell was on target after just seven minutes at Highbury, Arsenal could not break down the PSG defence again and had to endure a nervous 83 minutes before the final whistle confirmed they were through to the final.

It was Italian opposition once again for Graham and his team in the shape of Parma, the defending champions. Joint top-scorer Wright was suspended for the match in the Parken Stadium in Copenhagen but the back four which had conceded just three times in the earlier rounds remained *in situ* for the Anglo-Italian clash.

There was to be just one goal in the game and it came after 22 minutes. Parma captain Lorenzo Minotti mis-hit a clearance which fell to Alan Smith, who unleashed an instinctive, deadly left-foot volley that beat Luca Bucci in goal. The Gunners' back four shackled the threat of Gianfranco Zola and Faustino Asprilla for the rest of the match, and after 90 minutes Adams was preparing to lift the Cup Winners' Cup for the first time in the Club's history.

ABOVE: Arsenal beat Parma to win the Cup Winners' Cup in 1994 and made their mark on European football.

LEFT: Alan Smith proudly lifts the Cup Winners' Cup after an historic night in Denmark.

ARSENAL'S UEFA CUP RECORD

1978–79 – Third Round (Lost 2–1 on aggregate, Red Star Belgrade)

1981–82 – Second Round (Lost on away goals after 2–2 aggregate draw, Genk)

1982–83 – First Round (Lost 8–4 on aggregate, Spartak Moscow)

1996–97 – First Round (Lost 6–4 on aggregate, Borussia Monchengladbach)

1997–98 – First Round (Lost 2–1 on aggregate, PAOK)

1999–00 – Runners-Up (Lost 4–1 on penalties, Galatasaray)

European Records – Sequences

▶ LEHMANN'S LONG RUN

Jens Lehmann is the proud holder of the Champions League record for the longest time a goalkeeper has gone without conceding a goal, going a unprecedented 853 minutes without picking the ball out of the back of the net between February 2005 and September 2006.

The German keeper's unbelievable streak began in the last 16 of the 2004–05 campaign. Arsenal were defeated 3–1 by Bayern Munich away from home, with Lehmann beaten by Hasan Silihamidzic for the third goal in the 65th minute in the Olympiastadion but it was to be 20 months before another player scored against him.

Lehmann kept a clean sheet in the second leg against the Germans and, after missing the opening two group phase games in 2005–06, he returned to the side and successfully kept Sparta Prague, Real Madrid, Juventus and Villarreal at bay as Arsenal reached the final.

Arsene Wenger's side conceded two in the final against Barcelona but both goals came after the German had been sent off in the 18th minute for bringing down Samuel Eto'o – and so, albeit in bizarre circumstances, his unbeaten sequence continued.

He was finally beaten in the opening game of 2006–07 when Boubacar Sanogo scored a 90th minute consolation goal for Hamburg at the Imtech Arena, ending 853 minutes of glorious goalkeeping.

Lehmann's achievement eclipsed the previous record of 658 minutes set by Edwin van der Sar when he was an Ajax player in the 1990s.

▶ EUROPEAN EXILE

Following the Club's first foray into European football during the 1963–64 season in the Inter-Cities Fairs Cup, Arsenal's longest absence from European competition came in the 1970s when the Gunners spent six seasons reluctantly concentrating solely on domestic matters.

The side was eliminated from the European Cup at the quarter-final stage by Ajax on 22 March 1972 and did not feature in a UEFA tournament again until they lined up against Lokomotive Leipzig on 13 September 1978 in the first round of the UEFA Cup.

There was a nine-year exile from European action between 1982 and 1991 but six years of that absence were due to the ban on English clubs following the Heysel Stadium disaster.

ABOVE: Jens Lehmann went more than 14 hours without conceding a Champions League goal.

BELOW: Alan Sunderland in action against Lokomotive Leipzig in the 1978–79 UEFA Cup campaign.

CLEAN SHEET RECORD

The Gunners hold the Champions League record for the most consecutive clean sheets in the competition, going an amazing 10 matches during the 2005–06 campaign without allowing the opposition to score.

The miserly defensive streak started on 18 October 2005 in the third game of the group phase when Arsenal travelled to the Czech Republic to face Sparta Prague and returned to London with a 2–0 triumph.

The remaining three group games saw Sparta beaten 3–0 at Highbury, Swiss side FC Thun 1–0 away from home and Ajax held goalless in north London.

Real Madrid failed to breach the Gunners' defence in either leg of their last-16 meeting, as did Juventus in two quarter-finals clashes. Villarreal also fired blanks home and away in the semi-finals and it was not until the 76th minute of the final against Barcelona, when Samuel Eto'o scored, that Arsene Wenger's side finally conceded.

Before Eto'o, the last player to score against the team in the Champions League was Ajax's Markus Rosenberg in the 71st minute of the group game in September, meaning Arsenal had gone 995 minutes without conceding.

AC Milan had held the previous record, registering seven consecutive clean sheets in the 2004–05 season.

▶ UEFA CUP MILESTONE

Arsenal finished UEFA Cup runners-up in 2000 and it is no surprise that the team's longest unbeaten run in open play in the competition came en route to the final.

The sequence began with a 2–0 quarter-final, first-leg defeat of Werder Bremen at Highbury. The Germans were despatched 4–2 in the return match while Lens were beaten home and away in the semi-final.

The final in Copenhagen saw the Gunners face Galatasaray and, although it was the Turkish team who lifted the trophy, they only did so after beating Arsene Wenger's side in a penalty shootout, meaning Arsenal had still set a Club record of five UEFA Cup fixtures without defeat in open play.

ABOVE: Liam Brady surges forward in the European Cup Winners' Cup against Valencia in 1980. On this occasion, the Gunners succumbed to a penalty shootout.

▲ UNBOWED IN EUROPE

Arsenal had a real affinity with the UEFA Cup Winners' Cup – winning the competition once and twice finishing as runners-up – and between September 1979 and April 1995 the Club went an incredible 25 games in the tournament without suffering defeat in open play.

The remarkable streak began in September in the 1979–80 season with a 2–0 first-round, first-leg victory against Turkish side Fenerbahce at Highbury, and the side marched all the way to the final without loss. They were eventually beaten in a dreaded penalty shootout by Valencia but their unbeaten record inside 120 minutes remained intact.

The Gunners were back in Cup Winners' Cup action in 1993–94 and lifted the trophy without being beaten, extending the sequence to 18 games.

The 1994–95 campaign saw Arsenal reach the semi-finals with four wins and two draws and the run reached a phenomenal 25 matches when they overcame Sampdoria 3–2 in the first leg of their last-four encounter at Highbury.

It was finally ended in the second leg a fortnight later when the Italians emerged 3–2 winners in the Stadio Luigi Ferraris in Genoa, although Arsenal still reached the final after overcoming the home side in a penalty shootout.

BELOW: Thierry Henry and the Gunners were in impressive form during their 1999–2000 UEFA Cup campaign.

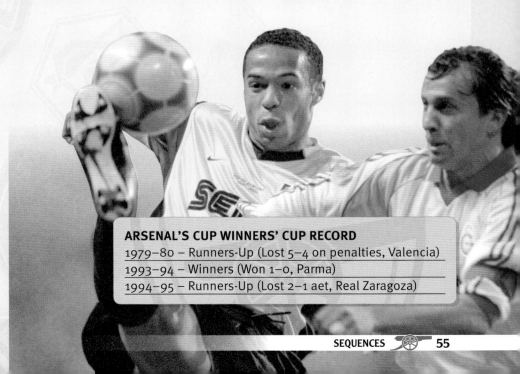

ARSENAL'S CUP WINNERS' CUP RECORD

1979–80 – Runners-Up (Lost 5–4 on penalties, Valencia)	
1993–94 – Winners (Won 1–0, Parma)	
1994–95 – Runners-Up (Lost 2–1 aet, Real Zaragoza)	

European Records – Miscellaneous

RECORD EIGHT VICTORIES

The Gunners won eight matches en route to the 2006 Champions League final, equalling the previous Club record of eight victories in a European campaign, set in 1969–70 when they won the Inter-Cities Fairs Cup.

In terms of a winning percentage, their feat of 1969–70 was the more impressive, with eight wins in 12 games compared to eight in 13 fixtures in 2005–06.

DEADLY CHAMAKH

Only one player has ever scored in six successive Champions League fixtures – Arsenal's Moroccan international Marouane Chamakh.

The striker began his prolific streak as a Bordeaux player, finding the back of the net against Olympiacos and Lyon twice in the knockout stages of the 2009–10 competition.

He signed for Arsenal on a free transfer in the summer of 2010 and continued his deadly form for the Gunners in the group phase of the 2010–11 tournament, netting in successive games against Braga, Partizan Belgrade and Shakhtar Donetsk.

ABOVE: John Lukic rolled back the years in Arsenal's 1–1 draw with Lazio at the Stadio Olimpico.

LUKIC AGAINST LAZIO

The oldest player to represent the Club in a competitive European fixture is goalkeeper John Lukic, who was 39 years and 311 days old when he was named in the starting XI for Arsenal's Champions League clash with Lazio in October 2000.

BELOW: Marouane Chamakh enjoyed a fine run in front of goal in 2010.

NATIONAL PRIDE

Arsenal have faced opposition from 24 different countries in their European history and have never suffered defeat against sides from 10 of those nations.

Teams from Croatia, Cyprus, the Czech Republic, Norway, Romania, Scotland, Serbia, Sweden, Switzerland and Turkey have all tried to beat the Gunners over the years in a total of 37 games ... without success.

FANTASTIC BACK FOUR

The foundations of the Gunners' progress to the final of the 2006 Champions League were built on a superb defensive effort, and the four goals Arsene Wenger's side conceded that season represent the Club's lowest tally ever in the competition.

Arsenal played 13 Champions League games in 2005–06 but only FC Thun and Ajax in the group phase and Barcelona in the final itself were able to find a way through the Gunners' back four.

► BENDTNER ON TARGET

Although they were eliminated by Barcelona at the quarter-final stage, the 2009–10 season was Arsenal's most prolific ever, with the side scoring 26 goals in 12 matches.

The Gunners racked up five in their aggregate victory over Celtic in the third qualifying round, and scored 12 more in finishing top of Group H. Their 6–2 demolition of Porto in the last 16 added to the tally and, although they were knocked out by Barcelona in the last eight, they still managed three over two legs against the reigning Spanish champions.

The goals were evenly shared among the squad. Nicklas Bendtner top-scored with five, Cesc Fabregas weighed in with four while Samir Nasri registered a treble. In total, 13 different Arsenal players found the back of the net during the campaign.

RIGHT: Nicklas Bendtner was the Gunners' top scorer in the 2009–10 Champions League with five goals.

► MARVELLOUS MACLEOD

The 1963–64 season saw Arsenal venture into Europe for the first time and their first match was against Danish side Stævnet in Copenhagen in the first round of the Inter-Cities Fairs Cup.

The Gunners triumphed 7–1 and, while Geoff Strong and Joe Baker made the headlines with a hat-trick apiece, it was Johnny MacLeod, a £400,000 signing from Hibernian, who made history with the Club's first-ever goal in a competitive European fixture.

Almost a month later winger Alan Skirton joined MacLeod in the record books when he became the first Gunner to score a European goal at Highbury as the side despatched Stævnet in the return leg.

ABOVE: Johnny MacLeod scored the Club's first ever goal in Europe in the 1963–64 season.

TEENAGER WILSHERE SETS NEW MARK

The youngest-ever player to feature for Arsenal in a European match was Jack Wilshere when he was named in the squad for the Champions League group stage clash with Dynamo Kiev at Emirates in November 2008.

The England midfielder started on the bench but was introduced to the action after 77 minutes in place of Carlos Vela, becoming the youngest European Gunner at the age of 16 years and 329 days.

It was only Wilshere's fourth appearance for the first team and broke the previous record set by Cesc Fabregas.

ARSENAL'S INTER-CITIES FAIRS CUP RECORD

1963–64 – Second Round (Lost 4–2 on aggregate, RFC de Liege)

1969–70 – Winners (Won 4–3 on aggregate, Anderlecht)

1970–71 – Quarter-Finals ((Lost on away goals after 2–2 aggregate draw, Cologne)

LONDON LANDMARK

When the Gunners beat Villarreal 1–0 on aggregate in the last four of the Champions League in 2006, they became the first Club from the capital to reach the final of European football's leading competition.

Tottenham had made the last four of the old European Cup in 1962 only to lose to Benfica 4–2 on aggregate, while Chelsea reached the semi-finals of the Champions League in 2004 and 2005, but it was Arsenal who set the record as the first London team to progress all the way to the final.

EMIRATES OPENER

Arsenal played their first competitive European match at Emirates in August 2007 when they faced Croatian side Dinamo Zagreb in the third qualifying round of the Champions League.

The Gunners were already 3–0 up following the first leg two weeks earlier, and they ran out 2–1 winners in north London to book their place in the group stages.

Freddie Ljungberg on 79 minutes and Mathieu Flamini in the final minute of the game were on target for Arsene Wenger's side, making Ljungberg the Gunners' first player to score a European goal at Emirates.

◀ KNOCKOUT SUCCESS

Arsenal's 2–0 victory over Montpellier at Emirates in November 2012 confirmed the team's place in the knockout stages of the 2012–13 Champions League, the 13th season in succession the Gunners had successfully got beyond the first group phase of the competition.

Only Real Madrid can boast a more impressive record, with 16 consecutive appearances in the knockout phase – making Arsenal English football's most consistent side in the tournament.

LEFT: Jack Wilshere was on target for the Gunners against Montpellier at Emirates in 2012.

▶ OVERMARS' EUROPEAN OPENER

Netherlands winger Marc Overmars holds the distinction as the first Arsenal player to score a Champions League goal for the Club, netting in the side's 1–1 draw with Lens in September 1998.

Arsenal qualified for the competition for the first time in 1998–99 after winning the Premier League the previous season and Overmars was on target in the Stade Felix Bollaert in the opening game of the group phase to earn his place in the record books. The Dutchman stroked home Emmanuel Petit's slide-rule pass in the 51st minute in France, but it was not quite enough to earn Arsene Wenger's side all three points, with Lens equalizing in the final minute.

RIGHT: Marc Overmars opened the Club's Champions League account against Lens, in 1998.

RED CARD FIRST

Jens Lehmann made 200 appearances for the Club between 2003 and 2011 but the German international will probably want to forget his performance in the Champions League final against Barcelona in 2006.

The Gunners' goalkeeper was sent off in the 18th minute of the game in the Stade de France in Paris for a foul on striker Samuel Eto'o, becoming the first player to see red in a Champions League final.

ABOVE: Jens Lehmann lasted just 18 minutes of the 2006 Champions League final against Barcelona.

BENDTNER'S BARRAGE

A Champions League hat-trick is a rare commodity and the first player to hit the fabled treble for the Gunners was Nicklas Bendtner, in March 2010.

The opposition was Porto at Emirates, in the last 16, and the Danish striker opened his account in the 10th minute when he pounced on a loose ball following a fine run from Andrey Arshavin. He doubled his tally 15 minutes later after more good work from Arshavin and completed his hat-trick in the final minute of the match from the penalty spot.

HENRY HITS FIRST

Arsenal's first two appearances in the Champions League resulted in elimination at the first group phase but Arsene Wenger's side did make it through to the quarter-finals in 2000–01, facing Spanish side Valencia.

The first leg at Highbury saw the Gunners emerge 2–1 winners, with Thierry Henry's 58th-minute opener the first-ever goal for the Club in the knockout stages of the competition.

RIGHT: Nicklas Bendtner hit a Champions League treble against Porto in 2010.

PART 2
Player Records

Football may be a game of 11 versus 11 but it's inevitable that individuals will make their mark and this chapter looks at the players who have rewritten the record books while wearing the red and white shirt.

The first six pages focus on the Club's most prolific and predatory marksmen over the years – from Thierry Henry's record haul of Arsenal goals, to Ted Drake's amazing exploits during the 1934–35 season, the Gunners' leading hat-trick heroes and Alan Smith's four-goal salvo in the European Cup.

The middle section is devoted to the likes of David O'Leary, Tom Parker and Ray Parlour who made Arsenal history with their number of appearances for the Club – the loyal servants who just kept on playing.

The Gunners' biggest transfers – from David Jack's British-record £10,890 move from Bolton in 1928 up to the recent past and Nicolas Anelka's massive £22.5 million switch to Real Madrid in 1999 – chart the Club's transfer dealings.

The final pages focus on the players from Great Britain and Ireland, and more recently those from beyond these shores, to have earned international recognition during their Arsenal careers, while the chapter also includes details of Alan Skirton's milestone appearance for the Club during the 1965–66 season.

ABOVE: Ted Drake (right) shoots during a match against Brentford in 1938.

RIGHT: David O'Leary (left) and Tony Adams celebrate Arsenal's 1990–91 League title success.

Player Records – Goalscoring

Goals win matches and over the years Arsenal have been blessed with some of the game's most prolific strikers – players who just couldn't stop scoring. From Cliff Bastin to Thierry Henry and Doug Lishman to Ian Wright, this section celebrates the Gunners whose eye for goal was without equal.

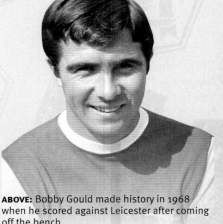

ABOVE: Bobby Gould made history in 1968 when he scored against Leicester after coming off the bench.

 GOULD STANDARD
Substitutions were first allowed in English football in the 1965–66 season but it was not until August 1968 that an Arsenal replacement came off the bench to score. The player who made history was striker Bobby Gould, who came on for George Graham in the Gunners' Division One clash with Leicester City and found the back of the net twice in a 3–0 victory.

 RECORD-BREAKING HENRY
The most prolific striker ever to pull on the famous red and white shirt of Arsenal, Thierry Henry scored 228 times in 377 appearances for the Gunners, to become the only player to surpass the 200-goal landmark in the Club's history. Surprisingly, it took the legendary Frenchman 10 games to open his Arsenal account following his £9 million move from Juventus in the summer of 1999, but once the legendary Frenchman had hit the winner against Southampton in September, coming off the bench at The Dell on 71 minutes and scoring just eight minutes later, the goals continued to flow with breathtaking regularity and style.

Henry reached a century of goals for the Club in his fourth season in England with a brace in a 4–0 demolition of Birmingham City at St Andrews in January 2003, and he reached the 150 milestone with a four-goal salvo against Leeds United at Highbury in April 2004.

On 18 October 2005, he became Arsenal's greatest-ever goalscorer. The game was a Champions League clash with Sparta Prague and, with his first of the evening, Henry equalled Ian Wright's previous record haul of 185. His second in a 3–0 victory saw him surpass the record Wright had set eight years and 35 days earlier, earning the Frenchman a unique place in the Club's illustrious history.

He hit the 200 mark in February 2006 with another goal at Birmingham while his 228th and final strike came exactly six years later while he was on loan back to the Gunners from the New York Red Bulls, hammering home an injury-time winner for Arsene Wenger's side at Sunderland in the Premier League.

The Frenchman still holds many other scoring records for the Club but his record-breaking career tally of 228 is undoubtedly his greatest.

LEFT: Thierry Henry registered the 100th goal of his Arsenal career in 2003 against Birmingham.

SEVENTH HEAVEN
Ted Drake's achievements in the 1934–35 campaign were phenomenal but his feat in December 1935 was almost unbelievable, scoring a Club-record seven goals in a single match. The unfortunate opponents were Aston Villa in a Division One clash at Villa Park and the final scoreline was 7–1 to the Gunners, with Drake netting all the goals for George Allison's team. According to contemporary reports, however, the striker could have actually had eight goals, had one of his efforts not struck the crossbar and the referee ruled the deflected ball did not cross the line.

SENSATIONAL SEASON FOR DRAKE

The great Ted Drake spent 11 superb seasons with the Gunners in the 1930s and 1940s and the Southampton-born centre-forward still holds the Club record for both the most goals and the most league goals scored in a single season. Unsurprisingly, he achieved his historic double in the same campaign, Arsenal's 1934–35 Division One title-winning season. In just 41 appearances, Drake contributed 42 of the 115 league goals the Gunners scored that year, and he took his overall tally to a record-breaking 44 with an FA Cup goal against Brighton & Hove Albion and another strike in the Charity Shield against Manchester City.

TWELVE-MATCH STREAK

The most consistent Gunner in terms of scoring in consecutive appearances for the Club is Ian Wright, who was on target in 12 matches on the bounce during the 1994–95 campaign. His amazing sequence began in mid-September, when he scored in Arsenal's 3–1 win in Cyprus against Omonia in the first round of the European Cup Winners' Cup and he subsequently scored against Newcastle in the league and twice against Hartlepool United in the League Cup.

West Ham, Omonia in the second leg and Crystal Palace all failed to stop the striker scoring and, although he missed the second leg against Hartlepool, Wright was back in business away to Wimbledon in the league before helping himself to a brace in a 3–1 league victory over Chelsea at Highbury. Goals against Danish club Brondby home and away in the European Cup Winners' Cup and Coventry in the league followed, and the prolific forward made it 12 matches in a row with a goal when he found the back of the net from the penalty spot in Arsenal's 2–1 win against Leicester at Filbert Street. Manchester United finally managed to shackle Wright in a goalless draw at Highbury at the end of November but his return of 16 goals in 12 successive games remains a Club record.

ABOVE: Ted Drake was in prolific form during the 1934–35 title-winning campaign.

PROLIFIC WRIGHT

Ian Wright holds the Club record for the most League Cup goals in an Arsenal career, scoring 29 during his seven seasons at Highbury. The England striker opened his League Cup account in September 1991 with the goal that earned George Graham's side a 1–1 draw with Leicester City at Filbert Street and he was on target five times in 1992–93 as the Gunners lifted the trophy. His final League Cup goal came in January 1998 with his strike in the 2–1 victory over West Ham at Upton Park in the quarter-finals.

RIGHT: The League Cup proved a happy hunting ground for Ian Wright.

TOP 10 GOALSCORERS

	App	Goals
Thierry Henry (1999–2007, 2012)	377	228
Ian Wright (1991–98)	288	185
Cliff Bastin (1929–46)	396	178
John Radford (1962–76)	481	149
Ted Drake (1934–45)	184	139
Jimmy Brain (1923–31)	232	139
Doug Lishman (1948–56)	244	137
Robin van Persie (2004–12)	278	132
Joe Hulme (1926–38)	374	125
David Jack (1928–34)	208	124

▼ HAT-TRICK HEROES

Twenty-five different players have scored three or more hat-tricks in competitive games for Arsenal since the Club was formed in 1886. Although Joseph Heath isn't on that list, he does hold the distinction as the player to score the first-ever league treble for the Gunners.

His brilliant triple came in a 4–0 victory over Walsall Town Swifts in a Second Division clash at Plumstead in September 1893 and he went on to register three more hat-tricks that season in friendlies against Chatham, London Caledonians and Crusaders.

The first-ever treble at Highbury was scored by Harry King in a 6–0 demolition of Grimsby Town in November 1914, one of the four hat-tricks of his Gunners career.

Dutch striker Dennis Bergkamp recorded the first hat-trick of Arsene Wenger's managerial reign at the Club in a 3–3 draw with Leicester City in August 1997, while the first treble of the Emirates era went to Emmanuel Adebayor in the 5–0 mauling of Derby County a decade later.

The youngest Arsenal player to hit the target three times in a single match was John Radford, who was just 17 years and 315 days old when the Gunners beat Wolves 5–0 at Highbury in January 1965.

Overall, Jack Lambert and Jimmy Brain head the career list with 12 Arsenal hat-tricks apiece. Ted Drake and Ian Wright both recorded 11 while Thierry Henry scored eight.

ABOVE: Joe Baker was on target 36 times for the Gunners in 1963.

► DEADLY DRAKE

Three players currently hold the record for the most goals for the Gunners in a calendar year. Yorkshireman Jack Lambert set the original mark back in 1930 when he was on target 36 times, but just five years later Ted Drake equalled his 12-month tally, while Liverpudlian Joe Baker joined the list in 1963.

HENRY IN EUROPE

Thierry Henry was the spearhead for some of Arsenal's greatest nights in Europe during his eight-year stay in north London and his 42 glorious goals remains a record return for the Club.

His first-ever European goal for the Gunners came on 22 September 1999 when he came off the bench for Marc Overmars at Highbury to score in a 3–1 victory against Swedish side AIK Solna. He was on target seven more times during the campaign to register his most prolific season for the Club.

The French striker was also to the fore during 2005–06 as Arsenal reached the Champions League final, with five goals in 11 appearances, and it was his famous strike against Real Madrid at the Bernabeu that saw the Gunners knock out the Spanish giants in the last 16 of the competition. He was also on target in the quarter-final triumph against Juventus.

In total, 35 of Henry's record-breaking 42 European goals came in the Champions League, while his last strike for the Club was in September 2006 in a 2–0 victory over Porto at Emirates.

LEFT: John Radford was still a teenager when he hit his first hat-trick for the Club.

FABULOUS FABREGAS

The youngest goalscorer in the Club's history is Cesc Fabregas, who was just 16 years and 212 days old when he was on target for Arsenal in their 5–0 win over Wolverhampton Wanderers at Highbury in a fifth-round League Cup clash.

The Spanish midfielder also holds the record as the Gunners' most youthful scorer in both league and European football.

He hit his first Premier League goal for the Club aged 17 years and 113 days against Blackburn Rovers in August 2004 while his maiden European strike came in the Champions League clash with Rosenborg at Highbury in December the same year – aged 17 years and 303 days.

► FOUR FOR SMITH

Henry holds the record for the most career European goals but Alan Smith holds the distinction as the player to have scored the most goals in a single European game for the Gunners. The England striker scored four in a 6–1 thrashing of FK Austria Wien at Highbury in the European Cup in September 1991.

RIGHT: Alan Smith was in deadly form in the 1991–92 European Cup campaign.

BELOW: The 2011–12 Premier League season was Robin van Persie's most prolific.

OLD-TIMER

The oldest player to find the back of the net for Arsenal is English winger Jock Rutherford, scoring in a 2–0 win over Sheffield United in Division One in September 1924. Rutherford was just 13 days short of celebrating his 40th birthday.

FASTEST TO 100 ARSENAL GOALS

Ted Drake (1934–45) – 108 appearances

Ian Wright (1991–98) – 143 appearances

Jimmy Brain (1923–31) – 144 appearances

Jack Lambert (1926–33) – 149 appearances

Joe Baker (1962–66) – 152 appearances

Reg Lewis (1935–53) – 152 appearances

David Jack (1928–34) – 156 appearances

Doug Lishman (1948–56) – 163 appearances

David Herd (1954–61) – 165 appearances

Cliff Bastin (1929–46) – 174 appearances

◄ PREMIER LEAGUE RECORD

Thierry Henry and Robin van Persie jointly hold the Club record for the most goals in a Premier League season. Henry scored 30 league goals in the 2003–04 campaign as Arsene Wenger's side were crowned champions while van Persie emulated the Frenchman's achievement in 2011–12 to finish as the division's leading marksman.

BASTIN'S CUP EXPLOITS

Arsenal's third-highest scorer of all time, Cliff Bastin is also the Club's leading marksman in the FA Cup – with 26 goals in 42 appearances between 1929 and 1947.

The Gunners won the FA Cup twice during the outside-left's Highbury career and, although Bastin didn't score in either final, his four goals in eight appearances in 1929–30 and six in seven in 1935–36 were pivotal in the team's progress to Wembley.

He also holds the record as Arsenal's youngest scorer in an FA Cup tie, hitting the net in a 2–0 win against Chelsea in the third round at the age of 17 years and 303 days.

▼ GOALS GALORE

Dutch striker Robin van Persie and England star Ian Wright jointly hold the Premier League record for scoring against the highest number of different sides in a single season, with the two former players both hitting the target against 17 of the 19 other top-flight clubs.

Wright first set the record during the Gunners' 1996–97 campaign when only Manchester United and Sunderland succeeded in stopping him in front of goal, and van Persie emulated his feat in 2011–12 when he hit the net against every Premier League team except Manchester City and Fulham.

▶ EXTRA-TIME EDDIE

The 1971 FA Cup final was a magical moment in Arsenal's history, with victory in extra-time against Liverpool at Wembley completing the fabled league and cup double for the first time.

The match, however, was also noteworthy for Eddie Kelly's strike in the 101st minute, the first time a substitute had scored in an FA Cup final. The Scottish midfielder came on for Peter Storey after 64 minutes at Wembley and his goal levelled the match after Steve Heighway had put Liverpool in front, paving the way for Charlie George's late winner.

ABOVE: Victory over Liverpool saw Arsenal lift the FA Cup for a fourth time in 1971.

BELOW: Van Persie found the back of the net 132 times in 278 games during his eight-year Arsenal career.

LEFT: Julio Baptista smashed four goals past Liverpool at Anfield in 2007.

◀ ANFIELD ANNIHILATION

Brazilian Julio Baptista spent a season on loan at Arsenal in 2006–07 and, although the midfielder's spell in English football was brief, he still found time to set a Club record for the most goals in a League Cup match.

He set the record in January 2007 when Arsene Wenger's side travelled to Anfield to face Liverpool in the fifth round, scoring twice either side of half-time for a personal haul of four goals in the side's remarkable 6–3 victory. Amazingly, Baptista also had a penalty saved by Jerzy Dudek as Liverpool crashed to their worst home defeat in 76 years.

LAMBERT LASHES FIVE

Jack Lambert averaged a goal in every 1.48 games during his seven-year-long Gunners career and his impressive strike rate received a significant boost when he scored five in a 9–2 demolition of Sheffield United on Christmas Eve 1932.

His haul is the Club-record tally for an individual in a competitive match at Highbury and helped Herbert Chapman's side storm to the Division One title.

▶ SILVA LINING

Brazilian midfielder Gilberto Silva registered a modest 24 goals in 244 appearances over six years for the Gunners, but he still holds the record as the scorer of the fastest-ever goal in the Club's history.

His amazingly rapid effort came in the group stages of the 2002–03 Champions League against PSV Eindhoven and when Silva converted Thierry Henry's cross for the opening goal of what proved to be a 4–0 victory, there had been a mere 20.07 seconds of play.

ABOVE: Gilberto Silva was on target for the Gunners after just 20 seconds against PSV in the 2002–03 Champions League.

MOST ARSENAL HAT-TRICKS

Jack Lambert (1926–33)	12
Jimmy Brain (1923–31)	12
Ted Drake (1934–45)	11
Ian Wright (1991–98)	11
Thierry Henry (1999–2007, 2012)	8
David Herd (1954–61)	7
David Jack (1928–34)	7
Doug Lishman (1948–56)	7
John Radford (1962–76)	6
Ronnie Rooke (1946–49)	5
Joe Baker (1962–66)	5

AWAY-DAY CONSISTENCY

Robin van Persie was in sensational form in the final two seasons of his Arsenal career, and during his purple patch the Dutchman set a new Club record for scoring in the most consecutive away fixtures in the league.

His prolific sequence began on New Year's Day 2011 when he was on target in a 3–0 victory over Birmingham at St Andrews. In the next three-and-a-half months, the striker scored away from home against West Ham, Newcastle, West Brom and Blackpool.

He continued the run with a goal in the 3–3 draw against Spurs at White Hart Lane in April and extended the streak further with strikes against Bolton and Stoke. His record-setting effort came in a 2–2 draw at Craven Cottage against Fulham in the team's final game of the season, making it nine games on the bounce.

Player Records – Appearances

Injury, age and loss of form can all curtail a professional career but some Arsenal players have defied all these obstacles to clock up a breathtaking number of games for the Club. This section looks at the players who refused to quit.

▶ EIGHTEEN YEARS FOR O'LEARY

Republic of Ireland defender David O'Leary holds the record for the most appearances for Arsenal, playing 722 times for the Club between 1975 and 1993 in a glittering career which saw him claim two Division One winner's medals, as well as two FA Cups and two League Cups.

Signed as an apprentice in 1973, the centre-half graduated through the Club's reserve team ranks, and just three months after his 17th birthday he was handed his first team debut by manager Bertie Mee – in the opening fixture of the 1975–76 season against Burnley at Turf Moor. He made an instant impression on the side and went on to play 26 more times in the league for the Gunners in his first season.

The youngest player ever to reach both the 100 and 200-match milestones, O'Leary made his 400th appearance for the Club at the age of 26 and surpassed George Armstrong's previous record of 621 senior games in November 1989 when he played in the dramatic 4–3 victory over Norwich City at Highbury.

His last game for the Club was the 1993 FA Cup final replay against Sheffield Wednesday at Wembley, when he came off the bench after 81 minutes to replace Ian Wright in the Gunners' 2–1 extra-time victory. He signed for Leeds United on a free transfer in July 1993 after 18 years at Arsenal, bringing to an end a superb career in which he also set a Club milestone of 558 league appearances.

ABOVE: David O'Leary spent almost two decades in the Arsenal ranks, making him a legend at the Club.

RIGHT: Tom Parker was an incredibly consistent performer for the Club during the 1920s.

◀ RELIABLE PARKER

Signed from Southampton for £3,250 in March 1926, right-back Tom Parker captained Arsenal to their first major trophy – the 1930 FA Cup – and also holds the record for the most consecutive appearances in Gunners history.

His unbroken sequence of games began against Blackburn Rovers in April 1926, a game Arsenal won 4–2 at Highbury, and continued until Boxing Day 1929 when he was in the side that lost 2–1 to Portsmouth in north London.

In total Parker played in 172 consecutive matches for the Gunners. In his seven seasons with the Club, he missed just six games.

TEENAGE STAR

The youngest player to appear for the Gunners in an FA Cup match is Stewart Robson. The young midfielder registered the milestone in the Gunners' 1–0 loss against Tottenham at White Hart Lane in the third round of the 1981–82 competition, only 57 days after he had turned 17.

◀ EXPERIENCED GUNNER

The oldest player to wear the Arsenal shirt in a competitive match is Jock Rutherford, who was 41 years and 159 days old when he featured against Manchester City at Highbury in March 1926.

The outside-right signed for the Club from Newcastle in 1913 and a decade later left to become the manager of Stoke City. He resigned from his new role after just two months and returned to Highbury as a player. He hung up his boots in 1925 but was tempted out of retirement for a third stint as an Arsenal player later the same year, paving the way for his record-setting appearance against Manchester City.

▼ PARLOUR'S PREMIER LEAGUE MILESTONE

A product of the Arsenal junior ranks, Ray Parlour joined the Club as a trainee in 1989 and, with 333 games on his impressive CV, the midfielder is the most-experienced-ever Gunner in terms of Premier League appearances.

Parlour made his first team debut in the old First Division in January 1992 but the first of his 333 Premier League matches came the following season when he was selected for the clash with Liverpool at Anfield in August.

The midfielder went on to feature heavily in all three of the Club's Premier League title triumphs, playing 34 times in 1997–98, 27 in 2001–02 and a further 25 in 2003–04.

His final Premier League appearance for the Gunners came in the penultimate game of the 2003–04 season, a 1–0 victory over Fulham at Craven Cottage.

ABOVE: Jock Rutherford (front row, first player on the left), continued to play into his forties.

LEFT: Ray Parlour set a Club record for Premier League appearances.

CHAMPIONS LEAGUE RECORD

Thierry Henry has played more Champions League games for the Club than any other player, appearing 78 times in European football's marquee competition.

The Frenchman made his Gunners debut in the tournament as an 81st-minute substitute for Dennis Bergkamp in a goalless draw against Fiorentina in the group stages in 1999, while his first start for the Club came 12 months later in a 1–0 victory over Sparta Prague.

His last Champions League game was during his loan spell at Emirates during the 2011–12 season, replacing Theo Walcott at half-time in the Gunners' 4–0 loss in Italy to AC Milan in February.

TOP 10 APPEARANCES

	App	Goals
David O'Leary (1973–93)	722	14
Tony Adams (1983–2002)	669	48
George Armstrong (1961–77)	621	68
Lee Dixon (1988–2002)	619	25
Nigel Winterburn (1987–2000)	584	12
David Seaman (1990–2003)	564	0
Pat Rice (1966–80)	528	22
Peter Storey (1965–77)	501	17
John Radford (1964–76)	481	149
Peter Simpson (1960–78)	477	15

ABLE SEAMAN

Only five goalkeepers have made over 300 appearances for the Club in Arsenal's history and David Seaman stands head and shoulders above his rivals in terms of total number of games played.

The England custodian was signed from Queens Park Rangers for a British record fee of £1.3 million in 1990 and made his first team debut on the opening day of the 1990–91 campaign against Wimbledon at Plough Lane. Seaman was ever-present in the league for the Gunners throughout the season, conceding just 18 goals in 38 matches as George Graham's side claimed the title.

He spent 13 years as an Arsenal player and his final appearance was a fittingly triumphant send-off, keeping a clean sheet as the Gunners beat Southampton 1–0 in the 2003 FA Cup final at Wembley.

In total, Seaman played a Club-record 564 times for Arsenal. Welsh keeper Jack Kelsey is second on the all-time list with 352 appearances in the 1950s and 1960s, while Irish legend Pat Jennings is third with 327. Bob Wilson played 308 times for the Gunners while James Ashcroft featured in 303 games for the Gunners at the start of the 20th century.

John Lukic and George Swindin both narrowly missed out on the 300-match career milestone, playing 298 and 297 times respectively.

▼ SWEET SIXTEEN

The youngest player to feature in the Arsenal first team is Cesc Fabregas after Arsene Wenger selected the Spanish playmaker for the Club's League Cup clash with Rotherham United at Emirates in October 2003 at the age of 16 years and 177 days. Fabregas played 85 minutes of the 1–1 draw before being substituted.

RIGHT: David Seaman joined Arsenal from Queens Park Rangers in the summer of 1990.

BELOW: Cesc Febregas broke into the Gunners' first team as a 16-year-old.

► AMAZING ARMSTRONG

George Armstrong is third on the all-time list of appearances for the Gunners, with a magnificent career tally of 621 matches, and also holds the unique distinction of having played exactly 500 league games.

The winger made his debut as a teenager in a First Division clash with Blackpool at Bloomfield Road in February 1962 and, although it was his only appearance for George Swindin's team that season, he was in the starting XI for new manager Billy Wright for the opening game of the 1962–63 campaign against Leyton Orient.

Over the next 15 years, Armstrong was a fixture in the Gunners' team and made his 500th and final league appearance for the Club in a 3–2 win over Manchester United at Old Trafford in the final game of the 1976–77 season.

He signed for Leicester City in the summer of 1977 but returned to Highbury in 1990 as part of the reserve team coaching staff.

BARGAIN DEAL FOR DIXON

The Gunners' three leading players in terms of appearances – David O'Leary, Tony Adams and George Armstrong – were all home-grown and made their professional debuts for the Club, making Lee Dixon's 619 games a record for a player signed from another team.

Dixon began his career in the early 1980s with Burnley and, after brief spells with Chester City, Bury and Stoke City, George Graham brought him to London in January 1988 in a £350,000 deal.

The full-back made his debut in a Division One clash against Luton Town the following month and established himself as a first team regular with 33 league appearances during the 1988–89 campaign as Arsenal were crowned First Division champions.

His Highbury career was to last 14 years with the last of his 619 games coming against Everton in the final fixture of the 2001–02 season.

ABOVE: George Armstrong is third on Arsenal's all-time appearance list.

► DUTCH DELIGHT

The first 17 players on the all-time Arsenal appearance list all hail from Britain or Ireland, making Dutchman Dennis Bergkamp in 18th the foreign player with the most career games for the Club.

Signed from Inter Milan for £7.5 million in June 1995, the striker made his league debut in August in a 2–0 victory against Everton at Goodison, and for his 11 seasons in north London he was a key figure in one of the most successful eras of the Club's history.

He retired at the end of the 2005–06 campaign, bidding farewell to the Gunners in May with an 11-minute cameo appearance from the bench in a 4–2 win against Wigan at Highbury.

It was his 423rd and final appearance for Arsenal, eclipsing the 406 games Frenchman Patrick Vieira played for the Club.

RIGHT: Dennis Bergkamp scored 120 goals in his 423 games for the Club.

ARSENAL APPEARANCE RECORDS

Most League Games:	558, David O'Leary
Most Premier League Games:	333, Ray Parlour
Most Champions League Games:	79, Thierry Henry
Most League Cup Games:	70, David O'Leary
Most Consecutive Games:	172, Tom Parker (3 April 1926–26 December 1929)

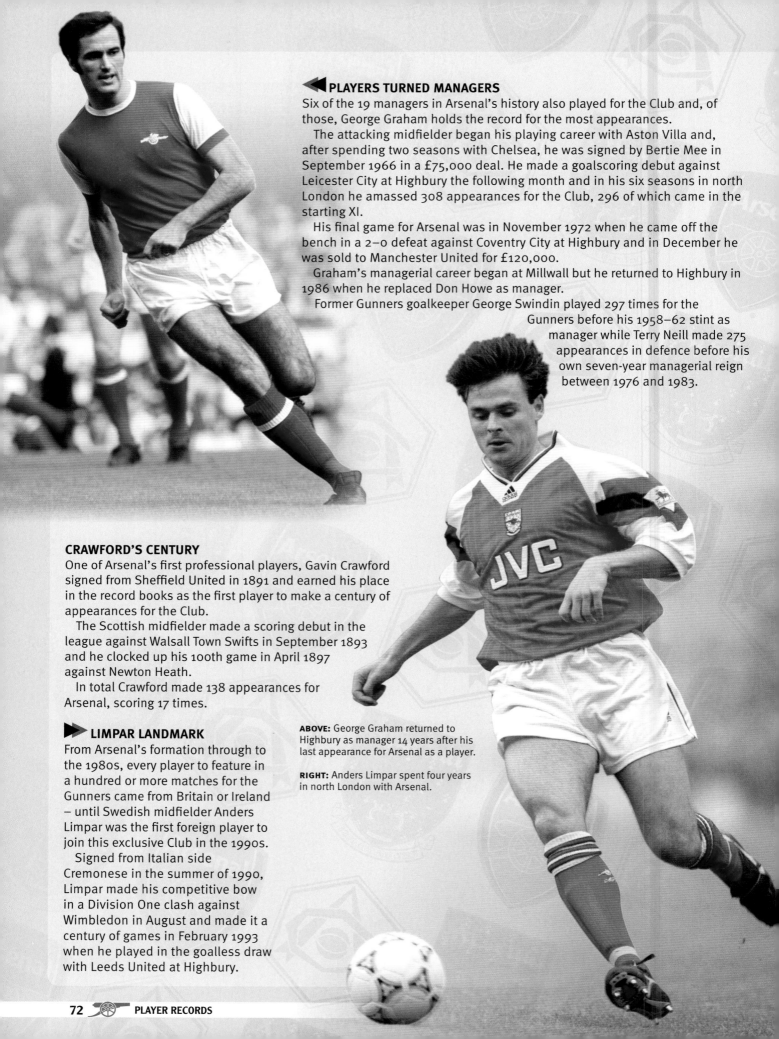

PLAYERS TURNED MANAGERS

Six of the 19 managers in Arsenal's history also played for the Club and, of those, George Graham holds the record for the most appearances.

The attacking midfielder began his playing career with Aston Villa and, after spending two seasons with Chelsea, he was signed by Bertie Mee in September 1966 in a £75,000 deal. He made a goalscoring debut against Leicester City at Highbury the following month and in his six seasons in north London he amassed 308 appearances for the Club, 296 of which came in the starting XI.

His final game for Arsenal was in November 1972 when he came off the bench in a 2–0 defeat against Coventry City at Highbury and in December he was sold to Manchester United for £120,000.

Graham's managerial career began at Millwall but he returned to Highbury in 1986 when he replaced Don Howe as manager.

Former Gunners goalkeeper George Swindin played 297 times for the Gunners before his 1958–62 stint as manager while Terry Neill made 275 appearances in defence before his own seven-year managerial reign between 1976 and 1983.

CRAWFORD'S CENTURY

One of Arsenal's first professional players, Gavin Crawford signed from Sheffield United in 1891 and earned his place in the record books as the first player to make a century of appearances for the Club.

The Scottish midfielder made a scoring debut in the league against Walsall Town Swifts in September 1893 and he clocked up his 100th game in April 1897 against Newton Heath.

In total Crawford made 138 appearances for Arsenal, scoring 17 times.

LIMPAR LANDMARK

From Arsenal's formation through to the 1980s, every player to feature in a hundred or more matches for the Gunners came from Britain or Ireland – until Swedish midfielder Anders Limpar was the first foreign player to join this exclusive Club in the 1990s.

Signed from Italian side Cremonese in the summer of 1990, Limpar made his competitive bow in a Division One clash against Wimbledon in August and made it a century of games in February 1993 when he played in the goalless draw with Leeds United at Highbury.

ABOVE: George Graham returned to Highbury as manager 14 years after his last appearance for Arsenal as a player.

RIGHT: Anders Limpar spent four years in north London with Arsenal.

TOURE THE TRAILBLAZER

Arsenal have become a genuinely global side in recent years and this was reflected in the seven-year Highbury career of Kolo Toure, whose 326 appearances for the Gunners is a record for a non-European player. The Ivory Coast centre-half joined Arsenal from African side ASEC Mimosas in 2002 and made 26 Premier League appearances in his debut season. He remained a first choice for Arsene Wenger for the following six years in north London and before leaving for Manchester City, in 2009, he won the Premier League and two FA Cups.

ABOVE: Kolo Toure arrived at Highbury in 2002, making his debut against Liverpool in the Community Shield.

HOMEGROWN HERO

Cesc Fabregas joined the Arsenal Academy as a 16-year-old in September 2003 and less than three years later made his 100th appearance for the Club, making him the most recent homegrown player in Arsenal history to reach a century of games for the Gunners.

The Spaniard reached the milestone when he featured in the Champions League clash with Dynamo Zagreb in early August 2006, joining an illustrious list of young players to graduate through the Club's junior ranks to first-team football and 100 or more senior appearances.

The midfielder clocked up 300 matches under Arsene Wenger against Blackpool at Bloomfield Road in April 2011, but little more than two months later he returned to his native Spain when he signed for Barcelona.

▶ JOHN FIRST TO 400

Just 20 players have reached the 400-game milestone for the Club and the first to do so was Welsh midfielder Bob John. A member of the Gunners side that won the title in 1931, 1933 and 1934 and the FA Cup in 1930, John signed from Caerphilly in January 1922 and spent 15 years in London before retiring.

He reached the 400-match mark in the 1932–33 season and made 470 appearances in total for the Club, placing him 11th on the all-time list.

RIGHT: Bob John's Arsenal career lasted 15 years.

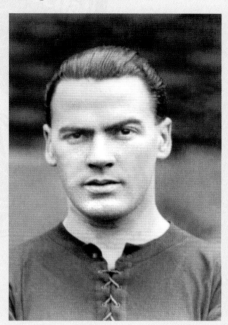

ARSENAL APPEARANCE RECORDS
YOUNGEST PLAYERS

Overall: Cesc Fabregas
(16 years 177 days v Rotherham Utd, League Cup, Oct 2003)

League: Jack Wilshere
(16 years 256 days v Blackburn, Sept 2008)

Premier League: Jack Wilshere
(16 years 256 days v Blackburn, Sept 2008)

Europe: Jack Wilshere
(16 years 329 days v Dynamo Kiev, Champions League, Nov 2008)

FA Cup: Jack Wilshere
(17 years 2 days v Plymouth, Jan 2009)

OLDEST PLAYERS

Overall: Jock Rutherford
(41 years 159 days, v Man City, League, March 1926)

League: Jock Rutherford
(41 years 159 days, v Man City, March 1926)

Premier League: Jens Lehmann
(41 years 151 days v Blackpool, April 2011)

Europe: John Lukic
(39 years 311 days v Lazio, Champions League, Oct 2000)

Player Records – Transfers

Arsenal have always attracted marquee players but quality invariably comes at a price and this section focuses on the milestone transfer fees the Club has paid to sign some of the game's biggest names.

▼ JACK'S FIVE-FIGURE DEAL

Arsenal have been involved in a British-record transfer deal five times in the Club's history and hit the headlines for the first time in October 1928 when manager Herbert Chapman secured the services of Bolton Wanderers inside-forward David Jack.

The previous record was the £5,500 fee paid by Sunderland to South Shields for England full-back Warney Cresswell six years earlier but Chapman had to dig deep to persuade Bolton to sell Jack and after prolonged negotiations the two clubs agreed on a figure of £10,890, the first time any player in the world had moved clubs for a five-figure sum.

Jack's reputation preceded him – he had become the first player ever to score at Wembley in the 1923 FA Cup final, and had a tally of 144 goals in 295 league appearances for Wanderers – but he arrived at Highbury aged 29 and the sceptics questioned whether Chapman had got value for money in the deal.

In his six seasons with the Gunners, Jack proved he was worth every penny. He finished his first season in the capital as the side's top scorer, with 25 goals in 31 games and he was an integral part of the team that beat Huddersfield 2–0 in the 1930 FA Cup final, the Club's first major trophy.

His most prolific campaign came in 1930–31 when he netted 34 times as Arsenal were crowned First Division champions. He would go on to add two further championship medals to his collection after the title triumphs of 1932–33 and 1933–34.

Jack finally hung up his boots in 1934 at the age of 35, having scored a remarkable 124 times in 208 games in all competitions – costing the Club roughly £88 for each goal during his Highbury career.

LEFT: David Jack became the first player ever to command a five-figure transfer fee.

▼ HUGE PROFIT ON ANELKA

No club likes to see its best players leave, but there was no arguing with the financial logic behind Arsene Wenger's decision to sell Nicolas Anelka to Real Madrid in 1999 for £22.5 million, then a record fee involving a British side.

The young French striker had cost the Gunners a modest £500,000 when Wenger had signed him from Paris Saint-Germain two years earlier. After helping Arsenal clinch the 1997–98 Premier League title with six goals in 26 appearances, he left Highbury for Spain for 45 times what they paid for him.

LEFT: Nicolas Anelka was sold to Real Madrid in the summer of 1999 after two seasons at Highbury.

BERGKAMP JOINS GUNNERS

The fourth time Arsenal were involved in a British-record deal was in 1995 – and it was arguably the Club's greatest piece of business, as it saw Dennis Bergkamp join the Gunners.

The Dutchman arrived at Highbury in a £7.5 million move from Italian giants Inter Milan, smashing the previous mark of £2.5 million paid for Ian Wright in 1991 and John Hartson four years later. In his 11 seasons with the Club Bergkamp certainly did not disappoint.

His debut season saw the striker on target 11 times in 33 league appearances and he was the Club's top scorer with 16 in 1997–98 as Arsenal claimed the Premier League title for the first time. Bergkamp won three league titles and four FA Cups with the Gunners and in total the sublimely-talented forward made 423 appearances, scoring 120 goals.

The love affair finally came to an end in 2006 when he called time on his playing career – and on more than a decade of Arsenal service.

BELOW: Alan Ball became Club captain following his £220,000 transfer from Everton.

ABOVE: Dennis Bergkamp's performances for the Club justified his record price tag.

BONUS BALL

Arsenal famously won the league and FA Cup double in 1970–71 but manager Bertie Mee was not one to rest on his laurels – and in December 1971 he persuaded the Highbury board to spend £220,000 on signing Alan Ball from Everton.

The deal eclipsed the previous British transfer record – the £200,000 Tottenham paid West Ham for Martin Peters almost two years earlier – and although Ball did not win a trophy with the Club, he was a hugely influential player who made 217 starts in five seasons in north London.

Ball was named captain for the 1973–74 season, and in a period of transition for the Club he was a key figure as the team preserved their top-flight status.

BRITISH TRANSFER RECORD

A decade after the Gunners made history by signing David Jack, they again set a new British transfer record when they paid Wolverhampton Wanderers £14,500 for the privilege of signing Welshman Bryn Jones in March 1938.

The inside-forward scored on his Division One debut for the Club, in a 2–0 win over Portsmouth at Highbury in August, but the outbreak of the Second World War the following year and the suspension of league football interrupted his Gunners career.

Jones served in the Royal Artillery during the conflict but, when competitive football resumed in 1946, he was 34 years old and past the peak of his powers.

He did play seven times during the 1947–48 season as Arsenal were crowned champions but it was not enough to earn him a winner's medal and in 1949 he was sold to Norwich City.

ARSENAL'S FIVE BRITISH RECORD TRANSFERS

Player	From	To	Date	Fee
David Jack	Bolton	Arsenal	Oct 1928	£10,890
Bryn Jones	Wolves	Arsenal	Mar 1938	£14,500
Alan Ball	Everton	Arsenal	Dec 1971	£220,000
Dennis Bergkamp	Inter Milan	Arsenal	Jun 1995	£7.5m
Nicolas Anelka	Arsenal	Real Madrid	Jul 1999	£22.5m

RUSSIAN RECRUIT

The January transfer window is usually a relatively quiet period for the top clubs but Arsenal were nothing if not noisy in January 2004 when they agreed a £17.5 million deal to sign Jose Antonio Reyes from Spanish side Sevilla.

The deal was made up of an initial payment of £10.5 million, with the Gunners committed to paying a further £7 million depending on appearances, making the potential combined fee the highest agreed in the Club's history.

The striker, however, made a modest 110 appearances before returning to Spain with Atletico Madrid in 2007 and it is unclear whether that was enough to trigger the full £7 million settlement.

The record one-off transfer fee in Arsenal's history was the £16.9 million they invested in Russian midfielder Andrey Arshavin when he joined the Club from Zenit St Petersburg in the 2009 January transfer window.

The Gunners paid £15 million of the £16.9 million out of their own pocket, with the remaining £1.9 million coming from Arshavin himself in the form of compensation and the forfeit of a loyalty bonus.

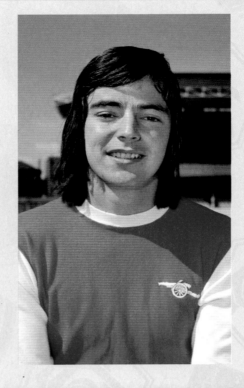

SIX-FIGURE MARINELLO

When the Gunners signed David Jack back in 1928, they became the first Club ever to pay five figures for a player. Forty-two years later Arsenal invested their first-ever six figure fee when Scottish striker Peter Marinello arrived at Highbury.

The then 19-year-old forward signed from Hibernian in January 1970 for £100,000 and made an instant impression on English football with a goal on his debut against Manchester United at Old Trafford.

Sadly, that was to be the highlight of a disappointing career in north London as Marinello struggled to break into the first team on a regular basis, and in July 1973 he left for Portsmouth – having made just 51 appearances and scoring five times in three seasons with the Gunners.

LEFT: Peter Marinello struggled to find form at Highbury after his switch from Hibs.

BELOW: Andrey Arshavin came to England in a £16.9 million deal in January 2009.

COSTLY CUSTODIAN

Goalkeepers don't tend to command the same high transfer fees as their outfield counterparts but David Seaman was an exception to the rule when he signed from Queens Park Rangers in 1990, a deal which cost Arsenal £1.3 million.

The transfer set two new records at the same time, making Seaman both the Gunners' first seven-figure player and the world's most expensive goalkeeper at the time.

The England star settled quickly into his new surroundings, and in his first season at Highbury he conceded a miserly 18 goals in 38 Division One games as Arsenal were crowned champions. Seaman went on to add two more Championship winner's medals, four FA Cups, a League Cup and the Cup Winners' Cup to his collection.

In total, the keeper spent 13 years at Arsenal and made 564 appearances for the Club before a swan-song season with Manchester City and his retirement in 2004.

▶ TEENAGE TALENT

Young talent comes at a premium and Arsenal certainly had to dig deep to sign Alex Oxlade-Chamberlain in the summer of 2011, agreeing a £12 million deal with Southampton to make the winger the most expensive teenager in the Club's history.

The youngster signed a three-year deal with the Gunners in August, five days after celebrating his 18th birthday and in the process broke the record set by Theo Walcott five years earlier as the most costly teenage recruit.

The deal agreed to bring Oxlade-Chamberlain to Emirates from St Mary's saw Arsenal pay £7 million up front with another £5 million due depending on performance-related targets. The Walcott transfer was initially also reported as a £12 million deal but was subsequently revised down to £9.1 million when Southampton agreed to an early but lower settlement.

▶ FAREWELL FABREGAS

The sale of Cesc Fabregas to Barcelona in the summer of 2011 brought to an end one of the most protracted transfer sagas in the Club's history – and earned Arsenal the biggest transfer fee it has ever received for a player.

The reported headline fee for the Spanish midfielder was £35 million but in reality Barcelona paid £25.4 million in advance to sign Fabregas, with the balance of the deal dependent on appearances and his new side's success in La Liga and the Champions League over the course of his contract.

But even allowing for the reduced down payment, the deal still eclipsed the £24 million the Gunners received when Robin van Persie joined Manchester United in August 2012.

ABOVE: Cesc Fabregas returned to Spain in 2011 but cost Barcelona a record fee.

LEFT: The Club were looking to the future when they signed Alex Oxlade-Chamberlain in 2011.

MILLIONAIRE FRENCHMAN

The advent of the Premier League sparked a sharp rise in transfer fees in English football and Arsenal followed the trend when they bought Thierry Henry to the Premier League from Juventus for £11 million, the first instance of the Club paying an eight-figure fee for a new player.

The prolific Frenchman swapped Turin for London in 1999 and proceeded to rewrite the record books in eight glorious years with the Gunners, eventually finishing as the Club's all-time top goalscorer with 228 in 337 appearances.

Two league titles and three FA Cup triumphs were no more than his scintillating performances deserved, and many still regard Henry as the Premier League's finest-ever foreign recruit.

Player Records – Miscellaneous

From the first Gunner to see red in a competitive game at Emirates, to Alan Skirton's unprecedented substitute appearance against Northampton and Alex Manninger's Premier League clean sheet record, this section looks at the players who made their own little bit of Arsenal history.

▶ RED CARD RECORD

Patrick Vieira was a famously combative presence in the Gunners' midfield between 1996 and 2005 and it's perhaps no surprise that the Frenchman holds the dubious distinction of being the Arsenal player to receive the most Premier League red cards.

In total, Vieira was sent off eight times in his 279 league appearances for the Club. His first dismissal came in January 1998 in a 2–2 draw with Coventry City at Highfield Road – for dissent after conceding a penalty for handball.

He began the 2000–01 season with successive sending-offs in the two opening fixtures, against Sunderland and Liverpool, while his eighth and final red card was in September 2003 in the goalless draw with Manchester United at Old Trafford – for fouling Ruud van Nistelrooy.

The Frenchman also set a Club record for the most yellow cards in the Premier League, with 72 – which means he was cautioned on average every 3.88 games. His first yellow came in only his second appearance for the Club, in September 1996.

RIGHT: Patrick Vieira was no stranger to the wrath of referees during his Highbury career.

BELOW: Thierry Henry knocks the ball past Wigan goalkeeper Mike Pollitt for one of his three goals in Arsenal's final competitive match at Highbury.

▼ FRENCH FAREWELL

Thierry Henry holds many of the Club's scoring records so it was appropriate that the Frenchman would be the player to score the final goal in a competitive match at Highbury.

The prolific striker netted with a 76th-minute penalty in a 4–2 win over Wigan Athletic on 7 May 2006 to complete his hat-trick and bid farewell to what had been the Club's home for 93 years.

Unsurprisingly Henry was on target two months later at Emirates to register the first goal at the Club's new stadium. The game was Dennis Bergkamp's testimonial against Ajax and the striker christened the ground with a 55th-minute strike, setting up a 2–1 victory.

FANTASTIC FABREGAS

Cesc Fabregas was a talisman for Arsenal during his eight years with the Club and his impact on the side is borne out by the team's phenomenal record in matches in which he scored.

The Spanish midfielder scored 57 goals for the Gunners in all competitions and on only one occasion did Arsenal suffer defeat when he found the back of the net.

That match was the 2005 Community Shield clash with Chelsea at the Millennium Stadium, a game the Blues won 2–1 thanks to two Didier Drogba goals.

In total Arsenal were unbeaten in the 49 league, European and cup games in which Fabregas was on target, winning 41 of them.

McDONALD'S TREBLE

Goalkeeper Hugh McDonald holds the distinction of being the first player to enjoy three different spells with the Club, amassing a total of 103 games for the Gunners between 1906 and 1913.

The Scottish custodian first signed for Arsenal in January 1906 as an understudy for England keeper Jimmy Ashcroft but, after making just two league appearances, he joined Brighton & Hove Albion at the end of the year.

McDonald spent two years on the south coast but returned to London in 1908 when Ashcroft was sold to Blackburn Rovers. He would be the Club's first-choice goalkeeper for two seasons, making 74 appearances in the league.

He was on the move again in 1910 when he was transferred to Oldham Athletic but, after a brief spell with Bradford Park Avenue, he was back at Arsenal in 1912 for a third time. It was to prove only a season-long reunion, however, and after 18 more league games for the Club he left to play for Fulham.

LEFT: Alan Skirton's substitute appearance was a watershed in the tactics of the game.

SILVA'S FIRST

The first competitive goal at Emirates was scored by Gilberto Silva in the side's 1–1 draw with Aston Villa in August 2006. The Brazilian midfielder found the back of the net seven minutes from time with an unstoppable volley, cancelling out Olof Mellberg's earlier effort to earn the Gunners a point in front of a crowd of 60,023 in north London.

ABOVE: Gilberto Silva celebrates after christening Emirates Stadium in 2006.

SKIRTON'S BENCHMARK

The 1965–66 season was the first in English football in which managers could make substitutions. Winger Alan Skirton became the first player in Arsenal's history to come off the bench in a competitive match when they played Northampton Town in September 1965.

The Gunners had already played nine Division One games without manager Billy Wright having to turn to the bench, but that all changed at Highbury against the Cobblers when Skirton was introduced to the action. Wright made six more substitutions over the course of the season, centre-half Peter Simpson leading the way with three appearances as a replacement.

CESC FABREGAS SEASON-BY-SEASON

	League	Cup	Europe	Goals
2003–04	0	3	0	1
2004–05	33	8	5	3
2005–06	35	2	13	5
2006–07	38	6	10	4
2007–08	32	3	10	13
2008–09	22	1	10	3
2009–10	27	1	8	19
2010–11	25	6	5	9
Total:	212	30	61	57

▶ MARVELLOUS MANNINGER

Austrian goalkeeper Alex Manninger made a modest 63 starts during his five-year stint in north London but he still holds the record for most consecutive clean sheets in the Premier League after debut.

His first Premier League appearance came in January 1998 when Arsenal beat Southampton 3–0 at Highbury. Eight days later the Austrian shut Chelsea out and kept a third consecutive clean sheet against Crystal Palace. A goalless draw with West Ham at Upton Park in March and a 1–0 victory away at Wimbledon extended the sequence and he made it six Premier League clean sheets in his first six games when a series of superb saves helped earn Arsene Wenger's side a 1–0 win over Manchester United at Old Trafford.

His feat remains a record – although his seventh league game for the Gunners did end in a thumping 4–0 defeat against Liverpool at Anfield.

DREADFUL DEBUT

Jason Crowe made just three appearances for the Club before he was transferred to Portsmouth in 1999 – and the full-back's debut was definitely one to forget.

His first team bow came as a substitute in extra-time during Arsenal's League Cup clash with Birmingham City at Highbury in October 1997. The 21-year-old had been on the pitch for just 33 seconds when referee Uriah Rennie showed him a red card for a high tackle on a Blues player. It remains the fastest dismissal on debut in the Club's history.

▶ BAD BOY BRADY

Republic of Ireland international Liam Brady was a cultured presence in the Gunners' midfield for seven years during the 1970s – but there was nothing stylish about his behaviour in Arsenal's Division One clash with Stoke City at the Victoria Ground in March 1977.

Midway through the first half, Brady was brought down by Stoke's Steve Waddington. Rather than allow the referee to punish the Potters player, the Irishman got up and struck him in the face with his forearm. The official was far from impressed and showed Brady a straight red card, making him the first Arsenal player ever to be sent off in a competitive match.

The Gunners were on a seven-match losing streak, but much to Brady's relief his team-mates held on for a 1–1 draw despite their numerical disadvantage.

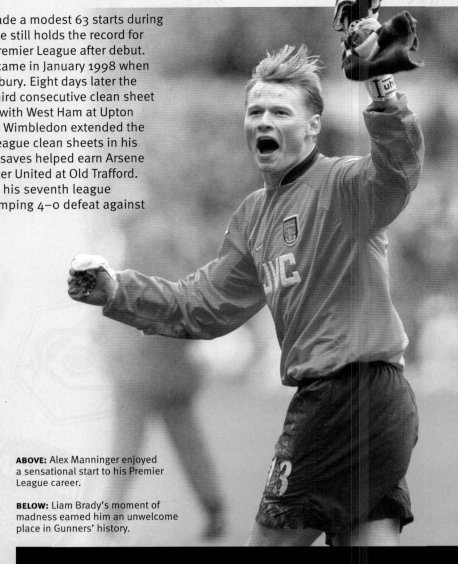

ABOVE: Alex Manninger enjoyed a sensational start to his Premier League career.

BELOW: Liam Brady's moment of madness earned him an unwelcome place in Gunners' history.

◀ BOULD NEW ERA

Steve Bould scored just eight times in his 372 career appearances for the Gunners but the long-serving centre-half does hold the distinction of having scored Arsenal's first-ever Premier League goal.

The defender was on target in the 28th minute of his side's 4–2 defeat to Norwich City at Highbury in August 1992, with the first of 40 goals the Gunners scored in their inaugural Premier League campaign.

LEFT: Steve Bould was the first on target in the inaugural Premier League season.

▼ YELLOW PERIL

The 1976–77 season in English football saw the introduction of yellow and red cards – and George Armstrong became the first Arsenal player to be booked, on 25 August 1976.

The Gunners winger was cautioned during a 3–1 victory over Norwich City at Carrow Road but was quickly followed into the referee's book by team-mates Pat Rice, Liam Brady and David O'Leary.

LEFT: Rarely in trouble with referees, George Armstrong's yellow card against the Canaries in 1976 was history-making.

QUICK-FIRE CAMPBELL

The first goal of a new season is always a moment to celebrate and striker Kevin Campbell holds the Club record for the fastest goal in the Premier League since the competition began in 1992–93.

His effort came in the first fixture of the 1994–95 campaign when he was on target after just two minutes against Manchester City at Highbury. An Ian Wright strike and a Michael Vonk own-goal completed the scoring as Arsenal recorded a 3–0 win.

SENDEROS SENDING-OFF

The Club's debut 2006–07 season at Emirates failed to produce a single red card for an Arsenal player, making Philippe Senderos the first Gunner to get sent off at Ashburton Grove.

The Swiss defender made history in September 2007 against Portsmouth in the Premier League, getting his matching orders in the 50th minute for a professional foul on Pompey striker (and former Gunner) Kanu.

Fortunately for Senderos, Arsene Wenger's side were still too strong for the visitors, running out 3–1 winners.

FIRST PREMIER LEAGUE GOALSCORER

1992–93 – Steve Bould (2–4 v Norwich City, 15 August)
1993–94 – Ian Wright (1–0 v Tottenham, 16 August)
1994–95 – Kevin Campbell (3–0 v Manchester City, 20 August)
1995–96 – Ian Wright (1–1 v Middlesbrough, 20 August)
1996–97 – John Hartson (2–0 v West Ham, 17 August)
1997–98 – Ian Wright (1–1 v Leeds United, 9 August)
1998–99 – Emmanuel Petit (2–1 v Nottingham Forest, 17 August)
1999–2000 – Dennis Bergkamp (2–1 v Leicester, 7 August)
2000–01 – Lauren (2–0 v Liverpool, 21 August)
2001–02 – Thierry Henry (4–0 v Middlesbrough, 18 August)
2002–03 – Thierry Henry (2–0 v Birmingham, 18 August)
2003–04 – Thierry Henry (2–1 v Everton, 16 August)
2004–05 – Dennis Bergkamp (4–1 v Everton, 15 August)
2005–06 – Thierry Henry (2–0 v Newcastle, 14 August)
2006–07 – Gilberto Silva (1–1 v Aston Villa, 19 August)
2007–08 – Robin van Persie (2–1 v Fulham, 12 August)
2008–09 – Samir Nasri (1–0 v West Bromwich, 16 August)
2009–10 – Denilson (6–1 v Everton, 15 August)
2010–11 – Pepe Reina OG (1–1 v Liverpool, 15 August)
2011–12 – Theo Walcott (2–8 v Manchester United, 28 August)
2012–13 – Lukas Podolski (2–0 v Liverpool, 2 September)

Player Records – International

Welshman Caesar Jenkyns became Arsenal's first ever international in 1896 and this section celebrates the records and feats of the Club's players who have followed in his footsteps and represented their countries.

The Gunners have boasted hundreds of internationals and their unprecedented tally of 15 players at the 2006 World Cup finals in Germany was more than any other Club in the world.

From goalkeeper Jimmy Ashcroft, the Club's first England cap in 1906, to the magnificent midfield duo of Emmanuel Petit and Patrick Vieira, the first Gunners to play in a World Cup final in 1998, and German centurion Lukas Podolski, Arsenal players have consistently been at the forefront of the international game.

These pages also commemorate some of the Gunners' more unusual achievements, including Paddy Sloan's unique career as a dual international in the 1940s, Gerry Keyser's game for the Netherlands in the 1930s which began a new chapter in Arsenal history and the infamous 'Battle Of Highbury' against Italy.

The section concludes with a nod to the increasingly global nature of the Gunners' squad and the trailblazing players such as Christopher Wreh, Junichi Inamoto and Frank Simek who have come to north London from far and wide to play for the Club.

BELOW RIGHT: Adams leads England out in September 2000 for the final international played at the old Wembley Stadium.

BELOW LEFT: Tony Adams was a stalwart for England for more than a decade, making 66 appearances between 1987 and 2000.

RIGHT: Adams and Dennis Bergkamp briefly put club allegiances aside when England faced the Netherlands at Euro 96.

KEEPING IT IN THE FAMILY

The first father and son to play for England were George Eastham Senior and George Eastham, the latter winning his 19 caps for his country in the 1960s while he was an Arsenal player.

Eastham Senior played just once for the Three Lions when he was a Bolton player, featuring in a 1–0 victory over Holland in May 1935. His son made his Three Lions debut 28 years later in the 1–1 draw with Brazil at Wembley, making the Easthams the first family to supply England with two generations of players.

SANSOM'S RECORD

Arsenal signed Kenny Sansom from Crystal Palace in the summer of 1980 and the full-back still holds the Club record for the number of England caps amassed while a Gunner.

The defender made his international debut against Wales in May 1979 while he was still a Palace player but 12 months later, and after eight more appearances for his country, he made the switch from Selhurst Park to Highbury.

In total, Sansom won 77 of his 86 England caps while he was with Arsenal, featuring in the 1982 and 1986 World Cup finals and the 1988 European Championship campaign in West Germany.

The first and only goal of his Three Lions career came in a 5–0 win over Finland in a World Cup qualifier in October 1984 at Wembley while his final appearance was against the USSR in June 1988 in Frankfurt.

Eastham Junior was part of Sir Alf Ramsey's squad for the 1966 World Cup campaign and, although he did not play in the tournament in which England were crowned world champions, he was retrospectively awarded a winners' medal by FIFA in 2009.

He scored twice for the Three Lions in his 19 appearances. His second international goal came in his final game, a 2–0 friendly victory over Denmark in Copenhagen in July 1966 – just eight days before England's opening game of the World Cup finals.

RIGHT: George Eastham proudly followed in his father's footsteps when he played for England in the 1960s.

BELOW: With 77 appearances while with Arsenal, Kenny Sansom is still the Gunners' most capped English player.

ENGLAND FIRST

Signed by Harry Bradshaw from Gravesend United in the summer of 1900, goalkeeper Jimmy Ashcroft spent eight years with Arsenal and in his sixth season at the Club he became the first-ever Gunner to represent England.

His Three Lions debut came in the opening fixture of the British Home Championship in February 1906 against Ireland in Belfast. A brace from Dicky Bond and further strikes from Arthur Brown, Stanley Harris and Samuel Day earned England a 5–0 victory.

Ashcroft kept his place in the side and another clean sheet in a 1–0 win over Wales at the Arms Park in Cardiff a month later and he won his third and final cap in April 1906 against Scotland at Hampden Park in Glasgow. This time, however, the Liverpool-born keeper was unable to shut out the opposition as Scotland won 2–1.

WORLD CUP BREAKTHROUGH

England first sent a team to the World Cup in 1950 but it was not until 1982 that English players from Arsenal represented the Three Lions in the finals.

The Gunners who led the way were Graham Rix and Kenny Sansom, who both played in the Ron Greenwood starting XI that beat France 3–1 at the Estadio San Mames in Bilbao in June 1982.

▼ CAPTAIN JACK

A key figure in Arsenal's emergence as a major force in English football in the 1930s, David Jack also holds the distinction of being the first Gunners player to captain England.

The famous inside-right won his first four caps as a Bolton Wanderers player but he made a record-breaking £10,890 transfer to Highbury in October 1928, and in April 1930 he led England out for the first time in the Home Championship clash with Scotland at Wembley.

England won the game 5–2 and Jack wore the captain's armband for the Three Lions in three more matches: a 3–3 draw with Germany in Berlin and goalless draws with Austria and Wales.

BELOW: David Jack (front row, second left) was the first Arsenal player to captain England.

ABOVE: Goalkeeper Jimmy Ashcroft blazed the trail for Arsenal players with the Three Lions, making his debut against Ireland in 1906

BATTLE OF HIGHBURY

Arsenal hold the record for the most players from a single club to represent England in an international, supplying seven of the Three Lions XI that faced Italy at Highbury in November 1934.

The seven Gunners were Frank Moss, George Male, Eddie Hapgood, Wilf Copping, Ray Bowden, Ted Drake and Cliff Bastin and – in an ill-tempered and violent game that became known as the "Battle of Highbury" – England beat the World Cup holders 3–2.

Manchester City's Eric Brook scored the first two goals while Drake added the third as early as the 12th minute.

TOP 10 MOST CAPPED ENGLAND PLAYERS	
Ashley Cole	101 caps
Kenny Sansom	86
David Seaman	75
Sol Campbell	73
Alan Ball	72
Tony Adams	66
David Platt	62
Martin Keown	43
Tony Woodcock	42
Paul Mariner	35

DELAYED DEBUT

Leslie Compton won just two caps for England but his first international appearance set a Three Lions record for the oldest outfield debutant ever.

The Gunners centre-half was 38 years and 64 days old when he played for England in the team's 4–2 victory against Wales at Roker Park in November 1950, eclipsing Newcastle United's 35-year-old Frank Hudspeth as the Three Lions' oldest first-timer.

Wanderers goalkeeper Alex Morten is the oldest-ever England debutant at 41 years and 113 days (set in 1873) but Compton remains the most senior outfield player in the history of the national side.

CAMPBELL ON TARGET

Only one Arsenal player has ever scored for England in a World Cup finals game – and the honour is held by Sol Campbell after his effort for the Three Lions against Sweden in 2002.

The central defender scored with a 24th-minute header against the Swedes in the Saitama Stadium in Japan in the group stages to earn Sven-Goran Eriksson's side a 1–1 draw.

Former Gunners Paul Mariner and Matthew Upson have also scored for England in the finals but neither were with Arsenal at the time they found the net.

Mariner scored in a 3–1 defeat of France in Bilbao at the 1982 World Cup in Spain, two years before he signed for the Gunners from Ipswich Town, while Upson's effort against Germany at the 2010 finals in South Africa came seven years after he'd left Highbury for Birmingham City.

ABOVE: Leslie Compton left it late to play for his country in a full international, making his debut two months into his 39th year.

CAPTAIN FANTASTIC

Tony Adams won 66 caps for England in an international career that spanned 13 years and the legendary Gunner holds the record for captaining the Three Lions at the most matches in European Championship finals.

The centre-half was named skipper by manager Terry Venables for the Euro 96 tournament and he led the side against Switzerland, Scotland and the Netherlands in the group stages.

He also wore the captain's armband for the quarter-final victory over Spain in a penalty shootout, and in the agonizing defeat to Germany in another shootout at Wembley. His five Championship appearances as skipper remains a Three Lions record.

Adams was also the first Arsenal player to captain England in the finals.

EUROPEAN BOW

Adams was the first Gunner to lead England at the European Championships. He and Highbury team-mate Kenny Sansom were the first Arsenal players to play for the Three Lions at the finals.

The duo made their Championship debut at the 1988 tournament in West Germany, playing in the Three Lions' 1–0 defeat against the Republic of Ireland in Stuttgart.

RIGHT: Tony Adams was an inspirational leader for both club and country.

BASTIN'S DOZEN

Cliff Bastin scored 178 times in 396 appearances for the Gunners while his 12 goals for England in 21 games is still a record for an Arsenal player.

The iconic outside-left was first capped by the Three Lions against Wales in November 1931 and in May 1933 he opened his England account in a 1–1 draw with Italy in Rome. He scored two braces for his country, the first coming just seven days after the Italy game when he was on target twice in a 4–0 demolition of Switzerland in Berne. His second double was in February 1935 in the 2–1 defeat of Ireland at Goodison Park.

LEFT: Cliff Bastin's 12-goal haul for England remains a Club record.

England lost only twice when Bastin scored, a 2–1 reverse against Wales at Ninian Park in October 1936 and a 2–1 defeat to Switzerland in May 1938. His final goal for the Three Lions came later that month, in a 4–2 rout of France in Paris.

Former Gunners David Platt and Tony Woodcock both scored more goals for England but they were not Arsenal players for the whole of their international careers.

Midfielder Platt scored 27 international goals but only one – his strike in the 3–0 defeat of Hungary at Wembley in May 1996 – came while he was at Highbury.

Woodcock found the back of the net 16 times in England colours but the first seven of his goals came while he was playing in Germany for Cologne. He signed for Arsenal in the summer of 1982 and hit nine England goals as a Gunner before returning to Cologne in 1986.

TEENAGE KICKS

Theo Walcott made history in May 2006 when he became the youngest player ever to represent the senior England side. Signed to Arsenal from Southampton in January 2006, the winger was just 17 years and 75 days old when he came off the bench in the Three Lions' clash with Hungary at Old Trafford, replacing Michael Owen after 65 minutes.

Walcott's appearance eclipsed the previous record of 17 years and 111 days set by Wayne Rooney against Australia in February 2003.

LEFT: Theo Walcott beat Wayne Rooney's record as England's youngest debutant.

CLIFF BASTIN'S ENGLAND GOALS

England 1 Italy (3 May 1933)
England 4 (2 goals) Switzerland 0 (20 May 1933)
England 3 Scotland 0 (14 April 1934)
England 2 (2 goals) Northern Ireland 1 (6 February 1935)
England 3 Germany 0 (4 December 1935)
England 1 Wales 2 (17 October 1936)
England 3 Northern Ireland 1 (18 November 1936)
England 6 Germany 3 (14 May 1938)
England 1 Switzerland 2 (21 May 1938)
England 4 France 2 (26 May 1938)

DUAL INTERNATIONAL

Inside-forward Paddy Sloan signed for Arsenal from Tranmere Rovers in 1947 and has the unusual claim to fame of having represented both the Republic of Ireland and Northern Ireland at full international level.

Sloan's curious international career began in 1945, while he was still a Tranmere player when he was selected by the Irish Football Association, the governing body of the game in Northern Ireland, to play against England at Windsor Park. He won his second cap against Wales at Ninian Park in May the following year.

Following his move to Highbury, however, he was called up by the Football Association of Ireland to tour with the Republic of Ireland side in the summer of 1946, playing in a 3–1 defeat to Portugal in Lisbon and a shock 1–0 victory over Spain in Madrid.

In April 1947 he made a third and final appearance for Northern Ireland against Wales in Belfast.

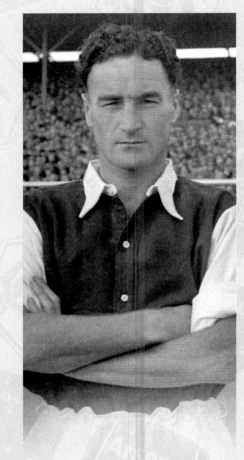

IRISH LEGENDS

Niall Quinn (92), Liam Brady (72) and Frank Stapleton (71) all won more caps for the Republic of Ireland than David O'Leary – but the centre-half appeared in more games than any of them for the Republic while he was an Arsenal player.

All 68 of O'Leary's caps came while he was at Highbury. The highlight of his international career was at the 1990 World Cup in Italy when he scored the winning penalty in the shootout against Romania, in the last 16 of the tournament.

WORLD CUP MILESTONE

The inaugural World Cup was staged in Uruguay in 1930, but it was not until the 1958 instalment of the competition in Sweden that Arsenal players were involved.

The two trailblazers were inside-half Dave Bowen and goalkeeper Jack Kelsey, who were both named in the Wales XI to face Hungary in the tournament opener at the Jernvallen Stadium in June. Wales drew the match 1–1 and eventually qualified for the quarter-finals.

Both Bowen and Kelsey were subsequently in the side that lost 1–0 in the last eight to Brazil in Gothenburg – to a Pele goal.

ABOVE: Paddy Sloan played for both the Republic of Ireland and Northern Ireland in a five-match international career.

BELOW: Jack Kelsey was the first goalkeeper to concede a World Cup goal scored by Brazil's legendary Pele.

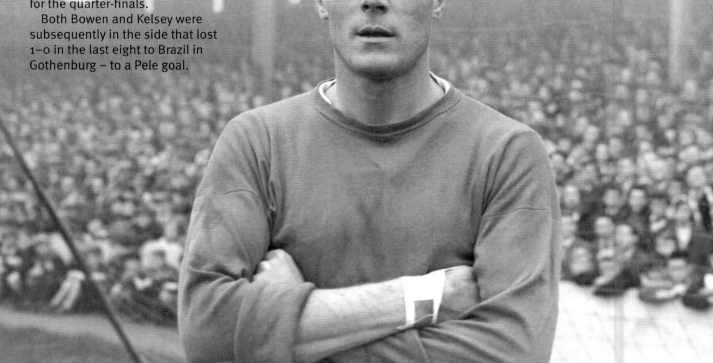

HAIL CAESAR

Jimmy Ashcroft was the first Arsenal player to be capped by England, in 1906, but a full decade before his appointment with the Three Lions it was Welshman Caesar Jenkyns who earned the distinction of being the Club's first-ever full international.

The centre-half from Powys joined the Club from Small Heath in April 1895, three years after making his Wales debut, and in March 1896 he became the Gunners' first international when he was selected to play against Scotland in Dundee.

He won eight caps for his country but spent just one season with Arsenal, ending his association with the Club in May 1896 when he signed for Newton Heath.

BELOW: Chesterfield-born Bob Wilson headed north of the border to kickstart his international career.

ABOVE: Caesar Jenkyns (back row, fourth left) was Woolwich Arsenal's first international, playing for Wales, during his one season with the Club.

SCOTTISH SWITCH

A veteran of 308 games for Arsenal, goalkeeper Bob Wilson was born in Chesterfield but played twice for Scotland, becoming the first Englishman in almost a century to be selected by the SFA.

Wilson's parents both hailed from north of the border and a change in the rules on eligibility in 1970 paved the way for his Scotland debut against Portugal in a European Championship qualifier in Glasgow in October 1971. His second cap came against the Netherlands in Rotterdam two months later.

In total, 18 players have represented Scotland while on the books at Arsenal.

RICE'S RECORD

Belfast-born Pat Rice holds the Club record for the most caps for Northern Ireland, playing 49 internationals for his country between 1968 and 1979.

The full-back won his first cap against Israel in September 1968 while his final appearance for Northern Ireland was against England in a European Championship qualifier in October 1979.

Just behind Rice are former Gunner Sammy Nelson, who played 47 times for Northern Ireland, and Terry Neill, who won 44 caps.

A CENTURY OF CAPS

The likes of Thierry Henry, Patrick Vieira and Ashley Cole have gone on to reach the 100 international appearances milestone after leaving the Club – but Lukas Podolski is the only man with a century of caps to play for Arsenal.

The midfielder played his 100th game for Germany in a 2–1 victory over Denmark in the group stages of Euro 2012 and officially became a Gunners player on 1 July.

He won his 102nd cap in a World Cup qualifier against the Faroe Islands in September 2012 to become the first Arsenal international centurion.

▶ THE FRENCH CONNECTION

Thierry Henry graced Highbury and subsequently Emirates for eight glorious seasons – and during his record-breaking spell in north London he also set the Club record for the most caps accumulated by an Arsenal player.

The striker played for France 123 times between 1997 and 2010, and 81 of his caps were earned while he was a Gunner. His international debut came as a 20-year-old against South Africa in October 1997, while his first game for *Les Bleus* after signing for Arsenal was against Scotland at Hampden Park in March 2000, where he scored in a 2–0 victory.

Henry continued to represent his country after joining Barcelona in 2007 but his 81 appearances while with Arsenal remains a record. He scored 38 goals in those 81 matches, which is also an Arsenal milestone.

Compatriot Patrick Vieira is second on the all-time list with 79 games for France during his nine-year association with the Club.

WORLDWIDE GUNNERS

Up to October 2012, Gunners players past, future and present had represented 43 different countries beyond Britain and Ireland at international level.

France led the way with 18 capped players who had also represented Arsenal in their career while the Netherlands were second on the list with six. Brazil and Sweden were joint third with five international Gunners.

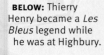

BELOW: Thierry Henry became a *Les Bleus* legend while he was at Highbury.

◀ VICTORIOUS VIEIRA

Legendary midfielder Patrick Vieira is the most successful international player in terms of silverware in Arsenal's history. The Frenchman lifted the 1998 World Cup and 2000 European Championship with *Les Bleus* and made it an unprecedented hat-trick of trophies in 2001 when France beat Japan in the final of the 2001 Confederations Cup.

Vieira scored the only goal of the match in the 30th minute of the match against the hosts in the Yokohama International Stadium to seal his trophy treble.

LEFT: Patrick Vieira won three major international trophies during his Arsenal career, including helping France to claim the FIFA Confederations Cup against Japan in 2001.

ABOVE: Emmanuel Petit scored France's third goal in the 1998 World Cup final against Brazil, the last World Cup goal of the 20th century.

LEFT: John Kosmina signed for Arsenal from his hometown club Adelaide City.

◀ FINAL FIRST

The first Arsenal players to play in a World Cup final were Emmanuel Petit and Patrick Vieira, who both featured in France's 3–0 victory over Brazil in Paris in July 1998.

Petit was named in Aime Jacquet's starting XI for the clash with the South Americans in the Stade de France and scored the third goal in injury-time in a famous 3–0 triumph. Vieira started the match on the bench but entered the fray after 74 minutes when he replaced Youri Djorkaeff.

Midfielder Cesc Fabregas emulated the achievement 12 years later when he was part of the Spanish squad that won the 2010 World Cup in South Africa. Named on the bench for the final against the Netherlands in Johannesburg, Fabregas came on for Xabi Alonso in the 87th minute as the game headed towards extra-time.

Alan Ball, Thierry Henry, Robert Pires and Gilberto Silva all won World Cup winner's medals – but not while they were with Arsenal.

◀ AUSTRALIAN ARRIVAL

The only Australian international to play for the Gunners is John Kosmina, a £20,000 buy from Adelaide City in March 1978. Capped 60 times by the Socceroos, the striker made just one league appearance for the Club, as a substitute in a 2–2 draw with Leeds United at Highbury in August 1978, and headed back to Australia the following year when he signed for the West Adelaide Hellas club.

MOST CAPS AS AN ARSENAL PLAYER

Thierry Henry (France)	81 caps
Patrick Vieira (France)	79
Kenny Sansom (England)	77
David Seaman (England)	72
David O'Leary (Republic of Ireland)	68
Robin van Persie (Netherlands)	68
Tony Adams (England)	66
Freddie Ljungberg (Sweden)	60
Cesc Fabregas (Spain)	58
Nicklas Bendtner (Denmark)	55

EUROPEAN CHAMPIONS

France's 2–1 victory over Italy in the final of Euro 2000 saw Patrick Vieira and Thierry Henry become the first Arsenal players to claim the European Championship crown.

The midfielder and the striker were both in the starting XI for the clash in Rotterdam, a game the French won 2–1 in extra-time courtesy of David Trezeguet's golden goal.

Future Gunners Robert Pires and Sylvain Wiltord also featured in the final, signing for the Club after France's triumph.

Midfielder Cesc Fabregas is Arsenal's only other European Championship winner, claiming the title with Spain in 2008 after a 1–0 victory against Germany in Vienna. Santi Cazorla also played in the match in the Ernst-Happel-Stadion, four years before signing for Arsenal from Malaga.

John Jensen was in the Danish side that beat Germany 2–0 in the final of the 1992 European Championship and became an Arsenal player two months later when George Graham signed him from Brondby.

 EASTERN PROMISE

Three international players from Asia have represented the Gunners. Japanese midfielder Junichi Inamoto led the way when he signed for Arsenal from Gamba Osaka in the summer of 2001, and a decade later compatriot Ryo Miyaichi signed his first professional contract with the Club.

South Korea winger Park Chu-Young became Arsenal's third Asian signing in August 2011 when he signed from Monaco, making his debut in a 3–1 League Cup victory over Shrewsbury at Emirates in September.

 THE HALF-CENTURY

A total of 12 players have won 50 or more caps for their respective countries while they were on Arsenal's books. The first player to reach the milestone was England full-back Kenny Sansom, while the most recent was Danish striker Nicklas Bendtner.

The other players on the elite list are Thierry Henry, Patrick Vieira, David Seaman, David O'Leary, Robin van Persie, Tony Adams, Freddie Ljungberg, Cesc Fabregas, Gilberto Silva and Ashley Cole.

ABOVE: Junichi Inamoto had already been capped by Japan when he arrived at Highbury.

LEFT: Nicklas Bendtner of Denmark is one of a dozen Gunners to play 50 international matches.

ABOVE: Christopher Wreh swapped Liberia for London when he signed for the Gunners.

CONTINENTAL CUSTODIAN

Dutch goalkeeper Gerry Keyser was the first non-British or Irish player to represent Arsenal in competitive action and made 12 league appearances for Herbert Chapman's side in the 1930–31 season as the Gunners were crowned Division One champions for the first time.

Keyser spent just one season at the Club, and after brief spells with Charlton and QPR he returned to the Netherlands to play for Ajax. It was during his time in Amsterdam that he won two caps for Holland in 1934, making him the first (albeit former) Gunner to play international football for a non-Home Nations team.

AMERICAN CONTINGENT

Six full South American internationals have played for the Gunners, with Brazilians Silvinho, Edu, Gilberto Silva, Julio Baptista and Andre Santos and Argentina's Nelson Vivas all pulling on the famous red and white shirt.

Central America is represented by Mexico's Carlos Vela, who made 62 appearances for the Club between 2008 and 2012, while the only international player from North America is USA defender Frank Simek whose one game for Arsenal came in a League Cup clash against Wolves in December 2003.

AFRICAN PIONEER

South African winger Daniel Le Roux was the first player from Africa to play for Arsenal, in the 1950s, but it was not until 1997 that the Gunners had a full African international in their ranks. Signed by Arsene Wenger from Monaco in a £300,000 deal, the player was Liberian striker Christopher Wreh.

The West African spent three seasons at Highbury, winning the 1997–98 Premier League and starting in the 1998 FA Cup final victory over Newcastle. His international career spanned seven years, winning 36 caps for the Lone Stars.

Le Roux did represent South Africa in his career but his appearances came during the side's amateur era.

In addition to Liberia, nine further African nations have supplied the Gunners with current or future international players. The countries are Togo, Senegal, Ivory Coast, Libya, Guinea, Ghana, Cameroon, Morocco and Nigeria.

GLOBAL INFLUENCE

The 2006 World Cup in Germany saw Arsenal supply 15 players to their respective countries, more than any other club.

Three Gunners represented England – Ashley Cole, Sol Campbell and Theo Walcott – while Kolo Toure and Emmanuel Eboue were on duty for the Ivory Coast. Johan Djourou and Philippe Senderos were selected by Switzerland while Cesc Fabregas and Jose Antonio Reyes were part of the Spain squad.

The other Arsenal players at the tournament were Jens Lehmann (Germany), Freddie Ljungberg (Sweden), Robin van Persie (Holland), Gilberto Silva (Brazil), Thierry Henry (France) and Emmanuel Adebayor (Togo).

RIGHT: Dutch goalkeeper Gerry Keyser broke the mould when he joined Arsenal ahead the 1930–31 season.

MOST INTERNATIONAL HONOURS AS AN ARSENAL PLAYER

Patrick Vieira – 3 (1998 World Cup, Euro 2000, 2001 Confederations Cup)
Thierry Henry – 2 (Euro 2000, 2003 Confederations Cup)
Sylvain Wiltord – 2 (2001, 2003 Confederations Cup)
Cesc Fabregas – 2 (Euro 2008, 2010 World Cup)
Robert Pires – 2 (2001, 2003 Confederations Cup)
Gilberto Silva – 2 (2005 Confederations, 2007 Copa America)
Lauren – 2 (2000 Olympics, 2002 Africa Cup of Nations)

PART 3
Other Records

Arsenal are one of the best-supported teams in the world and over the years hundreds of thousands of fans have streamed through the turnstiles to watch the Gunners in action.

The first pages of this chapter detail all the Club's record attendances – from the modest days of matches on Plumstead Common in the 1880s to the crowds seen at Emirates since Arsenal moved into their state-of-the-art new home in the summer of 2006.

Next up is a review of the achievements of the Club's managers with a special focus on George Graham and Arsene Wenger, the two most successful coaches in Arsenal's history and the winners of 13 major trophies between them.

The Gunners' stadiums from the old Invicta Ground, the team's 93-year love affair with Highbury and the recent relocation to Ashburton Grove are detailed in the middle section before four pages devoted to the north London derby and Arsenal's enduring and passionate rivalry with neighbours Tottenham.

The chapter ends with miscellaneous Club records, including the side's landmark European firsts, its unique role in the development of televised football, Australian John Kosmina's bizarre claim to Gunners fame and details of the last time the Club started a game with 11 Englishmen in the starting line-up.

ABOVE: Highbury's fabled marble hall, with its bust of legendary manager Herbert Chapman.

RIGHT: The Gunners faithful show their true colours as Arsenal begin a new era at Emirates.

Other Records – Attendances

From the record 73,295 fans who were at Highbury in 1935 for the visit of Sunderland to the 60,023 supporters in attendance for the first-ever competitive match at Emirates, this section focuses on the biggest crowds in Arsenal's history.

▶ WEMBLEY WOE

The Gunners' first two seasons of Champions League football saw the Club hierarchy take the decision to play "home" games at Wembley rather than Highbury. The team's supporters flocked in their thousands to watch.

The record attendance for a Wembley game was the 73,707 who watched Arsene Wenger's side tackle Lens in the group stages of the competition in November 1998.

Unfortunately Arsenal were unable to deliver the win the crowd craved and slipped to a 1–0 defeat after a Mickael Debeve goal – a result which saw them eliminated from that season's tournament.

The Gunners played six Champions League group phase games at Wembley between September 1998 and October 1999 with an aggregate total of 438,072 supporters attending the matches.

ABOVE: Wembley was packed when French side Lens were the opponents in 1998.

BELOW: The League Cup visit of Shrewsbury Town failed to capture the imagination of the Gunners faithful.

▼ LEAGUE CUP LOW

The early rounds of the League Cup do not always produce the most glamorous of matches and Arsenal's third-round clash with Shrewsbury Town certainly failed to capture the imagination as a record-low crowd of 46,539 turned up at Emirates for the game in September 2011.

Arsene Wenger selected an experimental side but, despite the empty seats at Emirates, his unfamiliar team still ran out 3–1 winners against their League Two opponents with the goals coming from Kieran Gibbs, Yossi Benayoun and Alex Oxlade-Chamberlain.

 EMIRATES ERA

The first-ever competitive match staged at Emirates saw Aston Villa travel to north London for the opening game of the 2006–07 Premier League campaign. But the christening of the new stadium in August didn't go exactly according to plan.

A crowd of 60,023 swelled the Club's new home, but an Olof Mellberg goal for Villa threatened to spoil the party, and the Gunners faithful were grateful when Gilberto Silva's 84th-minute equalizer saved the day.

HIGHBURY HIGH

Arsenal spent 93 years at Highbury before relocating from London N5 to Emirates in the summer of 2006. The biggest crowd ever to cram into the famous old stadium was the 73,295 who watched the Gunners play Sunderland in a First Division clash in March 1935.

The Wearsiders had beaten George Allison's side 2–1 at Roker Park earlier in the season, but hopes of exacting revenge at Highbury fell flat as Arsenal were held to a goalless draw by the visitors.

FEWEST FANS

The 1960s was a relatively lean period for Arsenal and the lack of success on the pitch was reflected by the meagre crowd of just 4,554 who were at Highbury to watch the side play Leeds United in the First Division in May 1966.

It was a record low attendance and the lack of support didn't do Billy Wright's side any favours as the Gunners crashed to a 3–0 defeat, with two goals from Jim Storrie and one from Jimmy Greenhoff.

ABOVE: Sunderland goalkeeper Jimmy Thorpe kept a clean sheet when he played in front of Highbury's record crowd, 73,295, in 1935.

ABOVE: The move to Emirates Stadium in 2006 has seen Arsenal's attendances soar.

 TICKET BONANZA

The 1934–35 season was undoubtedly a good one for Arsenal on the pitch as George Allison's side claimed the Division One title for a fourth time in the Club's history.

The Gunners' accountants were also extremely happy, with the Club generating an estimated £100,000 in gate receipts over the course of the season, the first time an English side had reached six figures for ticket sales.

One of the biggest crowds of the campaign was the 70,544 at Highbury who paid to watch the north London derby against Spurs in October. Their loyalty was rewarded as the Gunners crushed the old rivals 5–1 courtesy of a Ted Drake hat-trick.

The record attendance of the season, however, came for the Sunderland match in March. The Wearsiders were Arsenal's main title rivals and the importance of the game was reflected by the 73,295 who packed Highbury to watch what turned out to be a goalless draw.

HOME ATTENDANCES – HIGHEST

Highbury
73,295 v Sunderland, 9 March 1935 (League)

Emirates Stadium
60,161 v Manchester United, 3 November 2007 (Premier League)

Wembley Stadium
73,707 v RC Lens, 25 November 1998 (Champions League)

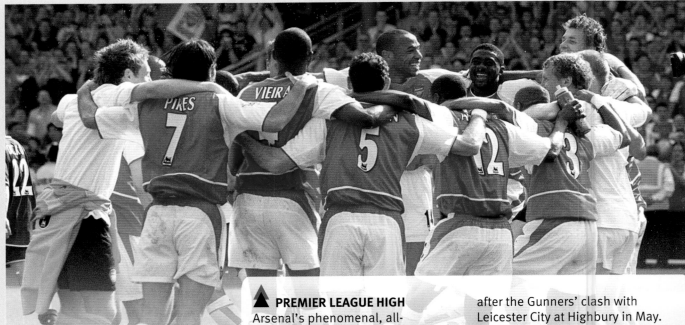

ABOVE: The Invincibles celebrate their record-breaking achievement before collecting the Premiership trophy at Highbury in May 2004.

▶ LEAGUE DEBUT

The Manor Ground in Plumstead was Arsenal's home for 20 years from 1893 and the stadium was the venue for the Gunners' first-ever Football League fixture.

The Division Two match in September 1893 saw Newcastle United in town and goals from Walter Shaw and Arthur Elliott were enough to earn Arsenal a 2–2 draw in front of a 10,000-strong crowd.

Attendances fluctuated over the rest of the Second Division campaign with a modest 2,000 turning up to watch the 3–1 victory over Grimsby Town in September, while a season-best 13,000 were in the stands for the 2–1 defeat against Notts County in March.

The biggest crowd of the year, however, was in November for the FA Cup third qualifying-round encounter with Millwall, a game which attracted an impressive gathering of 20,000 fans to the Manor Ground.

The Gunners players responded admirably to the support, winning the tie 2–0 courtesy of goals from wing-half Fred Davis and outside-left Charles Booth.

▲ PREMIER LEAGUE HIGH

Arsenal's phenomenal, all-conquering 2003–04 season saw Arsene Wenger's Invincibles wrap up the Premier League title by the end of April with a 2–2 draw with Tottenham at White Hart Lane. But it was not until the final day of the season that the side were officially presented with the trophy.

The presentation was scheduled after the Gunners' clash with Leicester City at Highbury in May. After goals from Thierry Henry and Patrick Vieira sealed a 2–1 victory and preserved the side's incredible unbeaten record, the silverware was handed over.

Captain Vieira was the first to hold the trophy in front of a crowd of 38,419, the highest attendance at Highbury in Premier League history.

BELOW: The Manor Ground in Plumstead witnessed the start of Arsenal's Football League adventure in 1893, but this match against Liverpool was in 1906.

Arsenal v. Liverpool at Plumstead 6·10·06.

SECOND-TIER FAREWELL

Arsenal's long and proud record as a top-flight club began in 1919 after the end of the Second World War, making their Division Two clash with Nottingham Forest in April 1915 the Gunners' last lower-league game.

The match at Highbury saw George Morrell's team thrash the visitors 7–0, with Harry King scoring four. A crowd of 10,000 were on hand to witness the Club's farewell to the Second Division.

HIGHBURY DEBUT

The Gunners bid farewell to the Manor Ground in Plumstead in the summer of 1913 and headed north of the river, relocating to Highbury and signalling a new era for the Club.

The first-ever competitive match at the stadium saw George Morrell's team play Leicester Fosse in a Division Two clash in early September 1913, and a 20,000-strong crowd flocked to the new ground to see the action.

The visitors threatened to spoil the party with a first-half goal but a George Jobey strike and an Archie Devine penalty, awarded for handball, ensured Arsenal christened their new home in appropriate winning style.

HIGHBURY SWANSONG

The last-ever competitive match to be staged at Highbury was Arsenal's Premier League clash with Wigan in May 2006, a game that drew a crowd of 38,359 for an emotional afternoon in the Club's history.

A Thierry Henry hat-trick and a Robert Pires goal sealed a 4–2 victory for the Gunners.

The attendance for the Wigan match was 219 bigger than the crowd of 38,140 who poured through the turnstiles for Arsene Wenger's first match in charge at Highbury, a goalless draw with Coventry in October 1996.

ABOVE: Arsenal goalkeeper George Swindin prepares to block a header from Manchester United's Jimmy Delaney, watched by a League-record crowd of 83,260 at United's temporary Maine Road home

GUNNERS TREBLE

The three highest attendances in the history of the old Division One were all for matches featuring Arsenal, underlining the enduring popularity of the Club.

The First Division's crowd record was set in January 1948 when Tom Whittaker's side headed north to face Manchester United, a game witnessed by 83,260 supporters and one which the Gunners drew 1–1 courtesy of a goal from striker Reg Lewis.

Arsenal's visit to Stamford Bridge to play Chelsea in October 1935 attracted the division's second-highest-ever attendance with 82,905 fans, and it was another 1–1 stalemate thanks to a Jack Crayston strike.

Another trip to Manchester in February 1935 – this time to face City at Maine Road – drew Division One's third-biggest crowd with 79,491 spectators – and yet again the points were shared as Ray Bowden scored in the 1–1 draw.

DERBY RECORD

Tickets for the north London derby are invariably snapped up within minutes of going on sale but the 1991 FA Cup semi-final between Arsenal and Tottenham presented a record number of fans with the opportunity to watch the two old rivals do battle.

Wembley was chosen as the neutral venue for the last-four showdown, meaning 77,893 supporters were able to watch the game.

Unfortunately for the Gunners contingent in the record crowd, it was Spurs who emerged 3–1 winners and were back at Wembley for the final a month later.

LEFT: The 1991 north London derby at Wembley was watched by a record crowd

HOME ATTENDANCES – LOWEST
Highbury
4,554 v Leeds United, 5 May 1966 (League)
Emirates Stadium
46,539 v Shrewsbury Town, 20 September 2011 (League Cup)
Wembley Stadium
71,227 v AIK Solna, 22 September 1999 (Champions League)

▶ OLYMPIC VENUE

As well as playing host to England, Highbury was also used as a venue for the 1948 Olympics and hosted two matches during the course of the Games.

The first, at the end of July, saw the Great Britain side dramatically beat the Netherlands 4–3 after extra-time in the first round in front of a 21,000-strong crowd.

The quarter-final showdown between Denmark and Italy six days later, however, proved even more popular – with 25,000 fans in attendance as the Danes beat the Azzurri 5–3 to book their place in the last four at Wembley.

CHARITY BEGINS AT HOME

The Charity Shield became English football's traditional season opener at Wembley in 1974, but before the game was switched to the home of the England team Arsenal contested the fixture at Highbury five times.

The first time saw George Allison's team demolish Manchester City 4–0 in November 1934 in front of a crowd of 10,888, while the final Highbury instalment of the Charity Shield – a 3–1 victory over Blackpool in October 1953 – was watched by 39,853 fans.

The record crowd for the fixture, however, was in attendance for the game against Preston North End in September 1938 when 40,296 supporters packed Highbury to witness Ted Drake score twice in a 2–1 triumph.

RIGHT: Highbury staged two matches at the 1948 Olympic Games: this first-round match between Great Britain and the Netherlands and a quarter-final tie.

▼ CUP CONNECTION

During its 93-year-long life, Highbury was chosen as the neutral venue for a total of 12 FA Cup semi-finals.

The opening last-four clash at the ground saw Portsmouth beat Aston Villa in March 1929 while the last semi-final was between Chelsea and Wimbledon in April 1997, a game the Blues won 3–0 in front of 32,674 spectators.

BELOW: FA Cup semi-finals were held at Highbury for 58 years, but with all semi-finals now at Wembley, Emirates (top) isn't needed.

FIGHT NIGHT

In the football fraternity, 1966 is famed for England's pulsating extra-time victory over West Germany at Wembley in the World Cup – but in the same year Highbury played host to another famous sporting occasion, the second fight between Henry Cooper and Muhammad Ali.

The ring was built in the middle of the pitch at Highbury and 45,973 tickets were sold for the world heavyweight championship bout. Sadly for the Cooper fans, the fight was stopped by the referee in the sixth round due to a cut over the English champion's left eye. Ali retained his title.

INTERNATIONAL DUTY

England played matches at Highbury 12 times during the ground's lifetime and five times the games attracted 50,000-plus crowds to roar on the Three Lions.

The first time was in December 1931 when 55,000 thronged the Gunners' home to watch England demolish Spain 7–1 in a friendly. Three years later there were 56,044 supporters at the ground to witness a 3–2 win against the Italians courtesy of goals from Eric Brook (2) and Arsenal striker Ted Drake, a game which became known as the "Battle of Highbury".

The record attendance for an England game at Highbury, however, was in November 1950 when Yugoslavia were the visitors to north London. The game was watched by 61,000 people and ended in a 2–2 draw thanks to a brace from legendary Bolton Wanderers centre-forward Nat Lofthouse.

ABOVE: Henry Cooper and Muhammad Ali did battle at Highbury back in 1966.

RARE RUGBY VISIT

The Australian rugby league side embarked on its third tour of Britain in 1921 and in October the Kangaroos made an unlikely appearance at Highbury against England.

The rest of the matches were staged in the north of the country or Wales, but the tourists headed south for the eighth game of their trip, attracting 12,000 spectators to witness a rare game of rugby league in the capital – and a 6–5 victory for England.

BELGIAN MATCH

The second of England's visits to Highbury to play Belgium in March 1923 was also their first full home match against a side outside Great Britain and Ireland.

The Three Lions were far more accustomed to playing Wales, Scotland and Ireland, but found the new opposition to their liking, despatching the Belgians 6–1 in front of 25,000 delirious England supporters.

BELOW: A dozen internationals were played at Highbury, N5, starting with the 1931 clash between England and Spain.

ARSENAL'S TOP FIVE ATTENDANCES

83,260	Manchester United v Arsenal	17/01/1948	(Division 1)
82,905	Chelsea v Arsenal	12/10/1935	(Division 1)
79,491	Manchester City v Arsenal	23/02/1935	(Division 1)
75,952	Chelsea v Arsenal	09/10/1937	(Division 1)
74,918	Manchester City v Arsenal	10/04/1937	(Division 1)

Other Records – Managers

This section is devoted to the records, milestones and trophies of the Club's managers from Scotsman Thomas Mitchell in the late 1880s, the Gunners' first professional coach, to the arrival of Arsene Wenger in 1996.

ABOVE: Harry Bradshaw took the Gunners into the First Division for the first time.

ABOVE: George Morrell's seven-year reign as manager was not a successful one.

▲ MORRELL'S MISERY

Famously Arsenal have been relegated just once in the Club's illustrious history – and George Morrell holds the unfortunate distinction of being the manager who oversaw the season in which they went down.

Appointed manager in February 1908, the Scot was forced to sanction the sale of some of the Club's leading players to balance the books, and eventually the exodus of talent caught up with Arsenal.

Morrell's team flirted with relegation during the 1909–10 campaign, only to escape the drop with an 18th-place finish. But there was no hiding place in 1912–13 when the side finished rock-bottom with just three victories in 38 league games.

The manager stayed with the Gunners despite the disappointment.

The Club relocated to Highbury and, although the side failed to secure an automatic return to the top-flight in 1913–14, the team's fifth-place finish the following season proved enough to earn an unusual return to Division One and a degree of redemption for Morrell.

Fifth place, of course, would not have won automatic promotion, but league football was suspended in 1915 due to the First World War. When competitive football returned in 1919, Arsenal were included in a new First Division that been expanded from 20 to 22 teams.

The decision to elevate the Gunners was partly based on the strength of Morrell's fifth place and, although he had resigned at the end of the 1914–15 campaign, it provided a happy footnote to what otherwise might have been a wholly miserable managerial career.

▲ BRADSHAW'S TRIUMPH

The Gunners' third professional manager, Harry Bradshaw, arrived in north London in August 1899 from his home-town club of Burnley and earned his place in the Arsenal record books as the first man to mastermind a successful promotion campaign.

His groundbreaking achievement came in the 1903–04 season when he steered the Gunners into second place in the final Division Two table, finishing a single point behind champions Preston North End and earning the Club a place in the top tier of English football for the first time.

His team won 21 of their 34 league fixtures during the campaign and were beaten just six times. Bradshaw's side were the division's most prolific scorers with 91 goals, Irish forward Tommy Shanks top-scoring in the league with 24.

Bradshaw also holds the distinction of being the first Arsenal manager to take charge of the team for 100 games, but left the Club at the end of the 1903–04 campaign when he accepted a lucrative offer to join Fulham.

PLAYER TURNED BOSS

The first man to play for Arsenal and then go on to manage the Club was Tom Whittaker, a wing-half for the Gunners for six years after the end of the First World War and subsequently the team's manager in the wake of the Second World War.

Born in Aldershot, Whittaker signed for the Gunners in 1919 and made his debut in a 1–0 defeat to West Bromwich Albion at the Hawthorns in April 1920. In total he clocked up 70 games for the Club, but his playing career was prematurely cut short by a persistent knee injury and his appearance against West Ham at Highbury in March 1925 was to be his last.

After his enforced retirement, Whittaker studied physiotherapy before legendary boss Hebert Chapman appointed him Arsenal's first team trainer in 1927. Twenty years later he was given the job of manager, succeeding George Allison.

His nine-year Highbury reign was certainly a highly successful one, with the Gunners winning the 1947–48 Division One title in his first season at the helm. He claimed a second title for the Club in 1952–53 while his team were also triumphant in the 1950 FA Cup final, beating Liverpool 2–0 at Wembley courtesy of a brace of goals from Reg Lewis.

Whittaker died of a heart attack in October 1956, at the age of 58, but his successful transition from player to manager remains a milestone in the Gunners' history.

MITCHELL'S BRIEF REIGN

Arsenal's first-ever full-time manager, Scotsman Thomas Mitchell, joined the Club in August 1897, replacing "secretary-manager" Sam Hollis and ushering in a new professional coaching era for the Club.

Hailing from Dumfries, Mitchell was secretary at Blackburn Rovers for 12 years before accepting his new position with the Gunners and, although his short tenure was to end in March 1898 when he resigned, the team rose from 10th to fifth in Division Two under his guidance.

Arsenal played 26 times in total under Mitchell in all competitions, winning 14 games and drawing four. His reign remains the shortest of all of the Club's permanent rather than interim or caretaker bosses.

BELOW: Tom Whittaker made a successful transition from Gunners player to Arsenal manager.

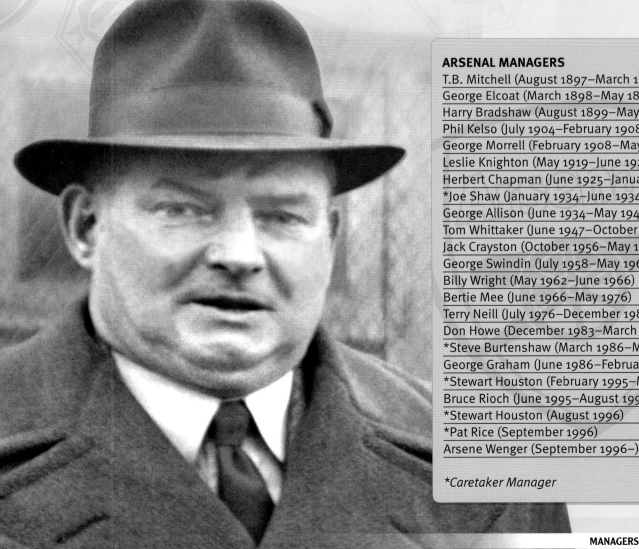

ARSENAL MANAGERS

T.B. Mitchell (August 1897–March 1898)
George Elcoat (March 1898–May 1899)
Harry Bradshaw (August 1899–May 1904)
Phil Kelso (July 1904–February 1908)
George Morrell (February 1908–May 1915)
Leslie Knighton (May 1919–June 1925)
Herbert Chapman (June 1925–January 1934)
*Joe Shaw (January 1934–June 1934
George Allison (June 1934–May 1947)
Tom Whittaker (June 1947–October 1956)
Jack Crayston (October 1956–May 1958)
George Swindin (July 1958–May 1962)
Billy Wright (May 1962–June 1966)
Bertie Mee (June 1966–May 1976)
Terry Neill (July 1976–December 1983)
Don Howe (December 1983–March 1986)
*Steve Burtenshaw (March 1986–May 1986)
George Graham (June 1986–February 1995)
*Stewart Houston (February 1995–May 1995)
Bruce Rioch (June 1995–August 1996)
*Stewart Houston (August 1996)
*Pat Rice (September 1996)
Arsene Wenger (September 1996–)

*Caretaker Manager

HERBERT'S CUP HEROICS

Herbert Chapman is remembered and revered in Arsenal folklore for many reasons, but perhaps his greatest achievement was his pivotal role in securing the first major trophy in Gunners history.

A journeyman inside-forward, the Yorkshireman joined the Club in the summer of 1925 after managerial spells with Northampton Town, Leeds City and Huddersfield Town (where he won four Division One titles and the FA Cup). Almost as soon as he arrived at Highbury, Arsenal's fortunes began to turn.

In his first season in north London, the Gunners narrowly missed out on a first league title when they finished as runners-up

behind Chapman's old side the Terriers. The Club's wait for silverware would not continue for much longer.

Chapman's moment of truth came in the 1930 FA Cup final against Huddersfield. Arsenal had already despatched Chelsea, Birmingham, Middlesbrough, West Ham and Hull en route to Wembley and goals from Alex James and Jack Lambert – both Chapman signings – ensured the journey was not wasted as they ran out 2–0 winners.

Under his astute and tactically innovative leadership, the Gunners famously went on to claim the First Division title for the first time in 1930–31 and again in 1932–33. But the FA Cup triumph was the major breakthrough the Club had

been waiting for since it had turned professional in 1891.

Chapman died suddenly in early 1934 after a brief illness, but his part in Arsenal's emergence as a heavyweight of English football is commemorated forever in the shape of a bronze statue of the ground-breaking Yorkshireman outside Emirates Stadium.

RIGHT: Bertie Mee made history in 1970–71 when his side completed the coveted Double for the first time.

RIGHT: Herbert Chapman was the mastermind behind Arsenal's first major trophy triumph.

END OF THE DROUGHT

Bertie Mee was Arsenal manager for a decade between 1966 and 1976 and his Highbury reign made history when the Gunners claimed the fabled League and FA Cup double for the first time.

Two successive but losing League Cup final appearances in 1968 and 1969 hinted at bigger and brighter things to come and when Mee's side won the 1970 Inter-Cities Fairs Cup, the Club's first piece of European silverware, to end a 17-year trophy drought, his team was almost at the peak of its powers.

The best, however, was yet to come and in 1970–71 Arsenal dominated. The league was a tightly-contested affair with Leeds United, but a Gunners surge towards the end of the campaign, in which they won eight of their closing 10 fixtures, was enough to secure the title – a point ahead of their Yorkshire rivals.

The climax of the season found Mee's team facing Liverpool at Wembley in the FA Cup final and, although the match went into extra-time, Charlie George's 112th-minute goal saw Arsenal complete the first double of the 20th century.

Mee remained at Highbury for five more years, in the process becoming the first man to manage the Club in 500 games.

ABOVE: Stewart Houston twice took charge of Arsenal as caretaker manager.

 LOYAL SERVANT

The only man to manage Arsenal twice, albeit briefly, is Stewart Houston who took charge at Highbury in 1995 in a caretaker capacity and again in 1996 on an interim basis.

The Scotsman joined the Club in 1990 as George Graham's assistant manager, but when his compatriot was sacked in February 1995 Houston stepped into the breach for the remainder of the 1994–95 season.

He stood aside that summer to make way for Bruce Rioch, but was elevated once again to caretaker manager when Rioch was dismissed in August 1996. The plan was for Houston to take charge of first team affairs until the arrival of Arsene Wenger from Grampus Eight in Japan. But the offer of the manager's job at QPR proved too tempting and he moved to Loftus Road in September, three weeks before the Frenchman's accession.

In total, Houston took charge of the side in 25 games during his two caretaker stints, winning nine matches and drawing five.

▶ **YOUNG GUN**

Terry Neill's seven-year stint as Arsenal manager saw the Club lift the 1979 FA Cup, but his reign is also notable for two other landmark achievements – he remains the youngest-ever man to coach the Gunners and he was also the first non-English or Scottish manager in the Club's history.

The Belfast-born centre-back spent 11 years at Highbury as a player, and three years after hanging up his boots he returned to the Club as manager at the age of 34.

Overall the Northern Irishman was in charge at Arsenal for 416 games, and as well as the FA Cup triumph he steered the team to the final of the 1979–80 Cup Winners' Cup against Valencia.

BELOW: Terry Neill was just 34 when he succeeded Bertie Mee in the Highbury hot seat.

▼ GLORIOUS GRAHAM

The most successful manager in Arsenal's history prior to the Arsene Wenger era, George Graham claimed six major trophies during nine celebrated and hugely successful years in the Highbury dugout, eclipsing even the great Herbert Chapman, George Allison, Tom Whittaker and Bertie Mee in terms of silverware.

The Scot spent 15 years at Highbury in total and, although his stint in the Gunners midfield yielded three trophies in the early 1970s, it was his reunion with the Club as manager between 1986 and 1995 that confirmed his legendary status.

Graham cut his managerial teeth at Millwall before his return to Arsenal and in his first season at the helm he ended the Club's eight-year wait for a trophy when he led his new side to victory in the final of the League Cup, beating Liverpool 2–1 at Wembley.

His coaching philosophy was to build from the back, and it reaped dividends with a second League Cup success in 1993 and the First Division title in 1988–89 and 1990–91.

Those triumphs put Graham ahead of his predecessors, but the final major act of his association with Arsenal was arguably his most significant as the Gunners won the 1994 Cup Winners' Cup. The Club had won the Inter-Cities Fairs Cup in 1970 under Bertie Mee, but it was not a UEFA-sanctioned competition, making Graham's 1994 success the first time Arsenal had lifted an official UEFA trophy.

The team despatched Danish side Odense and Belgians Standard Liege in the early rounds before edging past Torino 1–0 on aggregate in the quarter-finals courtesy of a Tony Adams strike in the second leg at Highbury. Paris Saint-Germain were beaten in the last four and defending champions Parma were the opponents in the final, staged at the Parken Stadium in Copenhagen in front of a 34,000 strong crowd.

Striker Alan Smith made the breakthrough in the first half with a superb volley after a mistake by the Italian defence, and for the rest of the match Graham's famed back four held firm as Parma pressed and Arsenal were champions.

The Gunners reached the final again 12 months later only to lose to Real Zaragoza in extra-time, but Graham had been sacked three months earlier, bringing down the curtain on an era in which the Scot had re-established the Club among the elite of English football.

BELOW: George Graham (with David O'Leary, left) made the Gunners a force to be reckoned with in English football.

OPPOSITE: Arsene Wenger revolutionised Arsenal and has won three Premier League titles and four FA Cups since 1996.

THE WONDER OF WENGER

The arrival of Arsene Wenger in north London in October 1996 from Japan was greeted with a mixture of anticipation and apathy. The new manager may have won the French League Championship and French Cup with Monaco but, following Bruce Rioch's ill-fated season-long reign at Highbury, he was not the household name many of the Arsenal faithful yearned for.

"The Professor", however, was unperturbed and the revolution he instigated at the Club was to see the Gunners enjoy the most prolific period in their history. Now, by any measure, Wenger is Arsenal's most successful and significant manager.

His first game in charge was away to Blackburn Rovers at Ewood Park on 12 October 1996 in the Premier League. Ian Wright scored both goals in a 2–0 win, but the 1997–98 campaign was Wenger's first full season and saw his increasingly cosmopolitan side dethrone Manchester United as champions. The icing on the cake was the subsequent 2–0 win over Newcastle in the FA Cup final and, less than two years after his appointment, Wenger had already emulated Bertie Mee's legendary 1971 double feat.

It was, of course, merely the beginning of a tide of silverware. Three more FA Cups and two further Premier League titles would follow, while the second double in 2001–02 and the staggering Invincibles season of 2003–04 cemented the Frenchman's place at the very top of the pantheon of the Club's great managers.

In October 2009, he surpassed George Allison's record of 4,748 days as Gunners manager. The team's stunning 5–3 win at Stamford Bridge against Chelsea in October 2011 was his 500th victory in all competitions at the helm, while the Premier League clash with Norwich in May 2012 saw him take charge of the side for the 900th time in an illustrious career.

His long list of individual awards includes Premier League Manager of the Season in 1998, 2002 and 2004, his 2006 induction into the English Football Hall of Fame, an honorary OBE and the accolade of World Coach of the Decade, awarded by the International Federation of Football History & Statistics.

His success on the pitch and his astute dealings in the transfer market are also credited with helping to fund the Club's 2006 move from Highbury to Emirates.

Wenger's reign has comprehensively rewritten the record books since he moved to north London and the Frenchman is now poised to join an elite and exclusive list of managers to take charge of 1,000 games at the same Club.

Other Records – Stadiums

Arsenal have played at six different grounds since the Club was founded in the 19th century and this section details all of the Gunners' homes from their early days on Plumstead Common to the £390 million Emirates Stadium.

COMMON PEOPLE

Arsenal's first "home" in the late nineteenth century was the open expanse of Plumstead Common in south-east London. But it was far from the height of luxury and, less than 12 months after the Club was founded, they were quickly on the move ahead of the 1887–88 season.

The Gunners won their first recorded match 6–1 against Erith in January 1887 and, although they were to play only a handful of games on the Common before relocating, it was to prove a happy albeit brief hunting ground – seven days later Arsenal demolished Alexandra United 11–0 in a friendly.

GROUND SWITCH

The Gunners' second home – the aptly named Sportsman Ground – was hardly more developed than their first and they spent just six months on the edge of Plumstead Marshes before they were on the move again.

The Club rented the Sportsman Ground from a local pig breeder and they played their first game there – a 5–1 victory over Alexandra United – in October 1887. But the pitch had a tendency to flood and the side's 5–0 win over Ascham in March 1888 was the Club's last fixture at the ground before the pigs reclaimed their old stamping ground.

▼ MANOR MOVE

Arsenal's itinerant existence continued in 1888 when they rented the Manor Ground in Plumstead, ignoring the inconvenient fact that a large open sewer ran along the southern side of the pitch.

By the Club's early standards, their two-year stay at the Manor Ground was relatively long. But with the players forced to change in the nearby Railway Tavern, the ambitious Gunners realized they needed a more modern facility and in 1890 they packed their bags once again.

BELOW: In 1893 Arsenal raised £4,000 to buy and redevelop the Manor Ground and the stadium regularly attracted 10,000 fans.

▲ TO THE MANOR REBORN

It was a case of déjà vu in 1893 when Arsenal returned to the Manor Ground. This time, though, after raising £4,000 through a share issue to buy 13-and-a-half acres of land for development, the Club was the owner rather than a temporary tenant.

Work quickly began on a large iron stand to house 2,000 fans and, with the terraces and military wagons that were wheeled in as viewing platforms for the big matches, the new-look Manor Ground was now capable of accommodating up to 20,000 supporters.

Thanks to scores of volunteers who worked tirelessly over the summer, the redevelopment was finished in time for the Club's debut in the 1893–94 Second Division. In the space of six years, Arsenal had grown from an amateur side into a fully fledged Football League team.

Around 10,000 descended on the new ground for the league opener against Newcastle United in September 1893 and the team christened the stadium with a 2–2 draw, courtesy of goals from inside-left Arthur Elliott and striker Walter Shaw.

The average gate during the Club's historic 1893–94 campaign was 6,000, while the highest attendance for a league match was the 13,000 who turned out to watch the visit of Notts County in March.

The Gunners spent 20 years at the Manor Ground, but crowds dwindled towards the end of their stay and just 3,000 were there to witness the final game, a 1–1 stalemate with Middlesbrough, in April 1913.

Arsenal were in financial trouble and new owner Sir Henry Norris decided the Club needed a new, more lucrative home. The Gunners were set to head north of the river and the Manor Ground quickly fell derelict. The old stand was demolished and the land redeveloped.

ABOVE: A packed Manor Ground watches Arsenal take on Liverpool during the 1905–06 season.

TRADING UP

The Invicta Ground in Plumstead was the Club's home between 1890 and 1893. With a stand that could house 1,500 spectators and terraces that were big enough for 3,000 more supporters, it signalled a new era for Arsenal.

Initially the average crowd was a modest 1,000, but a friendly game against Scottish Cup holders Hearts in March 1891 saw a record 12,000 fans in attendance.

The ground's owner first charged the Gunners an annual rent of £200. But after the Club turned professional in 1891 and were elected to the Football League two years later, the charges suddenly went up to £350 plus tax per year and the Arsenal accountants decided it was high time to seek alternative accommodation.

ABOVE: Work begins on the new Highbury stadium in the summer of 1913.

ARCHITECTURAL RIVALRY

Arsenal's move to Highbury would ignite a long-standing rivalry with neighbours Tottenham. But in 1913 the Gunners were more than happy to turn to renowned architect Archibald Leith, the man who had designed White Hart Lane, to draw up the first plans for the Club's new home.

The stadium was hurriedly built over the summer of 1913. It featured a stand on the east side of the pitch and banked terracing on the other three sides.

The total cost was £125,000 and although it was not completely finished in time for the opening game of the 1913–14 season – the team's 2–1 win over Leicester Fosse in September in the old Second Division – Highbury was open for business.

BUMS ON SEATS

The late 1980s and 1990s saw the last major improvements to Highbury, with the remodelling of the Clock End during the 1988–89 season which saw the addition of a roof and executive boxes, while the North Bank was demolished at the end of the 1991–92 campaign to make way for a new all-seater stand.

HANDS OF TIME

The construction of a roof over the North Stand presented Arsenal with the dilemma of what to do with the famous Highbury Clock that could no longer be accommodated at that end of the ground. In 1935 it was agreed to relocate the huge timepiece to the College End, the southern side of the stadium.

THE FINAL COUNT

The last-ever fixture at Highbury saw Arsene Wenger's side defeat Wigan Athletic 4–2 in May 2006, the 2,010th and final competitive match at the stadium that was the Club's home for more than nine decades.

Over those 93 years, the Gunners scored a grand total of 4,038 goals and won 1,196 games. They lost just 339 matches and conceded a miserly 1,955 goals.

The club's overall league record reads: played 1,689, won 981, drawn 412 and lost 296, while the team won 92 of the 142 FA Cup ties held in N5.

Only nine teams came to the stadium and went away victorious in 76 European fixtures, while Arsenal triumphed in four of the five Charity Shield games held at Highbury before the annual game was moved to Wembley.

The clock had been the idea of manager Herbert Chapman and initially it provided supporters with a 45-minute countdown during games – until the Football Association deemed that it undermined their referees and the Club were forced to change it to a conventional design.

The "striking" feature, however, proved so popular among the fans that College End was informally renamed the Clock End, and when the Club reluctantly moved to Emirates in 2006, they took the iconic clock with them.

BELOW: The Highbury Clock was a familiar feature at Highbury before it was moved to Emirates.

◀ LET THERE BE LIGHT

Until the 1950s, the Gunners were at the mercy of the sun when it came to staging matches, but in 1951 that all changed when the Club installed the first floodlights at Highbury.

Arsenal were the second English club (after Southampton) to experiment with artificial illumination and the lights were first put to the test in September in a friendly against Israeli side Hapoel Tel Aviv.

A healthy crowd of 44,385 turned out to watch the match – and a Cliff Holton hat-trick which secured a 6–1 victory for Tom Whittaker's side.

ABOVE: The introduction of floodlights in the 1950s added a new dimension to Highbury.

HOLY ORDERS

Arsenal owner Sir Henry Norris was desperate to increase the Club's potential supporter base. After considering relocating to Battersea and Harringay, he took the brave decision to invest in a plot of land in Highbury and the Gunners left south London for the north of the capital.

Norris negotiated a 21-year lease at a price of £20,000 and, despite initial opposition from local residents and other football clubs in the area,

the builders were commissioned and work began on the new stadium.

There were, however, restrictions. Norris leased the land from St John's College of Divinity and an initial condition of the deal was that Arsenal would not schedule matches for either Christmas Day or Good Friday. It was also agreed that no alcoholic drinks would be sold at the ground. The Club eventually bought the site outright in 1925 for £64,000 and the restrictions were lifted.

▼ HOME IMPROVEMENT

The 1930s saw the first significant addition to Leith's original design and in 1932 a West Stand, designed by Claude Waterlow Ferrier and William Binnie, was opened by the Prince of Wales (later King Edward VIII) after a £45,000 investment by the Club.

Four years later Arsenal decided to demolish Leith's old East Stand and replace it with a state-of-the-art edifice that could seat 4,000 spectators and boasted terracing for 17,000 more at a cost of £130,000. At the same time the North Bank terrace was given a roof and Highbury began to resemble a thoroughly modern stadium.

BELOW: In April 2007 a building site was all that remained of Arsenal Stadium, Highbury to generations of Gunners.

ARSENAL'S RECORD AT HIGHBURY

	P	W	D	L	F	A
League	1,689	981	412	296	3,372	1,692
FA Cup	142	92	32	18	305	123
League Cup	98	69	14	15	195	74
Europe	76	50	17	9	153	60
Charity Shield	5	4	0	1	13	6
TOTAL	2,010	1,196	475	339	4,038	1,955

► RECORD ATTENDANCES

Arsenal said goodbye to Highbury to increase match day capacity and the supporters have responded in their millions since the move across north London.

In the Club's first Premier League season at the ground, a grand total of 1,140,863 fans came through the turnstiles – an average of a 60,045-strong crowd for each of the Gunners' 19 league fixtures.

The biggest gate of the season came in March for the visit of Reading when 60,132 supporters filled the stadium to watch their side win 2–1, courtesy of a Gilberto Silva penalty and a Julio Baptista goal.

The second-highest attendance was the 60,128 spectators who witnessed Arsenal beat Manchester United 2–1 in January, while 60,115 fans were on hand for the 3–0 triumph over Tottenham in the north London derby in December.

TIMELY REMINDER

The famed Highbury Clock was taken down from the old stadium in July 2006. It took a 25-ton crane, four men and nine hours of painstaking manoeuvring to position the massive timepiece at Emirates.

It now sits high up on the outside of the new stadium and symbolically faces towards the Clock End Bridge.

ABOVE: More than one million fans flocked through the 104 turnstiles of Emirates during the 2006–07 season.

▼ BUILDING THE FUTURE

To describe the process of constructing the Club's state-of-the-art new stadium in Islington as a big job would be an architectural understatement. Once the planning permission and the all-important finances were in place, work finally began on the Herculean task in February 2004.

In total, it took 123 weeks and two days, 1,400 construction workers and six million man-hours, 55,000 cubic metres of concrete, 10,000 tons of reinforced steel (3,000 tons in the main roof alone) and 15,000 square metres of glazing to bring Emirates to life in time for the 2006–07 Premier League campaign.

The final cost of the ambitious project was £390 million and 2,500 legal documents had to be signed, sealed and delivered during the construction process of the 60,431-capacity stadium.

The highest point of the ground is 41.4 metres above ground level and the entire site at Ashburton Grove covers 17 acres.

BELOW: The construction of Emirates was a massive operation costing £390 million.

Emirates Stadium
12
months to kick off

Emirates Arsenal Sir Robert McAlpine

ABOVE: Arsene Wenger and his coaching staff watch the action from the spacious Emirates dugout.

DUGOUT DIMENSIONS
There's absolutely no shortage of space for the managers, players, coaches, medical staff and other Club employees in the dugouts at Emirates, with both teams provided with 40 seats apiece to watch the game.

LIQUID REFRESHMENT
There's little danger of going thirsty while watching a match at Emirates. The stadium has 250 food and drink outlets and match day staff can serve up to 2,400 pints of beer per minute across the ground.

FIXTURES AND FITTINGS
Once the shell of the stadium was completed, Arsenal set about installing the trappings of a modern football ground and the Club certainly didn't cut any corners when it came to the finishing touches.

Within Emirates there are 12,000 light fittings, 2,000 doors, 100 flights of stairs, 13 lifts and five escalators. Match days are monitored by 130 separate CCTV cameras and there are also 41 different camera positions to ensure broadcasters don't miss any of the action.

Nine hundred toilets and 370 metres of urinals mean supporters should never be caught short, while the ground's 104 turnstiles guarantee fans won't be late for kick-off.

SITTING PRETTY
Emirates is invariably full to capacity on match days. When the ground is full, 26,646 of the crowd are seated in the upper tier of the stadium. Another 24,425 supporters can watch the game from the lower tier while there are 7,139 more seats available at Club Level.

A lucky 2,222 spectators can feast their eyes on the action from executive boxes, while there is room for 128 guests in the Directors' Box. Arsenal also ensured there were 500 dedicated spaces for disabled supporters in the plans.

CAPTURED IN TIME
Almost two years before the official opening of the new stadium, the Club officially buried a time capsule in the foundations of Emirates to commemorate the Gunners' 93-year stay at Highbury.

Manager Arsene Wenger as well as Patrick Vieira and Thierry Henry were in attendance for the official ceremony in October 2004 as the capsule containing 40 items, 25 of which were chosen by Gunners fans, was lowered into place.

Among the keepsakes was a captain's armband worn by Tony Adams, a shirt worn by the late David Rocastle, marble from the old flooring at Highbury and a lock of Charlie George's hair.

Next to the capsule is the motto: "The deeper the foundations, the stronger the fortress."

BELOW: Inside the new state-of-the-art Arsenal dressing room at Emirates.

ARSENAL'S RECORD AT EMIRATES 2006–2013

	P	W	D	L	F	A
League	133	86	31	16	278	113
FA Cup	13	10	3	0	29	6
League Cup	13	11	1	1	35	7
Europe	37	27	7	3	86	23
TOTAL	196	134	42	20	428	149

Other Records – The Derby

The Gunners first faced Spurs in a competitive fixture in December 1900, but it was Arsenal's move to Highbury and north London 13 years later that ignited the rivalry between the two clubs. This section looks at the records produced by one of football's fiercest derby clashes.

GOALS GALORE

The highest aggregate scoreline in any derby game was Arsenal's dramatic 5–4 victory over Spurs at White Hart Lane in November 2004, a pulsating Premier League clash in which Arsene Wenger's side initially went behind before an unstoppable second-half salvo.

The home side took the lead after 37 minutes with a left-footed volley from Moroccan centre-half Noureddine Naybet, but moments before the break Arsenal equalized against the run of play with a breakaway Thierry Henry goal.

The second 45 minutes produced seven more goals. The Gunners stormed into a 3–1 advantage with a Lauren penalty and Patrick Vieira strike and, although Tottenham pegged them back with a Jermain Defoe goal, Arsenal restored their two-goal advantage when Freddie Ljungberg dissected the home defence on 69 minutes.

Spurs rallied again with a Ledley King header, but Robert Pires made it 5–3 with some nimble footwork. Although Freddie Kanoute reduced the arrears with the ninth goal of the contest two minutes from time, the Gunners held firm for a famous and record-breaking win.

DERBY FIRST

The first-ever competitive match between Arsenal and Tottenham saw the two sides meet in Division One at the Manor Ground in Plumstead in December 1909.

The Gunners won the game 1–0 courtesy of a goal from Walter Lawrence, making the English inside-forward the first Gunner to score against the Club's north London rivals.

O'LEARY'S LEGACY

Legendary centre-half David O'Leary has played in more games against Tottenham than any other Arsenal player, with 35 of his record 722 appearances for the Club coming against the old rivals.

The Irish defender's first taste of the action was in the goalless draw at White Hart Lane in September 1975, while his final involvement in the derby came in the 3–1 loss to the Lilywhites at Highbury in May 1993.

ABOVE: Alan Sunderland put Spurs to the sword in the derby in December 1978.

TRIPLE TRIUMPHS

Only two Arsenal players in the history of the derby have registered hat-tricks. Ted Drake was the first, in 1934, and it was to be 44 years before Alan Sunderland emulated his feat with a superb treble in the Gunners' 5–0 triumph at White Hart Lane 48 hours before Christmas Day in 1978.

BELOW: David O'Leary faced Tottenham a record 35 times during his 18-year Arsenal career.

SUPER SUB

The fastest-ever goal scored by an Arsenal substitute against Spurs was recorded in December 2007 when Nicklas Bendtner made an immediate impact for the Gunners from the bench at Emirates.

The derby clash was 74 minutes old and deadlocked at 1–1 when the Danish striker was brought on to replace Emmanuel Eboue – and just 1.8 seconds after his introduction, Bendtner headed Cesc Fabregas' corner past Paul Robinson.

It was the forward's first Premier League goal for Arsenal and enough to secure all three points for Arsene Wenger's side.

BELOW: Cesc Fabregas supplied the corner for the Gunners' quickest ever goal against Tottenham.

▶ EIGHT-GOAL MILESTONE

Three players jointly hold the record for career goals against Spurs, with Alan Sunderland, Robert Pires and Emmanuel Adebayor each finding the net eight times against the Lilywhites.

Togo striker Adebayor also holds the record as the highest individual scorer in the derby, with 10 goals. His first eight came in the red and white of Arsenal but he was on target for Tottenham for his ninth in the Gunners' 5–2 victory at Emirates in February 2012. Nine months later he made it 10 in another 5–2 loss for Spurs at Emirates.

ABOVE: Emmanuel Adebayor has scored for both clubs in the North London derby.

LEAGUE DOUBLE

Arsenal met Tottenham in competitive action for the first time in 1909 but it was not until the 1934–35 season that the Gunners recorded the club's first league double over their north London neighbours.

The first instalment of the historic feat came in October 1934 at Highbury when a goal from Albert Beasley, a Ted Drake hat-trick and an own goal gave George Allison's side a 5–1 success. The result still stands as the Club's biggest home win over Spurs.

Five months later the two teams met at White Hart Lane and Arsenal completed the double with a crushing 6–0 win, the goals coming from Alf Kirchen (2), Ted Drake (2), Peter Dougall and Cliff Bastin from the spot.

The victory also remains the Gunners' most comprehensive in the derby at White Hart Lane.

ARSENAL V TOTTENHAM RECORDS

Biggest Arsenal Home Win
Arsenal 5 Spurs 1 (20 October 1934, First Division)

Biggest Arsenal Away Win
Spurs 0 Arsenal 6 (6 March 1935, First Division)

Biggest Arsenal Home Defeat
Arsenal 0 Spurs 3 (14 December 1932, First Division)
Arsenal 0 Spurs 3 (27 February 1954, First Division)

Biggest Arsenal Away Defeat
Spurs 5 Arsenal 0 (25 December 1911, First Division)
Spurs 5 Arsenal 0 (4 April 1983, First Division)

Biggest Arsenal Premier League Win
Arsenal 5 Spurs 2 (26 February 2012)
Arsenal 5 Spurs 2 (17 November 2012)

Biggest Arsenal Premier League Defeat
Arsenal 1 Spurs 3 (11 May 1993)

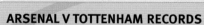

RECORD UNBEATEN STREAK

The first decade of the 21st century saw Arsenal enjoy a period of unprecedented dominance over their north London rivals. Between 2000 and 2008, Arsene Wenger's side were able to string together a Club-record 21 successive games without defeat to Tottenham.

The incredible run began in March 2000 when an own-goal from Chris Armstrong and a Thierry Henry penalty gave the Gunners a 3–1 victory at Highbury and continued for nearly eight years, climaxing in a 1–1 draw with Spurs at Emirates in January 2008.

The sequence finally came to an end 13 days later when the two sides met in the League Cup semi-final at White Hart Lane – a game the home side won 5–1.

In total Arsenal won 12 of the 21 fixtures during their unbeaten derby streak, scoring 42 goals and conceding just 23.

CROSSING THE DIVIDE

Transfers between Arsenal and Tottenham have remained a real rarity since the formation of the two clubs. The first man to play for both he Gunners and Spurs was a full-back by the name of Lycurgus Burrows.

Signed by Arsenal as an amateur in January 1892, a year before the Club was elected to the old Second Division, Burrows found his first team opportunities limited in the Gunners' new professional era and in October 1894 he signed for the Lilywhites.

The unusual part of the story was that, although Burrows was now a Tottenham player, his amateur status meant he was still registered with Arsenal. He made 10 league appearances for the Gunners during his unique "dual club" status.

▶ PULLING AWAY

The Gunners' Division One clash with Spurs at White Hart Lane on Boxing Day in 1983 was a hugely significant contest in the history of the north London derby. Two goals apiece from Charlie Nicholas and Raphael Meade saw Arsenal emerge 4–2 winners and in the process take the lead in the head-to-battle between the two clubs with 40 victories to Tottenham's 39. It is an advantage which the Gunners have not relinquished since.

▶ BROWN'S DERBY DOUBLE

A handful of players have featured for both Arsenal and Tottenham in the history of the north London derby, and the first to do so was striker Laurie Brown.

The Gunners signed Brown from Northampton Town in 1961 and in three seasons at Highbury he played in four clashes with the Lilywhites. He headed to White Hart Lane in February 1964 for a fee of £40,000, and in two years at Spurs he turned out against Arsenal three times.

Other players to represent both clubs in the capital's biggest game are David Jenkins, Jimmy Robertson, Pat Jennings, Willie Young, Sol Campbell and Emmanuel Adebayor.

BELOW: Charlie Nicholas (left) scored for Arsenal in the 1983 Boxing Day derby win.

ABOVE: Laurie Brown was the first player to play for both sides in the North London Derby.

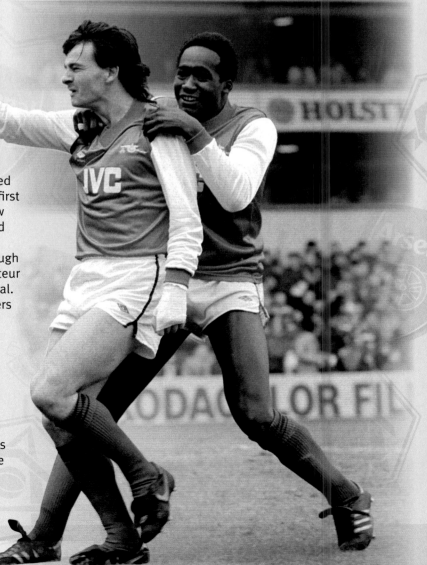

DRAMATIC DRAW

The first-ever stalemate between the two north London rivals saw Arsenal register a 1–1 result at White Hart Lane in April 1910. And the highest-scoring draw between the two sides was in the Premier League in October 2008, when they shared the points after an eight-goal thriller.

CUP CONTEST

The first FA Cup derby saw the Gunners face Spurs at Highbury in the third round of the competition in January 1949. Arsenal were the reigning First Division champions while Tottenham were a second-tier side, and the gulf in class told as Tom Whittaker's side emerged 3–0 winners.

Scottish right-wing Ian McPherson made history with the Club's first-ever FA Cup goal against Spurs, the second and third coming Don Roper and Doug Lishman respectively.

The Gunners have played Tottenham five times in FA Cup history and following the latest meeting – the 2–1 victory at Highbury in April 2001 – currently lead the series 3–2.

BELOW: Robert Pires celebrates after scoring at White Hart Lane in 2004 to secure the Premier League title.

Spurs took an early lead at Emirates through former Gunner David Bentley, but goals from Mikael Silvestre, William Gallas and Emmanuel Adebayor saw Arsenal storm into a commanding 3–1 lead.

Darren Bent pulled one back for the visitors but Robin van Persie restored the two-goal advantage just a minute later. The Gunners seemed certain to collect all three points until strikes from Jermaine Jenas and Aaron Lennon earned Tottenham an unlikely, last-gasp 4–4 draw.

BELOW: Frank McLintock is carried off the pitch by delirious Arsenal fans after the Gunners had wrapped up the 1970–71 League Championship with a 1–0 win over Spurs at White Hart Lane; five days later, Arsenal completed the double.

▶ **CHAMPIONS AT THE LANE**

The Gunners have twice been confirmed as English champions after league games at White Hart Lane.

The first instance was in May 1971 when Bertie Mee's side needed a win or a goalless draw at Spurs in the final match of the season to deny Leeds United the title. The contest was scoreless until the 87th minute when Ray Kennedy headed home a late winner to clinch the silverware at the home of the old rivals.

The second time was in April 2004 when Arsene Wenger's Invincibles needed only a point at White Hart Lane to become champions. Thanks to goals from Patrick Vieira and Robert Pires they came away with a 2–2 draw and the title.

ARSENAL V TOTTENHAM HEAD-TO-HEAD RECORD

	Arsenal Wins	Draws	Spurs Wins
League	64	43	49
League Cup	7	3	3
FA Cup	3	0	2
Other	0	1	0
TOTAL	73	47	54

Other Records – Miscellaneous

The next six pages focus on some of Arsenal's other notable records and milestones, including the Club's first experience of the dreaded penalty shootout, their unique visit to Buckingham Palace and the day Arsene Wenger made Premier League history.

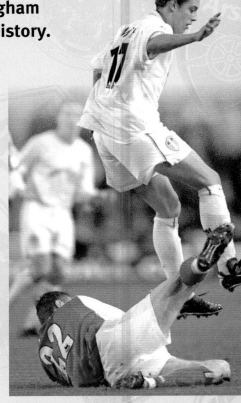

▶ CURSE OF INDISCIPLINE

Arsenal games against Leeds United are invariably fiery encounters and the November 2000 meeting at Elland Road was no exception.

A total of seven Arsenal players – Oleg Luzhny, Tony Adams, Martin Keown, Sylvinho, Ray Parlour, Lauren and Thierry Henry – were booked by referee Dermot Gallagher in a 1–0 defeat, a tally which remains the Gunners' most indisciplined display ever in the Premier League.

The Club's worst Premier League season in terms of yellow cards was the 1996–97 campaign when the team received a total of 81 bookings in 38 games. The average cards per team that season was a mere 60.

The Gunners also picked up five red cards during the campaign, with Tony Adams the first to take an early bath after picking up two yellows in just 22 minutes in the game against Newcastle United at St James' Park in November.

NATIONAL VARIETY

Three months after setting a Champions League record with 11 players from 11 nations, Arsenal repeated the trick in the Premier League when they faced Newcastle United at St James' Park.

Arsene Wenger's starting XI for the game on 10 December 2005 featured players from Germany, Ivory Coast, Cameroon, England, Switzerland, Sweden, Spain, Brazil, Belarus, Holland and France.

LEFT: Edu, from Brazil, was part of the 'foreign' 16-man squad named to play Crystal Palace in 2005.

ABOVE: Oleg Luzhny tackles Alan Smith and was one of seven Gunners to see yellow in the clash with Leeds United in 2000.

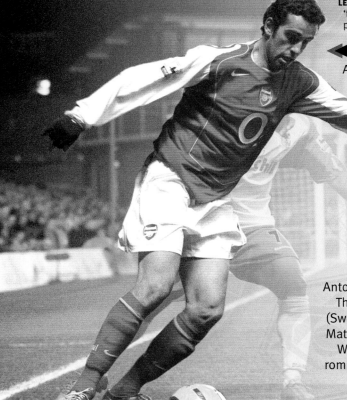

◀ GLOBAL GAME

Arsene Wenger is renowned for assembling cosmopolitan squads and in February 2005 the Frenchman broke new ground when he became the first manager in the history of the English game to name a 16-man match squad that featured no British players.

The Gunners boss was without English regulars Sol Campbell and Ashley Cole through injury and illness respectively for the Premier League clash with Crystal Palace, and fielded a team with an unmistakably global, albeit predominantly French, feel.

The Arsenal starting line-up at Selhurst Park was: Jens Lehmann (Germany), Lauren (Cameroon), Gael Clichy (France), Kolo Toure (Ivory Coast), Pascal Cygan (France), Robert Pires (France), Patrick Vieira (France), Edu (Brazil), Jose Antonio Reyes (Spain), Dennis Bergkamp (Holland), Thierry Henry (France).

The bench was warmed by Manuel Almunia (Spain), Philippe Senderos (Switzerland), Cesc Fabregas (Spain), Robin van Persie (Holland) and Mathieu Flamini (France).

Wenger's historic decision paid handsome dividends as his side romped to a 5–1 win over the Eagles.

LEAGUE OF NATIONS

The Gunners made Champions League history in September 2005 when they faced Hamburg in the group stages, becoming the first Club to field a side with players from 11 different countries.

Arsene Wenger initially named a side with two Ivorians (Emmanuel Eboue and Kolo Toure) and nine other nationalities for the match in the Volksparkstadion. But when Toure was forced off after 28 minutes with injury, he was replaced by Englishman Justin Hoyte and Arsenal became a side with 11 players hailing from 11 different countries.

That team was: Jens Lehmann (Germany), Emmanuel Eboue (Ivory Coast), Justin Hoyte (England), Johan Djourou (Switzerland), William Gallas (France), Alexander Hleb (Belarus), Cesc Fabregas (Spain), Gilberto Silva (Brazil), Tomas Rosicky (Czech Republic), Robin van Persie (Holland), Emmanuel Adebayor (Togo).

The introduction of Brazilian Julio Baptista for van Persie on 69 minutes disrupted the dynamic but history had still been made.

▶ EUROPEAN TRIUMPHS

The Gunners have enjoyed some famous nights in Europe over the years, but what must be two of their greatest results both came in the Champions League – against Real Madrid in 2006 and AC Milan two years later.

Arsene Wenger's side faced Real in the Bernabeu in the last 16 of the competition, and a superb solo goal from Thierry Henry earned Arsenal a brilliant 1–0 victory, the first time any English side had ever beaten the Spain heavyweights in Madrid.

In March 2008, they tackled Milan in the San Siro in the second leg of their last-16 fixture following a goalless draw in the first match at Emirates.

The Italians were the defending champions but late goals from Cesc Fabregas and Emmanuel Adebayor sent them crashing out – and in the process Arsenal became the first English club to beat the Serie A giants in the San Siro.

ABOVE: Paul Merson in action at Anfield in 1989 as Arsenal claimed a dramatic title triumph.

▲ TITLE DECIDER

Arsenal were the first club in the history of the old First Division to claim the title courtesy of the number of goals scored, edging out Liverpool in 1988–89 by the smallest of margins.

The Gunners claimed the trophy courtesy of their dramatic 2–0 victory at Anfield in the final match of the season, leaving the two clubs level on 76 points and both boasting a goal difference of plus 37.

George Graham's side, however, had scored 73 league goals compared to Liverpool's 65, which was enough to see Arsenal crowned champions.

THE ENGLISH ERA

Modern football is an increasingly global affair and the last time Arsenal fielded an entirely English XI was in April 1994 for the Premier League clash with Wimbledon at Highbury.

The Gunners team named by George Graham was: David Seaman, Lee Dixon, Martin Keown, Paul Davis, Steve Bould, Tony Adams, Kevin Campbell, Ian Wright, Alan Smith, Ray Parlour and Ian Selley.

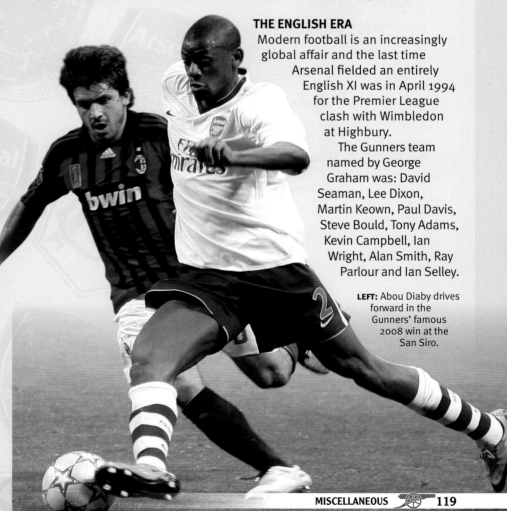

LEFT: Abou Diaby drives forward in the Gunners' famous 2008 win at the San Siro.

▶ GOING UNDERGROUND

The London Underground is part of the fabric of the capital and Arsenal remain the only Club in the city to have a tube station named after them.

The station next to the old Highbury Stadium was originally called Gillespie Road but manager Herbert Chapman campaigned vigorously to have it renamed.

The idea first occurred to him when he visited London as manager of Leeds City in 1913, and when he became Gunners boss 12 years later he began his quest to rebrand the station. After much lobbying and debate, the London Transport Board finally agreed to his request and in November 1932 Gillespie Road became Arsenal station.

ABOVE: The Gillespie Road tube station changed its name to Arsenal in 1932.

▼ TELEVISION PIONEERS

The Gunners have proven to be trailblazers in football on the box over the decades and the Club is in the history books as the very first to have been involved in a televised match.

In fact, Arsenal supplied both sides – the first team and the reserves – for a friendly at Highbury in September 1937 which was organized at the request of the BBC, eager to test new technology and their ability to broadcast sporting events.

No record of the result remains but clips of the start of the programme have survived, showing manager Herbert Chapman and his assistant Tom Whittaker introducing the first team before kick-off.

Twenty-seven years later Arsenal again broke new ground when their Division One clash with Liverpool became the first-ever game to be shown on the BBC's highlights programme *Match of the Day*. Unfortunately for Gunners fans, the show didn't make for happy viewing as Billy Wright's team were beaten 3–2 at Anfield.

On 31 January 2010, the Club made it a hat-trick of television firsts when its Premier League meeting with Manchester United became the first match in the world to be broadcast live in 3D.

Supporters at nine pubs in London, Manchester, Cardiff, Edinburgh and Dublin were the first to experience football in the new format as former Gunners striker Alan Smith provided the commentary.

BELOW: The Gunners' 3–1 home defeat against Manchester United in January 2010 was broadcast in 3D.

BADGE OF HONOUR

Under the visionary management of Herbert Chapman, Arsenal forged a reputation as one of the most innovative clubs in the country and in August 1928 the Club led the way again when it sent out a team wearing numbered shirts.

In an era of plain shirts, it was a bold move as the team ran out at Hillsborough to face Sheffield Wednesday in the First Division – and one which eventually paved the way for universal numbering.

Initially the Football League Management Committee didn't like the idea, but they relented after a meeting in 1939 and in August the Gunners ran out for their game with Blackburn Rovers at Highbury, proudly sporting officially sanctioned numbered shirts.

The Club badge appeared on the players' shirts for the team's first six FA Cup final appearances but did not become a regular feature of the Gunners' kit until the 1967–68 Division One season.

ABOVE: The Arsenal shirt, like the Club badge, has undergone a number of redesigns over the decades.

ROYAL VISIT

The Queen was scheduled to officially open Emirates in October 2006 but a back injury prevented her from giving the Club's new stadium her royal seal of approval. The Duke of Edinburgh did the honours instead – but four months later Her Majesty invited Arsene Wenger and his players to Buckingham Palace in lieu of her cancelled appearance, making Arsenal the first football club to visit the palace.

RADIO WAVES

Arsenal hold the distinction as the first club to stage a game broadcast live on radio, playing host to the BBC World Service in January 1927 for the Division One meeting with Sheffield United at Highbury.

The BBC had already trialled outside broadcasts for a rugby match at Twickenham, but the match against the Blades saw the use of two commentators for the first time, one providing a running commentary on the game while the other called out grid references to help listeners locate the action areas.

Gunners skipper Charlie Buchan opened the scoring at Highbury but Herbert Chapman's side were denied victory live on the airwaves when United equalized.

BELOW: Arsene Wenger and Peter Hill-Wood meet The Queen at Buckingham Palace.

ABOVE: The Gunners tackled Valencia in Brussels in the final of the 1980 Cup Winners' Cup.

◄ ON THE SPOT

The dreaded penalty shootout is a dramatic but frequently cruel way to settle a match. The Gunners' first experience of the lottery of spot-kicks was in May 1980 when they faced Valencia in the final of the Cup Winners' Cup.

The two teams could not muster a goal between them in 90 minutes or extra-time in the Heysel Stadium in Brussels, and so the final had to be decided from the spot. Mario Kempes and Liam Brady both had their opening efforts saved but the next eight were all converted, leaving the score level at 4–4. Ricardo Arias held his nerve to stroke home Valencia's sixth penalty and it was the unlucky Graham Rix who had his subsequent shot saved – to hand the trophy to the Spanish.

Twelve years later, however, the Gunners won their first penalty shootout, beating Millwall 3–1 from the spot in a League Cup second-round, second-leg clash. The game in October 1992 finished 1–1 but George Graham's side prevailed 3–1 in the shootout.

SUBSTITUTED SUBSTITUTE

Australian international John Kosmina made just four appearances for the Gunners in the 1970s. In three of those four games he came from the bench – and the Kangaroos striker holds the dubious distinction of being the first Arsenal substitute to be substituted in a competitive match.

The game was the Gunners' UEFA Cup second-round clash with Hadjuk Split at Highbury in November 1978. Kosmina was introduced to the action by manager Terry Neill in place of winger Mark Heeley. The Australian didn't last long, however, after picking up a knock and Neill duly replaced him with centre-forward Paul Vaessen.

LEAGUE TREBLE

The Gunners are one of only four clubs to have claimed the top-flight title for three successive years. Huddersfield Town were the first to achieve the championship hat-trick between 1924 and 1926 while Arsenal joined the elite club in 1935 with their third Division One title on the bounce. Liverpool were equally dominant in 1983, 1984 and 1985 while Manchester United emulated the feat in 2001 with their third successive Premier League triumph.

◄ CARDIFF DRAMA

Arsenal were involved in the first-ever FA Cup final to be decided on penalties, overcoming Manchester United from the spot in the Millennium Stadium in May 2005.

Despite the two sides boasting the attacking talents of Dennis Bergkamp and Wayne Rooney, Robert Pires and Ruud van Nistelrooy, neither side scored in normal or extra-time and the game headed to a shootout.

Cameroon defender Lauren, Freddie Ljungberg, substitute Robin van Persie and Ashley Cole were all on target, while Jens Lehmann saved Paul Scholes' second Manchester United effort.

It meant captain Patrick Vieira had to convert the Gunners' fifth penalty for glory, and he calmly beat Roy Carroll to seal the silverware.

LEFT: Patrick Vieria steps up to hit the winning penalty in the 2005 FA Cup final in the Millennnium Stadium.

THE NEWCOMERS

Since the advent of the Premier League, the 1993–94 season is the one in which Arsenal have handed league debuts to the smallest number of players, with winger Eddie McGoldrick the only newcomer to the first team during the course of the campaign.

In contrast, the 1999–2000 season saw Arsene Wenger introduce 11 new players to the side, the Club's highest number of debutants in Premier League history.

Arsenal's three Premier League title-winning campaigns resulted in a total of 20 players breaking into the first team. There were 10 debutants in 1997–98, six in 2001–02 and a mere four as Wenger's Invincibles completed an unbeaten league season in 2003–04.

HAT-TRICK HERO

Only one Arsenal player has ever scored hat-tricks in three successive home games – English centre-forward Doug Lishman.

Lishman's prolific streak came in the 1951–52 season and began with a treble in a 4–3 win over Fulham at Highbury in October. Two weeks later he hit another hat-trick in the 6–3 demolition of West Bromwich Albion, and he completed his amazing sequence at the end of November in a 4–2 victory against Bolton. In total, the striker hit 23 First Division goals for the Gunners in 38 appearances over the campaign.

RIGHT: Doug Lishman was in devastating form for the Club during the 1951–52 season.

BELOW: Eddie McGoldrick broke into the Arsenal side during the 1993–94 Premier League campaign.

ARSENAL'S RECORD IN PENALTY SHOOTOUTS

European Cup Winners' Cup Final (May 1980)
Valencia 0 Arsenal 0 – Lost 5–4 on penalties

League Cup, Second Round Second Leg (October 1992)
Millwall 1 Arsenal 1 – Won 3–1 on penalties

Charity Shield (August 1993)
Arsenal 1 Manchester United 1 – Lost 5–4 on penalties

European Cup Winners' Cup Semi-Final Second Leg (April 1995)
Sampdoria 3 Arsenal 2 (5–5 on aggregate) – Won 3–2 on penalties

FA Cup Third Round Replay (January 1998)
Port Vale 1 Arsenal 1 – Won 4–3 on penalties

FA Cup Quarter-Final Replay (March 1998)
West Ham 1 Arsenal 1 – Won 4–3 on penalties

League Cup Fourth Round (November 1999)
Middlesbrough 2 Arsenal 2 – Lost 3–1 on penalties

FA Cup Fourth Round Replay (January 2000)
Leicester 0 Arsenal 0 – Lost 6–5 on penalties

UEFA Cup Final (May 2000)
Galatasaray 0 Arsenal 0 – Lost 4–1 on penalties

Community Shield (August 2003)
Arsenal 1 Manchester United 1 – Lost 4–3 on penalties

League Cup Third Round (October 2003)
Arsenal 1 Rotherham United 1 – Won 9–8 on penalties

FA Cup Fifth Round Replay (March 2005)
Sheffield United 0 Arsenal 0 – Won 4–2 on penalties

FA Cup Final (May 2005)
Arsenal 0 Manchester United 0 – Won 5–4 on penalties

League Cup Quarter-Final (December 2005)
Doncaster Rovers 2 Arsenal 2 – Won 3–1 on penalties

League Cup Quarter-Finals (December 2012)
Bradford City 1 Arsenal 1 – Lost 3–2 on penalties

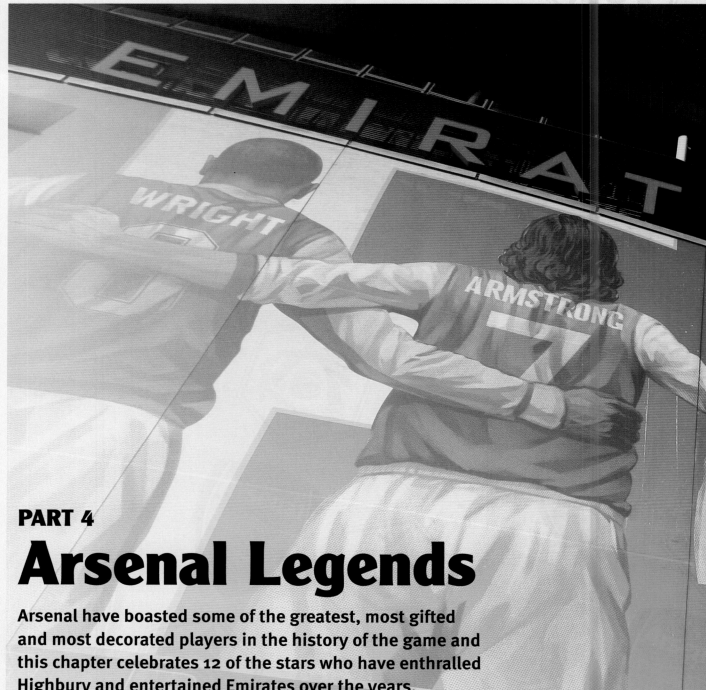

PART 4
Arsenal Legends

Arsenal have boasted some of the greatest, most gifted and most decorated players in the history of the game and this chapter celebrates 12 of the stars who have enthralled Highbury and entertained Emirates over the years.

The dozen legends played in different eras but share a common bond as players whose dazzling displays, years of loyal service and affinity with the Club made them firm favourites with the Gunners faithful.

The 1930s saw Cliff Bastin and Ted Drake both emerge as two of the Club's first true superstars, as the Gunners dominated English football for a decade, while Frank McLintock and Liam Brady are the men from the 1970s and 1980s respectively to feature on the list.

Four players synonymous with the George Graham era – Tony Adams, Ian Wright, David O'Leary and David Seaman – are also included while a trio of French players recruited by Arsene Wenger – Thierry Henry, Patrick Vieira and Robert Pires – and the dazzling Dutchman, Dennis Bergkamp, complete the famous dozen.

ABOVE: Emirates is adorned with striking images of some of the Club's greatest and most iconic players.

Tony Adams

The greatest captain in the Club's long and illustrious history, the lionhearted Adams bestrode Highbury like a colossus for 19 glorious years.

RIGHT: The Gunners skipper strikes a pose which became reassuringly familiar during his time with the Club.

BELOW: Tony Adams won 10 major trophies during his magnificent Arsenal career.

Although it was within the intimate surroundings of Highbury rather than the more expansive setting of the Club's new home in Ashburton Grove that Tony Adams forged his reputation as the Gunners' greatest-ever captain, it is outside Emirates that he is immortalized in bronze.

The striking statue of the former captain was unveiled in 2011 and when Arsenal deliberated on which three legendary servants to honour as part of the Club's 125th anniversary celebrations, Adams' inclusion was a foregone conclusion. He was joined by statues of Herbert Chapman and Thierry Henry but even their magnificent contributions to the Club's illustrious history cannot rival the impact Adams made

over 19 remarkable seasons in north London.

Few modern players graduate from the youth ranks to top-flight fame and fortune. Fewer still spend their entire careers with the same club. Adams did both and, despite his well-documented problems off the pitch, he did so with a unique blend of sheer stubbornness, fearless physicality and a sublime reading of the game.

His Arsenal odyssey began in 1980 when he signed schoolboy forms. Three years later he made his first team debut as a 17-year-old against Sunderland and in 1988 he became the Club's youngest-ever captain at the age of 21. He would not relinquish the armband for the remainder of his Highbury career, and under his leadership the Gunners blossomed and the trophy cabinet bulged.

Before George Graham appointed

him captain, Adams had already been part of the side which lifted the League Cup in 1987. Kenny Sansom had led the team out at Wembley that day but once the young centre-half assumed full-time command, the Gunners quickly graduated to even bigger and better things.

The first silverware of the Adams era was the 1988–89 Division One title, clinched in the most dramatic denouement to a season in living memory as his side beat Liverpool 2–0 at Anfield. Michael Thomas will live forever in Gunners folklore as the man who scored the decisive injury-time goal but it was the Arsenal rearguard, stoically led by Adams, that was equally instrumental in the Club's first title triumph in 18 years.

He was still just 22 years old on that famous night on Merseyside but the success was to prove far from transient and, as Adams' influence increased, the Gunners grew stronger.

The 1990–91 First Division title, the 1993 FA and League Cup double and the 1994 UEFA Cup Winners' Cup followed, but it was during the 1997–98 season that the skipper truly scaled the football summit as he led Arsenal to the elusive league and cup double.

Graham had given way to Arsene Wenger since the Club's last trophy.

Some believed the sophisticated Frenchman would struggle to find common ground with Arsenal's archetypal English central defender. But the captain found an added dimension to his game under the new manager and once the 1997–98 Premier League title was in the bag, edging out Manchester United by a solitary but priceless point, Adams guided the team to a 2–0 victory over Newcastle at Wembley.

Injury blighted him in the autumn of his Arsenal career but he underlined his enduring greatness in his swansong season, the 2001–02 campaign, leading his team to a superb second double. Adams' ageing legs could muster just 10 games in the league but he was a typically reassuring and abrasive presence for all 90 minutes of the FA Cup final victory over Chelsea in the Millennium Stadium in Cardiff.

The Gunners faithful did not know it then but it was to be his 669th and last appearance for the Club, leaving him 53 games shy of David O'Leary's record total. He announced his retirement three months after the final and, 19 years after his debut, he was no longer an Arsenal player.

The appearance milestone of O'Leary was one even Adams could

not quite eclipse but it mattered little compared to his other incredible accomplishments, not least his status as the Club's longest-serving and most successful leader, the first player to win top-flight titles in three different decades and the captain of two separate double-winning sides. Leading the side to its major piece of European silverware, not to mention the 66 caps for England, were merely the icing on the cake.

In 2004, he was inducted into the English Football Hall Of Fame but his statue outside Emirates remains a more fitting and more immediate tribute to the man known simply as "Mr Arsenal".

BELOW: The bronze statue of Adams which now proudly stands outside Emirates.

BOTTOM: Tony Adams was a cult figure with the Highbury faithful throughout his career.

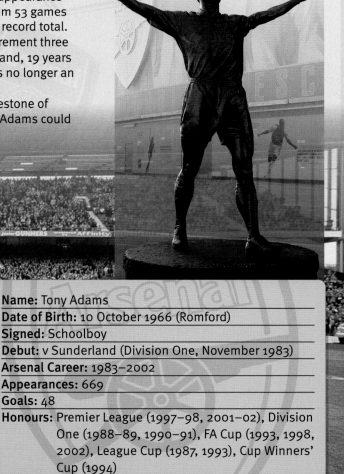

Name:	Tony Adams
Date of Birth:	10 October 1966 (Romford)
Signed:	Schoolboy
Debut:	v Sunderland (Division One, November 1983)
Arsenal Career:	1983–2002
Appearances:	669
Goals:	48
Honours:	Premier League (1997–98, 2001–02), Division One (1988–89, 1990–91), FA Cup (1993, 1998, 2002), League Cup (1987, 1993), Cup Winners' Cup (1994)

Cliff Bastin

A deadly goalscorer, Cliff Bastin spearheaded Arsenal's pre-War rise to First Division superpower status and the Club's successful quest for major silverware.

The unassuming, understated star of the first golden era in Arsenal's history, Cliff Bastin proudly held the record as the Club's greatest goalscorer for 58 years. His prolific exploits at Highbury in the 1930s are inextricably interwoven with the Gunners' emergence as an undisputed giant of the English game.

Bastin was football's original teenage sensation. By the age of 19, he had already won the Division One title and the FA Cup, and been capped for England. Although his glittering club career was prematurely curtailed by the Second World War, he still enjoyed a dazzling decade at Highbury in which he claimed five

LEFT: Cliff Bastin's dazzling skills made him an undisputed star of the English game during the 1930s.

Championship winner's medals and two FA Cups. His five titles remains a feat no subsequent Arsenal player has been able to surpass.

In fact, though, his Gunners career began purely by chance. Herbert Chapman spotted him playing for Exeter City against Watford in 1929 but the Arsenal manager was in reality at the game to scout a Hornets player called Tommy Barnett. A 17-year-old Bastin was not on his radar but Chapman's head was quickly turned. Despite Bastin having made just 17 appearances for the Grecians, Chapman decided he was worth the £2,000 it took to bring him to north London.

A stocky and powerful player, Bastin was a remarkably cool and clinical finisher for one so young and was equally comfortable shooting with either foot. These were attributes that served him well at Highbury and his debut season in 1929–30 culminated in a 2–0 victory over Huddersfield Town in the FA Cup final. At the time the fresh-faced Gunner affectionately known as "Boy Bastin" was the youngest player ever to feature in a final.

The following season Arsenal were crowned Division One champions for the first time. Chapman's side edged out Aston Villa for the title and Bastin played all 42 games, scoring 28 times.

Further Championship successes followed in 1932–33, 1933–34, 1934–35 and finally in 1937–38, and in each campaign he made at least 36 league appearances and in each season he reached double figures for goals scored.

His most prolific season was 1932–33 with 33 goals in 42 league games and, although the advent of Ted Drake in March 1934 saw the

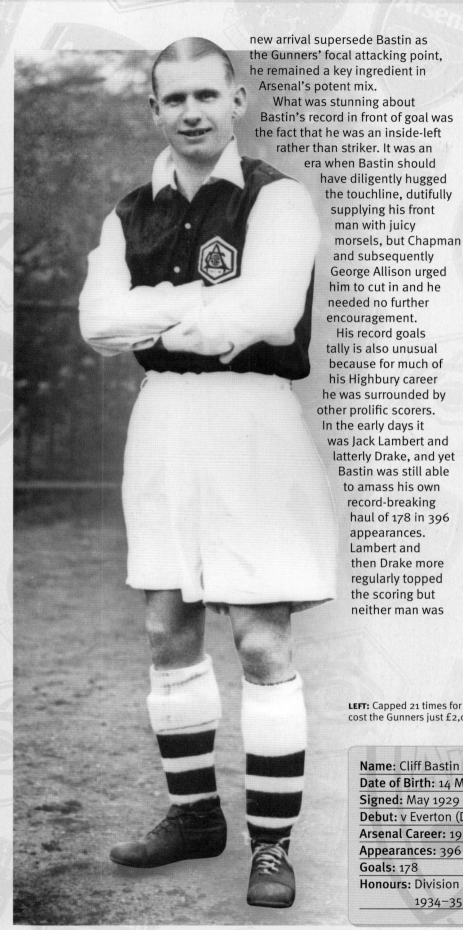

new arrival supersede Bastin as the Gunners' focal attacking point, he remained a key ingredient in Arsenal's potent mix.

What was stunning about Bastin's record in front of goal was the fact that he was an inside-left rather than striker. It was an era when Bastin should have diligently hugged the touchline, dutifully supplying his front man with juicy morsels, but Chapman and subsequently George Allison urged him to cut in and he needed no further encouragement.

His record goals tally is also unusual because for much of his Highbury career he was surrounded by other prolific scorers. In the early days it was Jack Lambert and latterly Drake, and yet Bastin was still able to amass his own record-breaking haul of 178 in 396 appearances. Lambert and then Drake more regularly topped the scoring but neither man was such an influential figure as Bastin throughout the Club's dominance of the decade.

His final full season in north London in 1938–39 was sadly disrupted by injury, restricting him to a modest 24 appearances in all competitions, and then the war came. He was still only 27 but his increasing deafness meant he was deemed unfit to fight and he spent the hostilities serving as an air raid warden.

He played a plethora of friendlies during the conflict but when the Football League returned for the 1946–47 season he was aged 34 and played just six times. His last appearance came in September against Manchester United at Old Trafford and at the end of the season he hung up his boots.

It was in 1997, nearly 60 years later, that Ian Wright finally went past his milestone. It was a bitter-sweet moment but did at least provide an opportunity for different generations of Arsenal supporters to collectively remember the amazing achievements of the Club's first superstar.

Whether Wright and subsequently Thierry Henry would have been able to topple Bastin as the Gunners' greatest goalscorer had it not been for the war years is a moot point but, while he was cruelly robbed of the autumn of his career, he achieved so much so young that it's difficult to imagine he was unduly aggrieved.

LEFT: Capped 21 times for England, Bastin cost the Gunners just £2,000 in 1929.

Name: Cliff Bastin
Date of Birth: 14 March 1912 (Exeter)
Signed: May 1929 (£2,000, Exeter City)
Debut: v Everton (Division One, October 1929)
Arsenal Career: 1929–46
Appearances: 396
Goals: 178
Honours: Division One (1930–31, 1932–33, 1933–34, 1934–35, 1937–38), FA Cup (1930, 1936)

Dennis Bergkamp

A goalscorer, a playmaker and a visionary – the striker was one of the most stylish players ever to represent the Club.

The history of Arsenal will forever remember the revolution that engulfed the Club in the wake of Arsene Wenger's arrival, as a flood of world-class players followed him to north London and the Gunners were reborn as the epitome of style and entertainment.

Dennis Bergkamp was perhaps the greatest of this new generation, a peerless combination of dazzling technique and natural vision. But for all his achievements as a manager, Wenger cannot claim the credit for bringing the Dutchman to Highbury and the 11 years of breathtaking artistry that followed.

That accolade goes to his predecessor, Bruce Rioch, who smashed the Club's transfer record to prise Bergkamp away from Inter Milan in June 1995. It cost £7.5 million to convince the Italians to part with him.

Whatever the failings of Rioch's brief reign as manager, the Dutchman was undoubtedly not one of them.

At times, it felt like Bergkamp was playing a different, altogether more cerebral game to everyone else on the pitch, such was his masterly ball control and unerring ability to think three or four passes ahead of other players. If Wenger was the Professor, Bergkamp was his star pupil.

All of the Dutchman's genius was encapsulated by the goal he scored at Newcastle United in early 2002, an effort so glorious that Arsenal supporters voted it the greatest goal in the Club's history. It is of course difficult to do it full justice but all those who witnessed his regal flick past Nikos Dabizas, his sublime spin behind the back of the bemused Magpies defender and his faultless side-footed finish past Shay Given will

LEFT AND BELOW: The Dutchman never failed to entertain with his sublime blend of instinct and skill.

never forget his touch, his movement and his vision.

There were many more similarly spectacular strikes during his Gunners career and his name remains a byword for elegance and style.

Bergkamp was educated at the Ajax Academy in "Total Football" in the Netherlands. He was handed his first team debut by the great Johan Cruyff in 1986, and after his two-year sojourn in Serie A with Inter he became a Gunner.

The frenetic pace of the English game in contrast to the more sedate philosophy he had encountered in Holland or Italy may have been a shock to the system but Bergkamp's speed of thought eased his transition, and in his first season under Rioch he scored 16 times.

Under Wenger, however, he became the heartbeat of the side and, although the goals continued, it was his wider contribution, his plentiful assists and his superb link-up play that defined him and made him a hero at Highbury.

Bergkamp's first silverware at Arsenal was the 1997–98 Premier League trophy, contributing 16 goals in 28 appearances. A hamstring injury ruled him out of the FA Cup final victory over Newcastle United as the Gunners completed the double but his goal in the fifth-round replay win at Crystal Palace

was pivotal in keeping the team in the competition.

His show-stealing displays throughout the campaign earned him the PFA Players' Player of the Year Award. He became only the second foreign player to claim the prize after Eric Cantona in 1993–94, cementing Bergkamp's reputation as one of the Premier League's true stars.

The Dutchman stayed at Highbury for eight more years and, as the Arsenal side evolved and matured, he became more influential. Thierry Henry enjoyed the lion's share of the headlines in terms of goals but it was Bergkamp, sitting behind the Frenchman, pulling the strings and knitting together the Gunners' increasingly expansive play, who frequently dictated the pace and direction of the attack.

The Club's second double in 2001–02 saw the striker miss just five Premier League games and he was on target three times, including the winner in the fourth round against Liverpool, as Arsenal marched to the

FA Cup final to face and beat Chelsea at Wembley.

Now in his 30s, Bergkamp's finely-honed technique defied the passing of time and he played 24 times in the league during the Invincibles season, collecting his third Premier League winner's medal.

The 2005–06 campaign was to be his last and it was fitting, for a player who had enriched Highbury for more than a decade, that he made a cameo appearance in the last-ever match at the old stadium, coming on for Jose Antonio Reyes with 10 minutes left on the clock as the Gunners despatched Wigan 4–2 on a emotional afternoon in north London.

Three days later Bergkamp celebrated his 37th birthday and the time had finally come to call time on his glittering career. Arsenal began a new era at Emirates a few months later without him but the memories of his 11 years in the red and white will never fade.

LEFT: Dennis Bergkamp was one of the most technically gifted players to grace the Premier League.

BELOW: Winning silverware became a habit during Bergkamp's 11-year stay in England.

Name:	Dennis Bergkamp
Date of Birth:	10 May 1969 (Amsterdam, Holland)
Signed:	June 1995 (£7.5m, Inter Milan)
Debut:	v Middlesbrough (Premier League, August 1995)
Arsenal Career:	1995–2006
Appearances:	423
Goals:	120
Honours:	Premier League (1997–98, 2001–02, 2003–04), FA Cup (1998, 2002, 2003, 2005)

Liam Brady

An elegant Republic of Ireland midfielder, Brady lit up Highbury during the 1970s with an intoxicating mixture of artistry and ambition.

RIGHT: The Irishman's technique and raw talent were second to none.

The beautiful game has always reserved a special place in its affections for an educated left foot. The sheer rarity of truly top-class left-footed players has always elevated such individuals above football's also-rans – and in Liam Brady, Arsenal boasted arguably the most mercurial, mesmerizing and magnificent of them all.

That the Dubliner was a Gunner during one of the leaner eras in the Club's history was irrelevant. When Brady was on song, Highbury was spellbound and he wielded

his legendary left boot as if it were the baton conducting the Arsenal orchestra.

His seven years in north London were certainly too brief; the lure of Italy eventually proved irresistible and he signed for Juventus in 1980. But while others played more games, scored more goals and served more seasons with Arsenal, Brady left as indelible a mark as anyone to wear the famous red and white shirt.

Like many of his countrymen before him, Brady left Ireland as a teenager to pursue his dreams of a professional career. His older brothers Pat and Ray had already crossed the Irish Sea to play for English clubs and on his 17th birthday, in 1973, Brady accepted the

BELOW: Liam Brady, on one of his trademark midfield surges, the ball seemingly glued to his feet.

Gunners' offer of a first professional contract.

Just eight months later he was thrust into first-team action, coming on as a substitute in the Division One game against Birmingham City at Highbury. A week later he was in the starting XI for the north London derby against Spurs at White Hart Lane. Despite his age and inexperience, he was rapidly becoming an integral part of Bertie Mee's team.

Slightly built but deceptively strong, Brady always seemed to have more time on the ball than those crashing around him. His beautiful balance, faultless close control and vision were the source of countless assists – and although his left foot was without equal, his right was far from a weakness. Brady almost glided over the grass at Highbury, and through the 1970s he was the player the fans yearned to watch.

It was in the latter years of the decade that Arsenal awoke from its slumbers and the Dubliner was at the heart of the revival. The 1978 FA Cup final may have ended in disappointment and a 1–0 defeat to Ipswich at Wembley, but the following season was arguably Brady's finest as the Gunners ended their eight-year wait for a trophy.

His brace of goals in the First Division season opener against Leeds United signalled the Irishman's intent, and in December 1978 he was famously on target with a sumptuous effort from outside the box, with the outside of that left boot, in a 5–0 rout of Spurs at Highbury.

The 1979 FA Cup final, however, was perhaps his finest 90 minutes for the Gunners. Manchester United were the opponents at Wembley and an inspired performance from Brady saw Terry Neill's team race into a 2–0 half-time lead courtesy of his deft assists for goals from Brian Talbot and Frank Stapleton... only to be dramatically dragged back to 2–2 in the dying minutes.

Extra-time seemed inevitable but Brady had other ideas and it was his surging run that was the catalyst for Alan Sunderland's late winner. The identity of the Man of the Match was the worst-kept secret in football.

The 1979–80 season was to be his last in north London. He was voted the PFA Player of the Year for 1979 (the first man from outside the United Kingdom to win the accolade) and his reputation now went before him. After two typically elegant displays in the two legs of Arsenal's Cup Winners' Cup semi-final win over Juventus, the Turin giants decided the Irishman

ABOVE: Brady proudly holds aloft the 1979 FA Cup which he did so much to win at Wembley.

belonged in Italy. It took £500,000 to convince Arsenal to sell in the summer of 1980 but the deal was eventually done and Brady quietly took his leave of Highbury.

After his two seasons at the Stadio delle Alpi his footballing journey took him to Sampdoria, Inter Milan, Ascoli and West Ham before he hung up the boots in 1990. Six years later he returned "home" when he was appointed as the new head of Arsenal's Youth Academy.

His 17 years nurturing future generations of Arsenal stars were widely regarded as an unqualified success – but, whatever his achievements as a coach and mentor, it was his seven seasons caressing the ball across Highbury's turf that most supporters remember. Brady in his pomp was a joy to behold and few players in the English game before or since have even come close to paralleling his instinctive elegance.

LEFT: Brady didn't play in the 1972 FA Cup final, but he did represent the Club in the competition's centenary parade before the game.

Name:	Liam Brady
Date of Birth:	13 February 1956 (Dublin)
Signed:	Schoolboy
Debut:	v Birmingham (Division One, October 1973)
Arsenal Career:	1971–80
Appearances:	307
Goals:	59
Honours:	FA Cup (1979)

Ted Drake

Lethal in front of goal, Ted Drake was a prolific and powerful centre-forward who left an indelible mark on the early history of the Gunners.

The legendary Herbert Chapman was Arsenal's first great manager. His untimely death in January 1934 robbed the game of one of its finest tactical innovators, but he left an enduring legacy and will forever be remembered as the man who guided the Gunners to the Division One title for the first time in the Club's history.

His reign, however, did have its disappointments and perhaps none greater than his failure to sign Ted Drake. Chapman tried to lure the centre-forward to Highbury in 1933 but Drake rebuffed his advances to remain with home-town club Southampton. It fell to Chapman's successor George Allison to seal the deal, and he eventually signed the prolific Saints striker for £6,500 in March the following year.

It's not hard to understand why both Arsenal managers were so eager to recruit Drake. His 47 goals in 72 league appearances for Southampton may have come in the Second Division but the forward was clearly destined for top-flight football. A goal on his Gunners debut against Wolves conclusively confirmed his credentials.

His arrival at Highbury saw him leading the line alongside Cliff Bastin – and while Bastin was the epitome of grace and guile, Drake's strengths were his pace, power and thunderbolt shot. Bastin supplied the artistry while Drake provided a physical cutting edge and their partnership reaped huge rewards.

In his first full season, the 1934–35 campaign, Drake was simply unstoppable in the First Division and his 42 goals in 41 games propelled Arsenal to the title. He was also on target in the FA Cup and the Charity Shield, and his overall haul of 44 remains a Club record for a single season that no Arsenal player has yet surpassed.

More records were to follow and in December 1935 Drake was at his

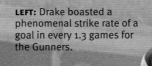

LEFT: Drake boasted a phenomenal strike rate of a goal in every 1.3 games for the Gunners.

BELOW: Ted Drake terrorised opposition defences with his physicality, fearlessness and devastating shooting.

destructive best when the Gunners faced Aston Villa, scoring all seven goals in a 7–1 victory at Villa Park. His incredible performance is still a record for goals in a competitive game.

Arsenal surrendered the title to Sunderland in 1935–36 despite Drake's 24 league goals but consolation came in the form of victory over Sheffield United in the final of the FA Cup at Wembley. The contest was settled by a single goal and unsurprisingly it was Drake who provided it, lashing Bastin's 74th-minute cross past Blades goalkeeper Jack Smith with his left foot to win the match.

Drake's physical and fearless approach, though, did not come without a price. For the remainder of his days as a Gunner he had to contend with a series of injuries which limited his appearances. Despite the knocks he was to finish as the Club's top scorer in all five of his full seasons in north London.

The 1937–38 campaign saw Arsenal crowned champions once again and although Drake featured in just over half of the league fixtures, his 17 goals were to prove priceless as Allison's side beat Wolves to the title by just one point.

The outbreak of the Second World War brought Drake's Highbury career to an abrupt and ultimately premature end. Aged just 27 at the start of the conflict, he regularly played in the Club's wartime fixtures but a back injury sustained in 1945 forced him to

BELOW: The striker is still the fastest player to register a century of goals for Arsenal.

retire and sadly he never featured in another league game.

Many more games and goals would surely have come had it not been for the War, but his goalscoring record remains an incredible testament to his talents. No Arsenal player before or since has found the back of the net as rapidly as Drake.

In total he scored 139 times for the Club in just 184 appearances. It took him a mere 108 games to record his century of goals – quicker than anyone in the Club's history – and while Thierry Henry, Ian Wright, Bastin and John Radford sit above him in the all-time list of Arsenal marksmen, his goals per game ratio is superior to them all.

After his playing days were cruelly cut short, Drake turned to management, and after spells with Hendon and Reading he was appointed Chelsea boss in 1952. Within three years the Blues were the Division One champions and Drake became the first man to win the title as both player and manager.

Chapman never had the chance to work with him but Drake's prolific if all-too-brief time with the Club certainly proved the iconic Arsenal manager knew a star when he saw one.

ABOVE: Sadly Drake's record-breaking Arsenal career was cut prematurely short by the Second World War.

Name:	Ted Drake
Date of Birth:	16 August 1912 (Southampton)
Signed:	March 1934 (£6,500, Southampton)
Debut:	v Wolverhampton Wanderers (Division One, March 1934)
Arsenal Career:	1934–45
Appearances:	184
Goals:	139
Honours:	Division One (1934–35, 1937–78), FA Cup (1936)

Thierry Henry

An irresistible force for eight incredible seasons, he rewrote the Club's scoring records as he ripped apart Premier League defences.

Elegant, explosive and extravagantly gifted, Thierry Henry was a match winner *par excellence* and even his phenomenal Club record of 228 goals in 337 appearances fails to tell the full story of the Frenchman's impact on both Arsenal and the Premier League.

Henry was two weeks short of his 22nd birthday when Arsene Wenger, his former manager at Monaco, signed him in August 1999 as a replacement for compatriot Nicolas Anelka. The £11 million fee seemed steep after a lacklustre season in Italy with Juventus and when his first eight appearances in the famous red and white failed to yield a goal, the cynics suggested the youngster was no more than an ill-advised import unable to adapt to the notoriously physical rigours of the English game.

On 18 September 1999, however, the story changed when Henry came off the bench in the 71st minute of a Premier League clash with Southampton at the Dell. Eight short minutes later, he collected a Nigel Winterburn pass, turned his marker and curled a glorious right-footed effort into the goal for the winner. A passionate love affair between player and Club had begun in earnest and, once he had ended his initial drought, Henry never looked back.

He finished the 1999–2000 campaign as the Gunners' top scorer with 26 in all competitions and for seven consecutive seasons he led the way for Arsenal in front of goal. It's a feat of prolific consistency that not even the great Ted Drake or iconic

LEFT: Thierry Henry was top scorer in both seasons in which he lifted the Premier League trophy.

BELOW: The Frenchman was as acrobatic as he was destructive during his remarkable Arsenal career.

Ian Wright could match, both players finishing six seasons each as the top scorer.

In 2001–02 Henry was on target 32 times in 49 games in all competitions as the Gunners completed the fabled league and cup double for the third time. Any lingering doubts about Henry's genius evaporated almost as rapidly as the hopes of the opposition defenders deployed to stop him.

The Frenchman's emergence as arguably the most feared striker in Europe coincided with one of the greatest eras in Arsenal's history. His deluge of goals, searing pace and dazzling dribbling were the catalyst for two Premier League and three FA Cup triumphs during his eight-year fairytale stay in north London.

Arsenal's success led inevitably to individual recognition and awards. A two-time PFA Player of the Year and three-time Football Writers' Association Footballer of the Year, Henry also won the Premier League Golden Boot four times and the European Golden Shoe twice.

At his imperious best, he was virtually unplayable and made a mockery of the old adage that some strikers score great goals while others are great goalscorers. The majority of Henry's 228 strikes for Arsenal were both beautiful and pivotal and, while he was ruthless from close range, he was also an artist outside the box.

His most prolific Premier League season for the Club inevitably came in 2003–04 as Wenger's unbeaten Invincibles majestically swept all before them. Henry scored 30 in 37 league appearances as the Gunners claimed the title, cementing his place in the pantheon of the Club's true greats.

When Henry was appointed Club captain in the wake of Patrick Vieira's departure in the summer of 2005, the burden of leadership did not dim his natural instincts in front of goal. In October 2005 his brace against Sparta Prague in the Champions League took him past Wright's record tally of 185. Set just eight years earlier, Wright's milestone seemed to many as if it would never be eclipsed – but Henry was evidently not reading the same script.

His final full season with the Gunners was 2006–07 and, although injury plagued what was to be his farewell campaign, he once again reached double figures in the league despite featuring just 17 times.

The sense of loss around Emirates when Henry signed for Barcelona in June 2007 was palpable. A year after he left for Spain, Arsenal fans still voted him the Gunners' greatest-ever player in an online poll conducted on the Club's official website.

The striker made an emotional if brief return to London in January 2012 when he rejoined on loan from New York Red Bulls. He made just seven fleeting appearances before returning to America but it surprised no-one when he scored a dramatic winner in the FA Cup against Leeds United in his first game back at his undisputed spiritual home.

Henry's individual records – the Club's all-time top scorer, leading Premier League and Champions League marksman – speak for themselves but his balletic displays on the pitch remain as memorable as the pure statistics.

RIGHT: Henry's record haul of 228 goals is a milestone which may never be eclipsed.

LEFT: A young Henry signs for the Gunners in 1999 and a new era for the Club begins.

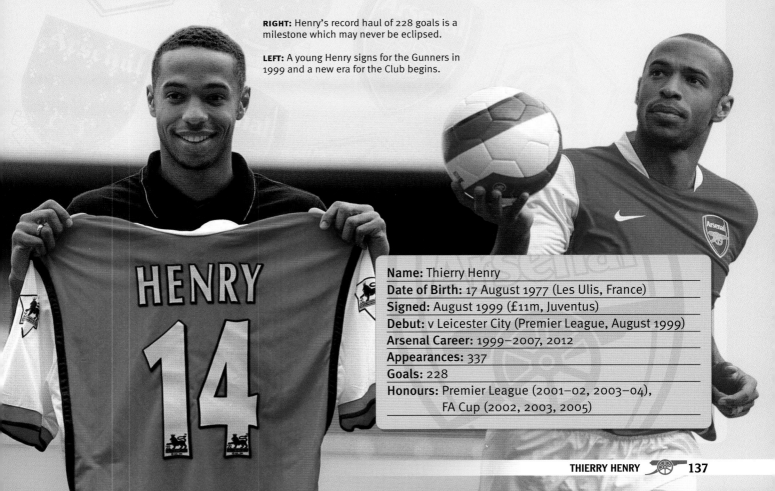

Name: Thierry Henry
Date of Birth: 17 August 1977 (Les Ulis, France)
Signed: August 1999 (£11m, Juventus)
Debut: v Leicester City (Premier League, August 1999)
Arsenal Career: 1999–2007, 2012
Appearances: 337
Goals: 228
Honours: Premier League (2001–02, 2003–04), FA Cup (2002, 2003, 2005)

Frank McLintock

Frank McLintock galvanized the Gunners for nearly a decade, and never took a backwards step in the Club's battle for trophies.

It was Billy Wright who brought Frank McLintock to Highbury, signing the Scottish international from Leicester City for a Club-record £80,000 in October 1964, but it was his successor Bertie Mee who was to harness the Glaswegian's abrasive talents and transform him into one of the greatest captains in the Club's history.

McLintock was just two months short of his 25th birthday when he arrived in north London. A wing-half by trade, the Scot was the epitome of youthful enthusiasm and aggression, and after making his debut in a defeat against Nottingham Forest, he quickly established himself as a key component in Wright's line-up.

The change of manager in the summer of 1966 saw McLintock's status as a first-team regular unaffected under Mee. But with Arsenal consistently finishing in mid-table, the side's prospects of silverware seemed frustratingly remote and the memories of the Club's 1952–53 title triumph were fading fast.

The 1969–70 season changed everything. A defensive injury crisis forced Mee's hand and he made the bold decision to switch McLintock to centre-half. It was to prove an inspired move and, with the Scot now

LEFT: Frank McLintock celebrates after captaining the side to a 2-1 win over Liverpool in the 1971 FA Cup final.

BELOW: McLintock's switch from wing half to the heart of the Arsenal defence transformed his career.

also wearing the captain's armband, the Gunners' fortunes began to improve dramatically.

Defeats to Leeds United and Swindon Town in the League Cup finals of 1968 and 1969 had at least hinted at progress but the first tangible evidence of McLintock's growing influence came in the 1969–70 Inter-Cities Fairs Cup campaign. With the Scotsman masterfully marshalling the back four, Arsenal conceded just three goals in 10 games en route to the final. Although they were beaten 3–1 by Anderlecht in Belgium in the first leg of the final, McLintock refused to be bowed and a 3–0 triumph in the return match at Highbury six days later saw the Scot lift the trophy.

The Club's first-ever European silverware was to be the hors d'oeuvres rather than the main course and in 1970–71 McLintock was ever-present as the Gunners famously completed the fabled League and Cup double.

By rights, Mee's team had no business claiming the Division One title. The team had finished a distant 12th in the table the previous season, 24 points

adrift of winners Everton, but Arsenal were now an altogether different proposition under the new skipper. They lost just six times as they narrowly edged out Leeds United to become champions.

McLintock was in imperious form throughout. He started all 42 league matches and his immaculate reading of the game, physical presence and forthright leadership saw the team concede only 29 times in a glorious campaign.

Five days after the climax of the league season, it was time for the FA Cup final against Liverpool and a possible place in the history books. McLintock led the side out at Wembley in front of 100,000 supporters and the stage was set for a day of real drama.

The 90 minutes of normal time failed to produce a goal but the Gunners went behind to a Steve Heighway goal early in extra-time and the double dream was dangling by a thread – until McLintock exhorted one last effort from his weary team.

His rallying cry did not go unheeded. Substitute Eddie Kelly equalized in the 101st minute, and when Charlie George beat Liverpool goalkeeper Ray Clemence with a thunderous 20-yard drive 10 minutes later the trophy and the double belonged to Arsenal.

The Football Writers' Association recognized McLintock's contribution to the Club's all-conquering season when they named him Footballer of the Year for 1971. The following year he was awarded the MBE and the Scot was confirmed as one of the Gunners' true greats.

LEFT: The Scottish international joined the Gunners from Leicester City in 1964 for a Club record £80,000.

He was to remain the king of Highbury for two more years. The team's 1–0 defeat in the 1972 FA Cup final against Leeds was painful but it could not tarnish the lustre of the previous season's achievements. When McLintock finally parted company with the Club, signing for QPR in the summer of 1973, Arsenal lost one of its finest and most feared leaders.

He was 38 when he finally hung up his boots. His brief forays into management with Leicester and latterly Brentford did not bring great success but that did little to detract from his reputation within Highbury and beyond.

In total, McLintock made 403 appearances for the Club, scoring 32 goals, and in 2009 he was inducted into the English Football Hall of Fame, a fitting tribute to a player who led the Gunners out of the Club's 17-year-long trophy drought.

BELOW: The former skipper was one of the greatest-ever Arsenal players.

Name:	Frank McLintock
Date of Birth:	28 December 1939 (Glasgow)
Signed:	October 1964 (£80,000, Leicester City)
Debut:	v Nottingham Forest (Division One, October 1964)
Arsenal Career:	1964–73
Appearances:	403
Goals:	32
Honours:	Inter-Cities Fairs Cup (1970), Division One (1970–71), FA Cup (1971)

David O'Leary

The epitome of class and staggering consistency, O'Leary's career spanned three separate decades and a record-breaking 722 first team appearances for the Club.

By his own admission, David O'Leary was far from a typical specimen in the abrasive world of centre-halves. Standing a modest six foot and built like a middle-distance runner rather than an archetypal rugged central defender, the adopted Irishman initially appeared ill-equipped for the physical rigours of his chosen profession.

But what O'Leary may have lacked in height or raw power, he more than made up for with his other attributes. Deceptively quick despite his unmistakable loping gait, unflappable, brave and composed, he oozed class while his Club-record 722 career appearances speaks

LEFT: A mainstay of the Gunners' defence for 18 years, the Irishman was a fans' favourite.

volumes about his mental and physical durability.

Born in Hackney, O'Leary moved with his family to Dublin when he was just three but returned to England in 1973 when he signed apprentice forms with the Gunners. Two years later he was thrust into Bertie Mee's side just three months after his 17th birthday.

Arsenal were struggling. The previous season the side had finished a lowly 16th, just four points clear of relegated Luton Town, and when O'Leary ran out for his first team debut against Burnley at Turf Moor in August even the most ardent supporters were apprehensively bracing themselves for another difficult campaign.

BELOW: O'Leary broke into the first team at the age of 17 and never looked back.

The Gunners came away from Burnley with a goalless draw but the fans' fears were confirmed as the season unfolded and once again the side limped home, finishing 17th in the table.

The one bright spot, however, was O'Leary. Partnering either Terry Mancini or Terry Powling in the heart of the defence, the teenager equipped himself with a maturity he had no right to display and made 27 appearances in the first of 17 seasons of loyal service for the Club.

The first silverware of his career came in 1979 when Arsenal faced Manchester United at Wembley in the FA Cup final. It was a pulsating encounter that Terry Neill's side won 3–2 courtesy of Alan Sunderland's last-gasp goal and O'Leary collected his first winner's medal. He was subsequently named in the PFA First Division Team of the Year and his reputation as one of the most accomplished centre-halves in the country continued to grow.

By now the Irishman was part of the furniture at Arsenal and his elegant distribution from the back, his beautifully-timed tackles and aura of calm confidence in even the most frenetic of situations were all reassuringly familiar to the Highbury faithful.

Part of the side that lifted the 1987 League Cup, O'Leary was yet to win the Championship but the arrival of George Graham in 1986 had seen the Gunners emerge as serious contenders and in 1988–89 they ended the Club's 18-year wait for the title. O'Leary played 26 times during the campaign and was part of the team that famously beat Liverpool 2–0 at Anfield in the final, winner-takes-all match of the season.

Although he was now in his 30s and vying with both Tony Adams and Steve Bould for selection, he continued to play regularly, albeit at right-back, and he clocked up another 21 games during the 1990–91 season as Graham's Gunners were crowned champions for a second time.

The 1992–93 campaign and the advent of the Premier League was to be his last in Arsenal colours and, although he made a modest 11 league appearances, O'Leary ensured he signed off in suitable style with two triumphant appearances at Wembley and two more winner's medals for his collection.

The first instalment of the farewell came at Wembley in April in the shape of the League Cup final against Sheffield Wednesday. O'Leary started in the 2–1 victory over the Owls and he was back at Wembley a month later for the FA Cup final against the same opposition.

This time he was named among the substitutes but came on for extra-time of the 1–1 draw and five days later he was again on the bench for the replay, coming on for Ian Wright after 81 minutes as the Gunners were taken into extra-time before clinching a 2–1 win.

The replay was the 35-year-old's 722nd and final game for the Club and in August he headed north when he signed for Leeds United. Not even team-mate Tony Adams was subsequently able to surpass his record number of appearances and many believe his phenomenal tally will never be eclipsed.

ABOVE: David O'Leary enjoyed the most successful period of his Highbury career under George Graham's management.

BELOW: The defender's elegant efforts earned him six major trophies in Arsenal colours.

Name:	David O'Leary
Date of Birth:	2 May 1958 (London)
Signed:	Apprentice
Debut:	v Burnley (Division One, August 1975)
Arsenal Career:	1975–93
Appearances:	722
Goals:	14
Honours:	Division One (1988–89, 1990–91), FA Cup (1979, 1993), League Cup (1987, 1993)

Robert Pires

The most entertaining of Arsene Wenger's French foreign legion, Pires' Gallic flair brought both style and silverware to north London in the 2000s.

The French invasion of Arsenal in the late 1990s and early 2000s was a revolution which transformed the Club's fortunes. The Gallic influx was the catalyst for one of the most successful and spectacular eras in Gunners' history and each of Arsene Wenger's new recruits from across the Channel added a new dimension to the side.

Thierry Henry supplied the goals, Patrick Vieira the power and the passion. Emmanuel Petit patrolled the midfield with menace while Sylvain Wiltord regularly rampaged the length of the pitch.

Robert Emmanuel Pires brought the magic. The midfielder scored goals too – 84 in 284 appearances – but it was his sublime skills, his ability to beat players with an audacious dribble and his sumptuous passing that made him a Highbury hero. At his peak, Pires was poetry in motion.

He arrived in north London in the summer of 2000. It cost the Gunners a modest £6 million to persuade Marseille to sell their Euro 2000 winner and, although the physical demands of the English game initially proved a challenge, he finished his debut season with a respectable eight goals in 51 appearances.

The 2001–02 campaign, however, was to be an altogether different story. The mercurial Frenchman

LEFT: Beautifully balanced and a natural crowd pleaser, the Frenchman made 284 appearances for the Club.

BELOW: Robert Pires scored the winning goal against Southampton in the final of the 2003 FA Cup in Cardiff.

unleashed his full array of attacking talents and he was to be a key figure as Arsenal famously completed a league and cup double.

Pires signalled his intent with a goal in the 4–0 mauling of Middlesbrough at the Riverside on the opening day of the season and never looked back as Wenger's side gathered momentum. The side lost just three times en route to the Premier League title and, while a cruciate ligament injury ruled Pires out of the Gunners' 2–0 win over Chelsea in the FA Cup final, it was his second-minute goal in the quarter-final replay against Newcastle that inspired the team's 3–0 triumph.

The double-winning side of course was brimming with stars, but it was Pires' cultured contribution to the cause that caught the imagination within Highbury and beyond. In 2002 he was named both the Arsenal Supporters' Club Player of the Year and the Football Writers' Association Footballer of the Year.

Pires, however, had unfinished business and 12 months after missing the FA Cup win against Chelsea he was to the fore as Arsenal retained the trophy, scoring the only goal in the final at the Millennium Stadium as Southampton were despatched 1–0.

His role in the Invincibles' breathtaking 2003–04 campaign was even more significant – he hit the winning goals in the league clashes with Everton in August, Liverpool the following month and Southampton in December before scoring the second against Tottenham at White Hart Lane in April to earn the side a 2–2 draw and confirm Arsenal as champions. In total, he scored 19 times from midfield in all competitions in 2003–04, as well as providing 15

assists, and his reputation as one of the English game's most dazzling but deadly performers was cemented.

His rich vein of form continued through the 2004–05 campaign. For the third consecutive season he scored 14 Premier League goals to finish as the division's third most prolific player and, although the title was to elude Wenger's team, there was more silverware in the shape of another FA Cup success. The trophy headed to Highbury for the third time in four years after Manchester United were beaten in a penalty shootout in Cardiff – but the Gunners might not have even reached the final had it not been for Pires' strike in the 1–1 draw with Sheffield United in the fifth round.

The final chapter of Pires' Gunners story was written in 2005–06 – but the climax to his glittering Arsenal career, the Champions League final against Barcelona in Paris, was not the fairy-tale ending he richly deserved.

The eagerly anticipated clash in the Stade de France saw goalkeeper Jens Lehmann sent off after just 18 minutes. Wenger was forced to bring on Manuel Almunia to wear the gloves for the remaining 72 minutes and the manager reluctantly sacrificed Pires as he reorganized his depleted line-up. Arsenal eventually suffered a 2–1 defeat in the French capital and Pires never played for the Club again.

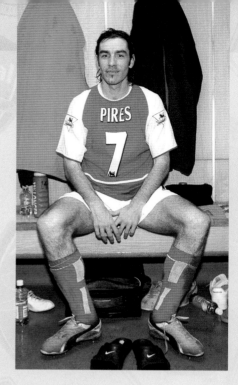

The popular Frenchman headed to Spain the following month when he signed for Villarreal on a free transfer. His six years at Highbury had come to an end but the bitter disappointment of defeat to Barcelona would not overshadow his other magnificent achievements and in 2008 supporters voted Pires as the sixth-greatest player in Arsenal history.

ABOVE: Robert Pires was an integral part of the Gunners' famed Invincibles throughout the 2003–04 season.

BELOW: Despite playing in midfield, Pires still scored 84 goals in six seasons for Arsenal.

Name:	Robert Pires
Date of Birth:	29 October 1973 (Reims, France)
Signed:	July 2000 (£6m, Marseille)
Debut:	v Sunderland (Premier League, August 2000)
Arsenal Career:	2000–06
Appearances:	284
Goals:	84
Honours:	Premier League (2001–02, 2003–04), FA Cup (2002, 2003, 2005)

David Seaman

Affectionately dubbed "Safe Hands", Seaman was Arsenal's unflappable last line of defence for 13 trophy-laden years at Highbury.

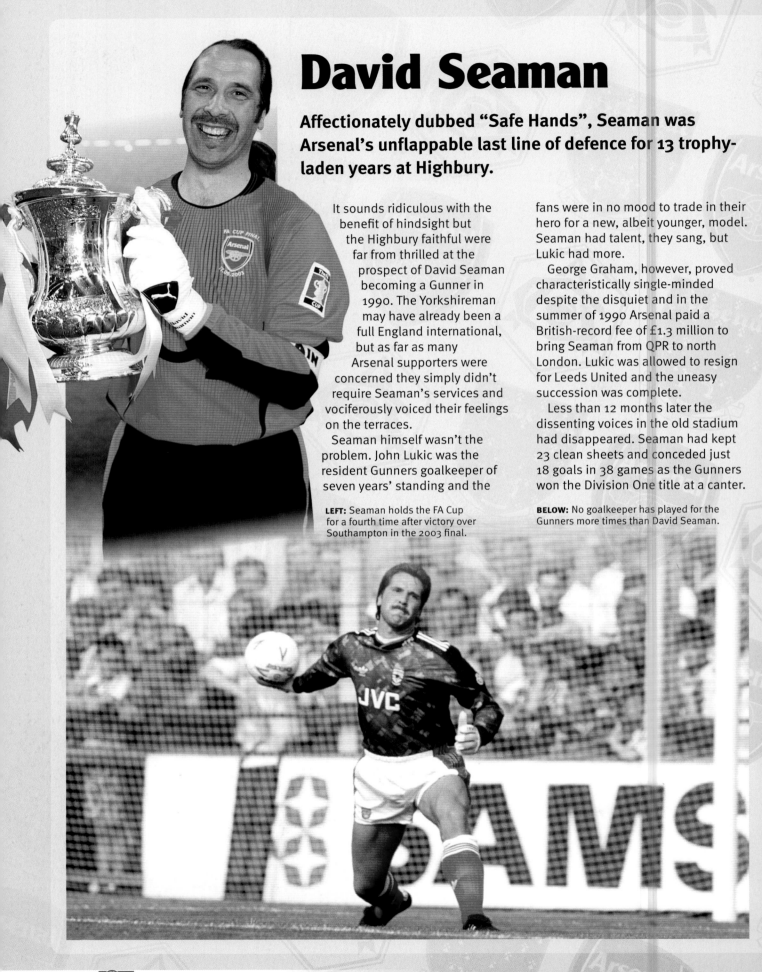

It sounds ridiculous with the benefit of hindsight but the Highbury faithful were far from thrilled at the prospect of David Seaman becoming a Gunner in 1990. The Yorkshireman may have already been a full England international, but as far as many Arsenal supporters were concerned they simply didn't require Seaman's services and vociferously voiced their feelings on the terraces.

Seaman himself wasn't the problem. John Lukic was the resident Gunners goalkeeper of seven years' standing and the fans were in no mood to trade in their hero for a new, albeit younger, model. Seaman had talent, they sang, but Lukic had more.

George Graham, however, proved characteristically single-minded despite the disquiet and in the summer of 1990 Arsenal paid a British-record fee of £1.3 million to bring Seaman from QPR to north London. Lukic was allowed to resign for Leeds United and the uneasy succession was complete.

Less than 12 months later the dissenting voices in the old stadium had disappeared. Seaman had kept 23 clean sheets and conceded just 18 goals in 38 games as the Gunners won the Division One title at a canter.

LEFT: Seaman holds the FA Cup for a fourth time after victory over Southampton in the 2003 final.

BELOW: No goalkeeper has played for the Gunners more times than David Seaman.

Highbury had a new hero and for the next 12 seasons the adulation showed no signs of waning.

Physically Seaman was the embodiment of a perfect keeper. Six-foot-three and athletic, he was blessed with sharp reflexes and innate bravery while technically he was faultless and read the game like a natural sweeper. Some keepers are famed for their shot-stopping prowess, others for their reliability under the high ball and crosses. Seaman could do it all.

His dazzling debut season was no one-off. The 1993 FA Cup, the first of the four in his career, and the League Cup earlier in the year added to his burgeoning reputation while his bravery was in evidence in the 1994 Cup Winners' Cup final against Parma, playing through the discomfort of a broken rib with a combination of pain-killers and archetypal Yorkshire grit as the Gunners completed a famous 1–0 victory that owed much to a stoical rearguard from Seaman and the

back four as the Italians searched insistently for the equalizer.

But as for so many of his Highbury contemporaries, he was yet to truly scale the heights and it was his typically uncomplicated contribution to the double-winning campaigns of 1997–98 and 2001–02 that cemented his legacy as the greatest keeper in the Club's history.

The 1997–98 season saw Seaman play 31 of the 38 Premier League fixtures en route to the title. He was preferred to Alex Manninger for the FA Cup final against Newcastle and, while the inevitable dimming of the light saw him sharing custodial duties in 2001–02 with Manninger and Richard Wright, he once again played in the Cup final as Chelsea were despatched 2–0 and yet another clean sheet was chalked up on his miserly CV.

The 2002–03 season proved a prolonged goodbye to the Club but there was time yet for both one more magnificent save and one emotional moment of celebratory farewell.

The save came in the FA Cup semi-final against Sheffield United. The Gunners were 1–0 up but seemed destined to be pegged back in the dying minutes when Paul Peschisolido's header flew towards goal – only for Seaman, just five months shy of his 40th birthday, to spectacularly claw his effort towards safety.

In the absence of the injured Patrick Vieira, Seaman captained the side in the final against Southampton in Cardiff. One last clean sheet and a Robert Pires goal were enough to see the veteran lift the famous trophy in his final act in an Arsenal shirt.

A little over two weeks later he was a Manchester City player, although his last hurrah in Manchester was cut short by a shoulder injury. In January 2004, he packed away the gloves and announced his retirement.

His Highbury career encompassed 564 appearances and eight major trophies. In the Premier League he played 344 times and kept 141 clean sheets. He also amassed 72 England caps while he was an Arsenal player. Like all goalkeepers, he made mistakes but they were notable for their rarity.

His trademark pony-tail and moustache were legendary but it is his nickname – "Safe Hands" – that encapsulates his 13 years with the Gunners and how he will always be remembered.

ABOVE: David Seaman kept a remarkable 141 clean sheets in 344 Premier League appearances.

LEFT: The goalkeeper was a pivotal player as Arsenal claimed the double in both 1997–98 and 2001–02.

Name:	David Seaman
Date of Birth:	19 September 1963 (Rotherham)
Signed:	June 1990 (£1.3m, QPR)
Debut:	v Wimbledon (Division One, August 1990)
Arsenal Career:	1990–2003
Appearances:	564
Goals:	0
Honours:	Premier League (1997–98, 2001–02), Division One (1990–91), FA Cup (1993, 1998, 2002, 2003), League Cup (1993), Cup Winners' Cup (1994)

Patrick Vieira

The indomitable heartbeat of the Arsenal side from 1996 to 2005, the French midfielder was both warrior and poet in a Gunners shirt.

When Arsene Wenger agreed to become the new Arsenal manager, he insisted on one condition before officially agreeing to take the Highbury job. It was neither a demand for a generous transfer budget nor a hefty performance-related bonus. The Frenchman simply insisted the Gunners hierarchy sign Patrick Vieira.

Wisely, the Club agreed. It cost £3.5 million to prise the 20-year-old away from AC Milan and, in the summer of 1996, the first recruit of the Wenger revolution arrived in London. The Arsenal faithful may have been unsure what to expect from their new, unheralded midfielder but their new manager knew exactly what the future held for his new signing.

From the very start, it was utterly impossible to ignore Vieira. His six-foot-four frame made him an intimidating physical presence but his raw power belied his artistry and intelligence and he quickly found the pace, aggression and passion of the English game fitted him like a glove. The Frenchman was a natural football Anglophile and, as he began to exercise a vicelike grip on the Arsenal midfield, the Gunners grew in confidence.

The side finished his debut season seven points adrift of champions Manchester United but 12 months

LEFT: Lifting trophies was a regular event during the Frenchman's nine-year career at Highbury.

BELOW: Patrick Vieira soon became the team's talisman after signing from AC Milan in the summer of 1996.

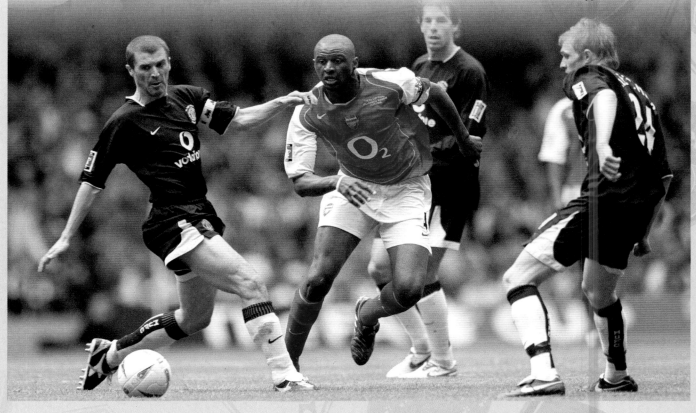

later, driven relentlessly and robustly on by Vieira, they were Premier League champions for the first time. The midfielder missed just five games and the best was yet to come as Arsenal despatched Newcastle 2–0 in the FA Cup final at Wembley to complete the double.

As the Gunners under Wenger continued to evolve, Vieira's influence increased. The likes of Marc Overmars, Thierry Henry, Freddie Ljungberg and Dennis Bergkamp were all brought in to provide the pyrotechnics but, without Vieira providing the cement, the new-look Arsenal would have been little more than a house built on sand.

The 2001–02 season saw the Frenchman once more integral to the Club's success, playing in 36 of 38 Premier League games as Arsenal once again claimed the title, before nullifying the threat of the Chelsea midfield as Wenger's side beat the Blues 2–0 in the final of the FA Cup to register a second double.

By now Vieira's reputation was almost as fearsome as his performances on the pitch. His angry spats with Manchester United's Roy Keane solidified his public image as a muscular midfield enforcer but he continued to be an infinitely more three-dimensional player who relished galloping forward with the ball at his feet as much as a physical confrontation. Arsenal scored a deluge of goals during his nine-season sojourn in the capital and, although he contributed a relatively modest 33 to that total, he never lacked a genuine goal threat.

In 2002 he assumed the Club captaincy. At any other time, Tony Adams' retirement could have left a dangerous vacuum but Vieira was hewn from the same rock and, in his first season wearing the armband, the team claimed the 2003 FA Cup despite the new skipper missing the final through injury.

The pinnacle of his Highbury career, however, came in 2003–04 as the unbeatable Invincibles ripped up the record books to claim a third Premier League crown. A hamstring injury limited Vieira's games early on in the historic campaign but 22 appearances in the closing 23 matches, scoring pivotal goals in the 2–1 win over Chelsea at Stamford Bridge in February and the 2–2 draw with Spurs at White Hart Lane in April, powered the Gunners to glory.

The 2004–05 campaign was to be his last but the football gods contrived to send him off in the most dramatic style.

The scene was the FA Cup final against Manchester United at the Millennium Stadium and, with neither side able to conjure a goal in 90 minutes or extra-time, the contest headed to a shootout.

After four penalties apiece, the score stood at 4–3 to the Gunners but it soon became 4–4 when Vieira's old sparring partner Keane converted.

The Frenchman only had to score to lift the trophy and in a fitting farewell to the team and the Club, to Wenger and the fans, he beat Roy Carroll and the party began.

A little less than two months later the Gunners accepted a £13.75 million bid from Juventus for the skipper. He was on his way back to Italy and an Arsenal adventure that encompassed 406 appearances was finished.

His departure, though, failed to arouse the ire of the Highbury faithful. They were undoubtedly sad to see him go but the memories of his majestic midfield displays, his rampaging runs and his brooding physical presence were still too fresh and too fond.

ABOVE: Patrick Vieira is one of an exclusive group of Arsenal players to have made more than 400 appearances for the Club.

LEFT: The midfielder succeeded Tony Adams as Arsenal captain in 2002.

Name:	Patrick Vieira
Date of Birth:	23 June 1976 (Dakar, Senegal)
Signed:	September 1996 (£3.5m, AC Milan)
Debut:	v Sheffield Wednesday (Premier League, September 1996)
Arsenal Career:	1996–2005
Appearances:	406
Goals:	33
Honours:	Premier League (1997–98, 2001–02, 2003–04), FA Cup (1998, 2002, 2003, 2005)

Ian Wright

A predatory, tireless and hugely popular marksman, Ian Wright was the man who finally broke Cliff Bastin's long-standing Arsenal scoring record.

There was always an irresistible, irrepressible sense of urgency to Ian Wright's Arsenal career. Perhaps it was the fact that the striker only arrived at Highbury two months short of his 28th birthday, or maybe it was merely his natural hunger for goals, but whenever Wright played, he was invariably in a hurry.

The striker's need for speed reaped phenomenal rewards. For six consecutive seasons he finished as the Gunners' top scorer and in September 1997 he famously broke Cliff Bastin's long-standing record of 178 goals for the Club with a hat-trick against Bolton Wanderers. Bastin took 396 games to set his milestone, Wright eclipsed it in just 266 appearances for the Club.

Wright scored a dazzling array of goals. A predator at close range inside the box, he also had the ability to produce the spectacular from long range and his explosive pace, energy and perpetual movement made him a constant thorn in the side of every team he faced.

George Graham brought the striker to Highbury in September 1991. Despite an impressive 117 goals in 253 starts for Crystal Palace, some still questioned the wisdom of

LEFT: Ian Wright's appetite for goals was as inexhaustible as the energy and desire he displayed on the pitch.

BELOW: Wright broke Cliff Bastin's Club goalscoring record in 1997 with a hat-trick against Bolton Wanderers.

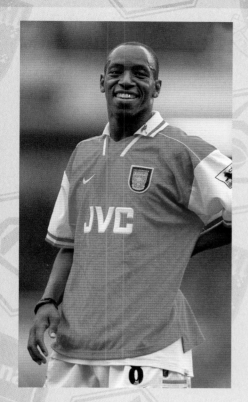

ABOVE: The striker claimed a Premier League winner's medal at the end of the 1997–98 campaign.

investing a then Club-record £2.5 million to persuade the Eagles to sell their prized centre-forward.

The sceptics also pointed out that Alan Smith was still scoring with reassuring regularity and a young Kevin Campbell was maturing into a proven marksman. The new signing, they feared, was an expensive luxury for the reigning First Division champions.

The doubts, however, were immediately dispelled when Wright scored a dazzling hat-trick on his league debut in a Division One clash with Southampton at the Dell. Twenty-three more goals followed during the 1991–92 campaign – including another hat-trick against the Saints on the final day of the season to snatch the Golden Boot from Tottenham's Gary Lineker – and Highbury had a new idol.

The first silverware of his Arsenal career came in 1993 as Graham's side completed a fabulous FA and League Cup double. Wright scored 15 goals in 15 cup appearances as the Gunners beat Sheffield Wednesday in the final of both competitions, including strikes in both the first Wembley match and the replay as they claimed

the FA Cup for the sixth time in the Club's history.

Suspension ruled him out of the team's 1–0 win over Parma in the 1994 Cup Winners' Cup final but the goals continued to flow and his youthful exuberance continued to counter his advancing years. Wright's appetite for the game was his hallmark and, even when he was not on target, his work rate and commitment were beyond question.

The arrival of Arsene Wenger in north London in September 1996 initially cast a shadow over Wright's future. The striker was just two months short of his 33rd birthday when the Frenchman was appointed – but rather than accept a changing of the guard under the new manager, Wright was spurred to even greater heights and under Wenger's watchful eye he responded with 23 goals in 35 Premier League games.

A Premier League winner's medal had so far eluded the centre-forward but there was still enough gas in the tank to complete his collection. Injury and the emergence of Nicolas Anelka limited Wright's appearances in 1997–98 but he characteristically refused to remain in the shadows and his winning goals against Coventry in August and Newcastle in December secured six points that ultimately proved pivotal as Arsenal narrowly edged out Manchester United for the title.

His Highbury farewell came in early May in a 4–0 romp over Everton. Surprisingly, Wright did not help himself to yet another Gunners goal but it was no more than a minor irritation as he said an emotional goodbye to the supporters who had witnessed him find the back of the net an incredible 185 times for the Club

over seven record-breaking seasons.

His last-ever Arsenal appearance came at Aston Villa a week later. Wright was booked, testament to the combative spirit that so naturally complemented his unerring eye for goal, and in the summer of 1998 the 34-year-old was sold to West Ham United.

His career with the Gunners may have been relatively short compared to longer-serving legends but Wright ensured he made the most of every minute of his time. The subsequent exploits of Thierry Henry may have rewritten many of the Club's goalscoring records but, in terms of goals per game for the Gunners, Wright remains the undisputed king.

RIGHT: Wright was the Gunners' leading goalscorer for six consecutive seasons.

Name:	Ian Wright
Date of Birth:	3 November 1963 (London)
Signed:	September 1991 (£2.5m, Crystal Palace)
Debut:	v Southampton (Division One, September 1991)
Arsenal Career:	1991–98
Appearances:	288
Goals:	185
Honours:	Premier League (1997–98), FA Cup (1993, 1998), League Cup (1993), Cup Winners' Cup (1994)

PART 5
Honours & Awards

The late, great Joe Mercer became the first-ever Gunner to win a major individual award when he was named the Football Writers' Association Footballer of the Year in 1949–50 – and ever since, Arsenal players and managers have been winning recognition from the wider football family.

From Liam Brady's breakthrough PFA Player of the Year success in 1978–79 to Thierry Henry's unprecedented double European Golden Shoe triumph, this chapter details the Arsenal players whose performances have earned them personal accolades and awards. There are also details of all of the winners of the coveted Arsenal Football Supporters' Player of the Year, as well as the Club's inductees into the prestigious English Football Hall of Fame.

ABOVE: Arsenal players over the decades have been no strangers to either team trophies or individual accolades.

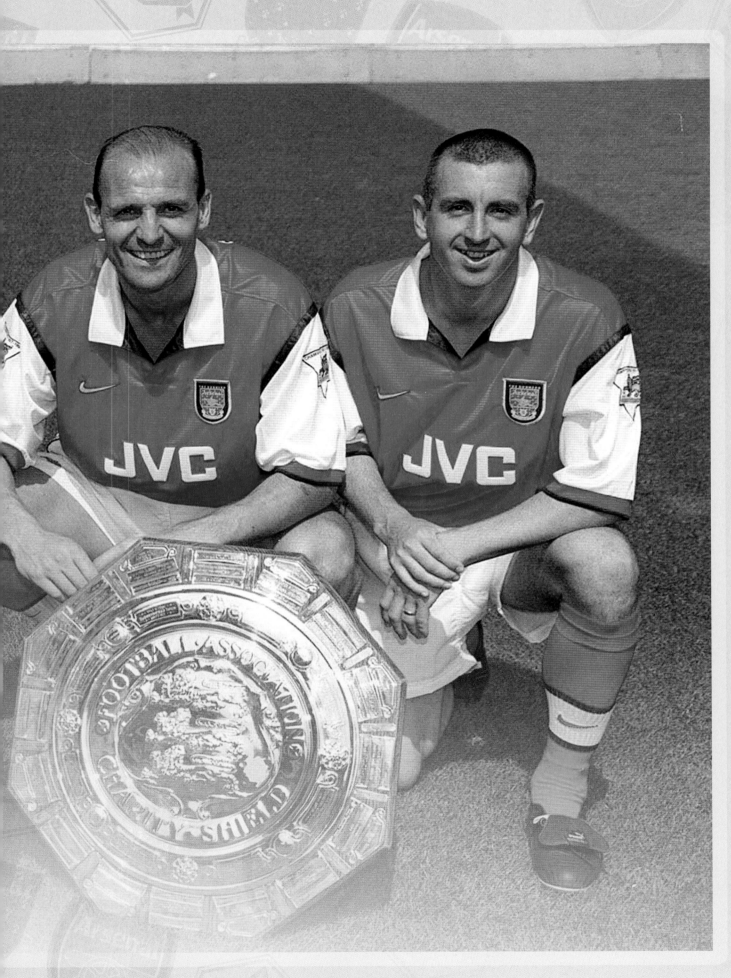

Honours & Awards – Individual

FOOTBALL'S FINEST

The English Football Hall of Fame was created in 2002 to honour the game's most iconic players and managers and the first Arsenal inductees to the exclusive club in 2003 were Alan Ball, Pat Jennings and Herbert Chapman.

Tony Adams and Viv Anderson joined them 12 months later while Ian Wright's name was added to the Hall of Fame in 2005.

In 2006 both Liam Brady and Arsene Wenger were recognized by the selection panel and the following year Dennis Bergkamp was also included after a supporters' poll was conducted by the BBC's *Football Focus* programme.

Thierry Henry joined the growing Arsenal contingent in 2008, as did former manager Bertie Mee, while Cliff Bastin, Frank McLintock and Joe Mercer were honoured in 2009.

Former centre-forward and co-founder of the Football Writers' Association Charlie Buchan was inducted in 2010, the most recent Gunner to be nominated for the Hall of Fame which is now housed in the National Football Museum in Manchester.

◀◀ DAZZLING DECADE

The 2000s were one of the finest eras in Arsenal's history and in 2011 Arsene Wenger's role in the Gunners' achievements was recognized when he was named as the decade's greatest manager by the International Football Federation of History & Statistics.

The Frenchman was honoured after the IFFHS devised a points-based system based on results and managerial awards over the past 10 years which saw Wenger beat runner-up Alex Ferguson and third-placed Jose Mourinho to the prize.

BRADY HONOURED

The Professional Football Association's Player of the Year Award is one of the most prestigious accolades in the game and the first Arsenal player to earn the recognition of his fellow players was Liam Brady after his stunning contribution during the 1978–79 season.

The Republic of Ireland midfielder was in vintage form with 13 goals in 37 appearances in the old First Division but it was his dazzling displays in the FA Cup, including a Man of the Match performance in the Gunners' 3–2 win in the final at Wembley against Manchester United, that ultimately clinched the playmaker the coveted PFA award.

▶ YOUNG TALENT

The PFA Young Player of the Year Award is presented annually to the most promising and exciting youngster in the top-flight and five Gunners players have received the accolade since its inaugural season in 1973–74.

Tony Adams was the first Arsenal recipient in 1986–87 and two seasons later he was followed by Paul Merson as a PFA winner. Nicolas Anelka won the award in 1998–99 while Cesc Fabregas was honoured in 2007–08.

The most recent young Gunner to be recognized was Jack Wilshere, who collected his award in 2010–11.

LEFT: Arsene Wenger was named Manager of the Decade in 2011 after two league and three FA Cup triumphs.

BELOW: Jack Wilshere's breakthrough in the 2010–11 season was rewarded with the PFA Young Player of the Year award.

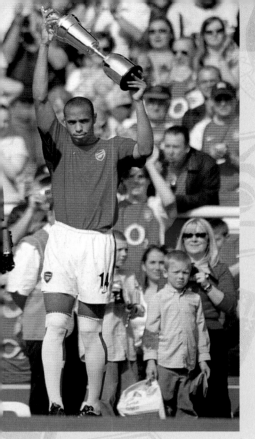

FANS' CHOICE

The Arsenal Football Supporters' Club have been voting for their Player of the Year since 1967 and Thierry Henry is the only player to date to have won the award four times. The Frenchman first won the fans' vote in 2000 and after repeating the success in 2003 and 2004, he made it a hat-trick of awards in 2005.

The first recipient of the award was Frank McLintock, while the first player to win it twice was John Radford, who attracted the lion's share of the vote in 1968 and then again in 1973.

The first player from outside Great Britain and Ireland to be honoured was Dennis Bergkamp, who was confirmed as the Gunners' Player of the Year in 1997.

LEFT: Thierry Henry recorded a brace of PFA awards during his Arsenal career.

▲ HENRY'S DOUBLE

Only five players – Mark Hughes, Alan Shearer, Thierry Henry, Cristiano Ronaldo and Gareth Bale – have ever won the PFA Player of the Year Award twice but Henry is the only one to have lifted the trophy in successive seasons.

The legendary French striker was first voted the winner after scoring 33 goals in 55 appearances for Arsenal in the 2002–03 season but was in even more prolific form during the Gunners' famed Invincibles campaign of 2003–04, hitting the back of the net 39 times in just 51 games to help the Club claim another Premier League title and himself back-to-back PFA awards.

▶ MERSON MAKES HIS MARK

The Alan Hardaker Trophy has been presented to the Man of the Match of the League Cup final since 1990 and to date the only Arsenal player to win the trophy is Paul Merson.

The midfielder won the prize in 1993 after the Gunners' 2–1 victory over Sheffield Wednesday at Wembley in recognition of his equalizing goal for George Graham's side and his subsequent assist for Steve Morrow's winner.

ARSENAL FOOTBALL SUPPORTERS' CLUB PLAYER OF THE YEAR

1967	Frank McLintock
1968	John Radford
1969	Peter Simpson
1970	George Armstrong
1971	Bob Wilson
1972	Pat Rice
1973	John Radford
1974	Alan Ball
1975	Jimmy Rimmer
1976	Liam Brady
1977	Frank Stapleton
1978	Liam Brady
1979	Liam Brady
1980	Frank Stapleton
1981	Kenny Sansom
1982	John Hollins
1983	Tony Woodcock
1984	Charlie Nicholas
1985	Stewart Robson
1986	David Rocastle
1987	Tony Adams
1988	Michael Thomas
1989	Alan Smith
1990	Tony Adams
1991	Steve Bould
1992	Ian Wright
1993	Ian Wright
1994	Tony Adams
1995	David Seaman
1996	Martin Keown
1997	Dennis Bergkamp
1998	Ray Parlour
1999	Nigel Winterburn
2000	Thierry Henry
2001	Patrick Vieira
2002	Robert Pires
2003	Thierry Henry
2004	Thierry Henry
2005	Thierry Henry
2006	Jens Lehmann
2007	Cesc Fabregas
2008	Cesc Fabregas
2009	Robin van Persie
2010	Cesc Fabregas
2011	Jack Wilshere
2012	Robin van Persie
2013	Santi Cazorla

LEFT: Paul Merson was in magnificent form as the Gunners beat Sheffield Wednesday in the 1993 League Cup final

Honours & Awards – Combined Team

The Professional Footballers' Association Team of the Year was first unveiled in 1973–74 but it was not until the 1977–78 season that an Arsenal player was included in the end-of-season XI when Liam Brady was named in a side that also featured Manchester United's Gordon McQueen, Martin Buchan, Steve Coppell and Joe Jordan, Nottingham Forest duo Peter Shilton and John Robertson, Aston Villa's John Gidman, West Bromwich Albion's Derek Statham, West Ham's Trevor Brooking and Birmingham's Trevor Francis.

The Gunners' largest contingent in the prestigious PFA team came 26 years after Brady's breakthrough on the back of the Invincibles' exploits during the 2003–04 campaign when six Arsenal players were named in the side.

The full line up was: Tim Howard (Manchester United), Lauren (Arsenal), Sol Campbell (Arsenal), John Terry (Chelsea), Ashley Cole (Arsenal), Steven Gerrard (Liverpool), Frank Lampard (Chelsea), Patrick Vieira (Arsenal), Robert Pires (Arsenal), Thierry Henry (Arsenal), Ruud van Nistelrooy (Manchester United).

ABOVE: Liam Brady was the first Gunner to be included in the PFA Team of the Year.

GOALS GALORE

The European Golden Shoe has been awarded to the leading goalscorer in matches from the top division of each European league since 1967–68 and Arsenal have twice boasted the Continent's most prolific marksman.

On both occasions it was Thierry Henry who collected the award, courtesy of his 30 Premier League goals in 2003–04 and his 25 strikes during the 2004–05 season.

MEDIA EXPOSURE

The Football Writers' Association Player of the Year award has been won eight times by six different Arsenal players since Blackpool's Stanley Matthews first received the accolade in the 1947–48 season.

The first Gunner to be recognized by the football scribes was left-half Joe Mercer in 1949–50, while centre-half Frank McLintock won the award 21 years later.

Dutch striker Dennis Bergkamp was honoured in 1997–98 and Robert Pires in 2001–02. Thierry Henry won his first FWA title in 2002–03 and completed his hat-trick, the only player in the award's history to be named the winner three times, in 2005–06.

The Club's most recent recipient was Robin van Persie in 2011–12, who was honoured after scoring 37 times in 48 Arsenal appearances.

RIGHT: Joe Mercer made history in 1950 when he was named the FWA Player of the Year.

▶ WENGER'S TRIUMPH

The League Managers Association has been naming a Manager of the Year since 1994 and Arsene Wenger is one of only four men to have received the accolade twice in his career.

The Frenchman was first recognized by his peers in 2002 after masterminding Arsenal's Premier League title triumph, and two years later he collected the award for a second time after his side famously went the entire league campaign unbeaten.

▶ GREATEST GOALS

The BBC's *Match of the Day* has organized its "Goal of the Season" competition since the 1970–71 season and on four occasions an Arsenal player has scored the winning effort.

Dennis Bergkamp was the first to be recognized for his spectacular score against Leicester City at Filbert Street during the 1997–98 campaign, a breathtaking example of first-time control and vision. The mercurial Dutchman made it a BBC double in the 2001–02 season with a sublime flick, turn and finish against Newcastle United at St James' Park.

The following season it was Thierry Henry who was the winner after a superb, long-range solo effort in the north London derby against Tottenham at Highbury,

while Emmanuel Adebayor was the 2007–08 recipient of the award after another clash with Spurs, beating Paul Robinson at White Hart Lane with a stunning volley from the edge of the area.

ABOVE: Arsene Wenger was honoured by his managerial peers in 2002 and again in 2004.

BELOW: Emmanuel Adebayor's spectacular strike against Spurs earned him the 2007–08 "Goal of the Season" accolade.

SANSOM'S RECORD

The player with the record number of appearances in a PFA Team of the Year is Kenny Sansom, with 11 separate nominations in the combined side.

The former Arsenal full-back was first included in the old Third Division Team of the Year in 1976–77 when he was a Crystal Palace player and subsequently made the First Division Team of the Year for 1980–81 after his summer switch from Selhurst Park to Highbury.

His 11th and final nomination came in 1986–87, featuring alongside fellow Gunners Viv Anderson, Tony Adams and David Rocastle.

ARSENAL'S FWA PLAYER OF THE YEAR AWARDS

1949–50	Joe Mercer
1970–71	Frank McLintock
1997–98	Dennis Bergkamp
2001–02	Robert Pires
2002–03	Thierry Henry
2003–04	Thierry Henry
2005–06	Thierry Henry
2011–12	Robin van Persie

Index

Picture Credits

The publishers would like to thank the following sources for their kind permission to reproduce the pictures in this book.